5

Remodeling Contractor's Handbook

by

Dan M. Wong

Craftsman Book Company
6058 Corte del Cedro, P.O. Box 6500, Carlsbad, CA 92008

Library of Congress Cataloging-in-Publication Data

Wong, Dan M.
    Remodeling contractor's handbook / by Dan M. Wong.
        p.   cm.
    Includes index.
    ISBN 0-934041-45-8
    1. Construction industry—Management. 2. Contractor's operations-
-Management. 3. Building trades—Management. 4. Buildings—Repair
and reconstruction—Management. 5. Buildings—Remodeling for other
use—Management.   I. Title.
HD9715.A2W645   1990   90-1875
690' .24'068—dc20   CIP

Contents

1

Start with Marketing

A thousand times in the last 35 years I've needed a good guide to the business of remodeling — a practical answer book that would solve the problems I (and every home improvement specialist) face every day. I looked. But I never found the book I needed. Maybe you've had the same experience.

Nearly every book store has a shelf of remodeling references. Most are picture books written for homeowners — completely useless to both you and me. Books with enough information to be useful are usually written by scholars or professional writers, people who've never made a living in the business.

To my mind, anyone who didn't apprentice in the contractor's school of hard knocks has missed a lot. I'm not sure they understand enough to give reliable advice. Would you take advice from a marriage counselor who was a life-long bachelor? I wanted to learn remodeling from a veteran, not a glib theoretician. I suspect you feel the same way.

I couldn't find a readable, practical, comprehensive reference for remodeling contractors. So a few years ago I set out to write one. The volume you're holding is the result.

I'm going to answer practical questions, make time- and money-saving suggestions, explain how to avoid the more common pitfalls, provide essential how-to information, and even occasionally entertain. But if you enjoy reading this book, don't think the information here is any less valuable. Everything in this book is here for just one reason: to help you make a good living in this competitive field. Your success depends on how well you play the game. And I intend to help you qualify as a world-class player.

Most of this book comes from my 35 years' experience as a contractor. I've been making notes and collecting valuable information for years, expecting that eventually I'd write a book on the subject I know best.

My first challenge was deciding how it should be organized. Where should I begin? Because every job begins with a sale (and because without sales you're going nowhere), I decided to start with the key to your success: marketing. Doing good work at reasonable prices is never enough. You have to sell as well as you build. So marketing will be my first topic.

Marketing Is Basic

Every remodeling contractor is in *business*. In this chapter, I'll explain how to market your service and suggest what you should and shouldn't do.

Let's start by defining terms. *Marketing* and *sales* don't mean the same thing. *Selling* is a craft. It's the steps you take to get orders. *Marketing* is an acquired discipline: an inexact science, but a science nevertheless. It includes defining your market, then examining, designing, assembling, evaluating, and fine-tuning a way to reach it. But what does "your market" mean? It's just a fancy way to define who your prospective buyers are.

Most good salespeople don't understand marketing — although most of them think they do. Marketing people may understand sales but they usually make lousy salespeople. For your business to prosper, you need to be good at both marketing and sales.

Be Smart and Prolific

The secret to success in any business, including remodeling contracting, is not to work harder, but to work *smarter*. And the first step to working smarter is to get more mileage from each marketing and sales dollar. Smarter marketing will increase your profit margin.

To increase it even more, you'll want to turn out more advertising to generate more leads. That's not too hard if you master the basic marketing procedures successful contractors use. Doing that should be part of your marketing strategy.

Whenever a business fails for any of the usual reasons — too little capital, bad estimating, weak or no business plan — it also suffers from *lack of sales*. No matter what kinds of problems your remodeling company faces, if you have enough sales, you can probably find a way to survive. When sales plummet, you have many fewer options. That should make marketing your highest priority.

A good supply of customers means your business will survive.

■ *Customers = business survival*

Good sales give you time to correct other problems. Given enough time, most remodeling contractors will find a way to grow and prosper.

■ *Customers + smart management = business profits*

That's why this section is so important. If you learn nothing else, learn how to market your services effectively.

Believe it or not, some remodelers do absolutely no marketing. And they wonder why their sales volume is so bad! They've bought the beautiful myth that quality work alone can produce enough leads and referrals. Of course, you want those referrals. You even expect them. They hold down your advertising costs. *But you can't depend on referrals alone to keep your company humming.*

Here's a word to the wise: Take care of marketing first and always. Why? Because marketing brings in *leads*. Without leads, you won't have any sales; without sales, you won't have a business.

Leads Keep You Going

Leads are to your remodeling business what gasoline is to your car. If you don't have any, you aren't going anywhere. If you have plenty, you can go a long way.

But what is a lead? It's just a prospective customer asking for an appointment to discuss a remodeling need. And how do you get leads? You identify your market and then give those people reasons to contact you. Sounds easy, doesn't it? And it can be, if you're doing it right. I'll explain.

Determine Your Market

Start by identifying your market. If you haven't defined exactly who your customers are, you can't focus promotion, advertising, and sales programs.

Are you targeting residences, businesses, apartments, or restaurants? Let's say you specialize in residential work. Old or new houses? What income group? Additions or repair? If you say, "all of them," you're not focusing on your market. Some call it *finding a niche*. When you're starting out in the remodeling business, it might be appropriate to take whatever you can get. You can't afford the luxury of picking and choosing. But you'll be wise to dump that attitude when volume picks up, or you'll find yourself scrambling from one type of job to another.

Zeroing in on a specialty has advantages. This doesn't mean you won't accept work outside your field. The whole purpose of having a niche is to help you build a solid reputation, a good base for further expansion.

Offer Design Services

Today we hear about contractors offering "revolutionary, new" design-build service. Nonsense! Remodeler builders have offered design and drafting services for as long as I can remember. They always will. You're already a builder. Offering to design what you build is no big deal.

There's a big advantage to offering design as well as construction. Of course, there's money to be made on design work. But more important, affluent owners expect it. Middle- and upper-income prospects want unique designs and high-quality work and are willing to pay for it.

Owners often prefer remodelers who offer design services. Customers like working with designer-remodelers because they take responsibility for the project from beginning to end. One-stop service is popular because it's convenient.

Another advantage of design-build contracts is that you have more control over the job. They also reduce the number of supervisors you, as the builder, must satisfy. Working with the owner's architect rather than carrying out your own design can lead to unpleasant surprises.

As the designer, you can tailor the job to fit the owner's budget and price. You're less likely to end up with a project that never gets built. Most remodelers have wasted more than a few late nights estimating jobs that never got the go-ahead. That's needless overhead. My experiences is that "no-go" projects happen because they're over-designed and over budget — often because of the architect's cavalier treatment of the owner's guidelines. Architect's fees are usually based on a percentage of the job. The more it costs, the more they make. Contractors who design-build are usually very practical about design and price. They design what they can build and nothing more.

". . . and that's the way it should be done."

Fortunately, the design-build concept is widely accepted by the people who count — the homeowners. You should be able to close more deals if you design what you plan to build.

How do you make the transition from a remodeler-builder to a design-remodeler-builder? You have two choices.

1) You can subcontract your design work. For projects requiring a professional's seal on the design drawings, hire an architect or engineer as the job requires. For small jobs that don't need the seal of a licensed professional to get a building permit, sub out your work to a design draftsman.

2) Hire someone to prepare drawings. Try hiring a draftsman with a few years' suitable experience. If the project is complex and you need sealed drawings, send them out to an architect or engineer for scrutiny and seal. You can even call on these professionals to supervise very complicated projects. If redrawing is necessary, your own people can do it. This holds down drafting costs.

Notice that the design-build approach requires more sales sophistication. You'll still have to convince prospective clients that your management, experience, and workmanship are top caliber. But now you also have to persuade them that you're innovative and well-grounded in design.

"Mind if I make one more change?"

A design-build operation may not suit every contractor, but for those of you capable of carrying if off, the rewards can be gratifying.

Effective Advertising

There's an old saying that goes something like this: "Any advertising, no matter how poorly done, is better than none at all." For you and me, it's not a question of *if* we will advertise, but *how well*.

Advertising is the best way to let the public know about your remodeling services. But it must be *effective advertising*. Good advertising needn't be complicated or mysterious. As a matter of fact, if you approach it logically, building a successful advertising plan can be both fun and profitable. Here are the rules I follow:

1) *Keep it simple.* Determine the most direct and cost-effective way to reach customers with your message.

2) *Be consistent.* Project the same image every time, over and over again, in all your advertising. Don't diffuse your message and confuse the audience. Focus on the message so you're not competing against yourself.

3) *Pull in leads.* That's the sole purpose of advertising. If it doesn't bring in leads, it's not working.

Your Advertising Budget

The percentage-of-sales method is probably the best way to set your advertising budget. Start with a minimum of 5 percent of gross sales. It's safer to make that 7 to 10 percent if you can manage it. That's not an unreasonable number. More advertising means more leads. More leads mean more sales. More sales mean you can be more selective in the jobs you accept — and enjoy a higher profit from each job.

After you've set your annual advertising budget, break it down into a monthly amount. For instance, suppose that you decide to spend 5 percent of your projected sales volume for advertising. You estimate annual sales of $500,000, so you'll be spending $25,000 on advertising over the next year. That gives you a monthly ad budget of a little over $2,000.

Of course, at the beginning of each year you don't know exactly what annual sales will be. But you can estimate sales from experience, intuition, or the goals you've set. Sales may fall to $450,000, or soar to $600,000. Adjust the ad budget according to actual sales. I figure our advertising budget on a monthly basis, using a plus and minus system to increase or decrease advertising expenditures in the following month.

Take a look at Figure 1-1. The second column shows the projected sales by month. The next column shows the monthly percentage of projected annual sales. Each month, you'd write in the actual sales. Under "+/-", put the accumulated total of the difference between actual sales and projections. The monthly advertising budget is calculated by multiplying the annual budget by the percentage in the third column.

For the sample company in Figure 1-1, sales are up by $1,000 at the end of the first quarter. This means an additional $50 (5 percent of $1,000) is available for advertising. The "carry forward" column shows that at the end of March, advertising expenses were $100 over budget. But because of the extra $50 available due to higher sales, the carry forward "overdraft" is reduced to $50 going into April.

Determining the Best Percentage

I've been asked many times how much remodeling contractors should spend on advertising. Of course, no percentage fits all. There are too many variables. But I believe most remodelers don't spend enough. My usual advice is: Don't be miserly with your ad budget. If you don't spend enough, you won't get enough sales leads. That's a simple equation to remember.

I'll also admit that most remodelers waste some advertising money. They spend without generating leads and go on doing more of the same

Advertising Budget Project

Goodguys Remodeling Company

Projected Sales for 19XX: $500,000

Projected Advertising Budget: 5% of $500,000 = $25,000

Month	Projected Sales	%	Actual Sales	+/-	Projected Budget	Actual Spent	Carry Forward
January	27,000	5.4	30,000	+3,000	1,350	1,000	+ 350
February	35,500	7.1	35,000	+2,500	1,775	2,000	+125
March	37,500	7.5	36,000	+1,000	1,875	2,100	- 100
April	45,000	9.0			2,250		- 50
May	39,500	7.9			1,975		
June	43,500	8.7					
July	38,500	7.7					
August	43,500	8.7					
September	46,000	9.2					
October	59,000	11.8					
November	46,000	9.2					
December	39,000	7.8					
	$500,000	100.0%			$25,000		

Figure 1-1   *Advertising budget worksheet*

until they run out of cash or patience. That's foolish. Don't spend a dollar that doesn't bring in results. And if you're getting good results, keep spending more until the results begin to tail off. In short, spend as much on advertising as you can afford, but be sure it's all spent wisely.

Some remodelers boast that 50 to 75 percent of their sales come through referrals. They don't need to do any advertising. Good for them! But it's likely their businesses are both small, and probably stagnant. For those of you who want more than an office in your house, more than mere wages — plan to prepare and launch an advertising program to get more leads, to sell more jobs, to grow, and to accumulate more profits. A comprehensive advertising program will help accomplish all this.

There are many things to consider in setting your ad budget. One is location. The harder it is for prospects to find you, the more you'll have to spend. If there's a competitor nearby, it's harder to keep or increase your market share. That adds to your advertising cost. If you're eager for new business, you'll spend more on ads. Hopefully, those higher costs will increase sales and profits.

You can base your advertising budget on the remodeling industry's advertising-to-sales ratios. These statistics are available from the associations of builders and remodeling contractors. Here are some you can write to:

International Remodeling Contractors Association
P.O. Box 17063
West Hartford, CT 06117

The National Remodelers Council
National Association of Home Builders (NAHB)
15th & M Streets N.W.
Washington, D.C. 20005
(800) 368-5242

National Association of Plumbing-Heating-Cooling Contractors (NAPHCC)
P.O. Box 6808
Falls Church, VA 22046
(703) 237-8100

National Association of the Remodeling Industry (NARI)
1901 N. Moore St., Suite 808
Arlington, VA 22009

You may find others in your local telephone book. Look under *Associations*. Some of them may offer cooperative advertising programs.

If you're just starting out, spend at least 5 percent on advertising. Don't spend less than that. Some successful contractors spend as much as 8 or 10 percent and don't consider that excessive. After all, they're making money or they wouldn't be doing it.

I've found that there's a direct relationship between the amount spent on advertising and the markup a contractor can expect. I'm not sure that increasing advertising by 10 percent will increase markup by exactly 10 percent. But generally the relationship holds true. Contractors who spend 2 percent or less of gross on advertising usually price jobs at about 140 percent of cost. But contractors spending 5 percent or more on advertising can usually sell their jobs at 170 to 210 percent of the labor and material cost. I assume this difference has something to do with the extra advertising. The more leads you can choose from, the more selective you can be, and the higher you can make your markup.

If you don't want to grow, to make more money, that's OK with me. To each his own. But if you're ambitious, pump some extra dollars into your advertising budget.

Keep Records to Judge Ad Effectiveness

Keep track of where your leads come from. Spending more on advertising is foolish unless you get better results. Ask each new prospect where they heard about your company. Record results for each ad: Yellow Pages, newspaper, signs, etc. If you're advertising in more than one paper, ask which one, and what issue. If the lead came from a referral, ask who recommended you and make a note of it in your book.

Record the cost of each type of advertising you buy every month. Match all the leads you get against the ads that produced those leads. Then analyze the cost per lead for each ad or type of ad. You'll see very quickly which type of ads are paying and which aren't. Cut back on what isn't working and do more of what's working best. If nothing is working, try something new.

Before you drop any form of advertising completely, do a little analysis. Is there any way you can improve it to increase the response? For instance, suppose you're spending $1,000 a month on newspaper ads and getting only four leads a month. That's way too much, $250 each. But before you cancel the ads, ask yourself these questions:

■ Is the ad properly done?

■ If not, can you improve it?

■ Is the basic message clear?

If you think the ad is good, try it again. But cut down its size. You might reduce a quarter-page ad to an eighth of a page. If you continue to get the same number of leads, you've cut the cost for each lead in half. That might make the cost per lead more acceptable.

Cost of Leads

What's an acceptable cost of leads? If advertising is 5 percent of gross and your average contract is $20,000, you can spend $1,000 for advertising on each job. That's easy. But let's go one step further. Every lead doesn't result in a sale. If you close one job from each ten leads, you can spend $100 per lead. In our example, the $1,000 should produce ten leads and one sale. Your 5 percent advertising budget is about right.

If you begin averaging one sale for each five leads, then you're really flying! But if that happens, don't cut back on advertising. Keep up the advertising and watch your volume grow!

Record advertising costs and results for a few months and you'll know your cost per lead and cost per job. But suppose you suddenly begin closing only one job in fifteen leads. You know this shouldn't happen because your average closing rate is one in ten or better. (You know it because you keep good records.) If the closing rate slips, you've got a problem. Some adjustments are needed. Maybe you need to improve the sales pitch. Or maybe your sales staff is coasting. Because you know right away that something's wrong, you can fix it before a small problem becomes a crisis.

Here's another problem. Suppose your sales staff is closing one out of three leads. That's great performance. But suppose your cost per lead is $500. That's $1,500 per job. My guess is that there's something wrong with your advertising.

Choosing Your Advertising Media

Every remodeling contractor has a wide choice of advertising media. There must be a thousand ways to get your message in front of the public. Here are a few of the more popular choices, not necessarily in order of decreasing popularity:

- Yellow Pages

- Direct mail

- Newspapers

- Telemarketing

- Canvassing

- Radio

- Television

- Showrooms

- Signs

- Miscellaneous advertising

Let's look at these one at a time, beginning with the ever-popular Yellow Pages.

Yellow Pages

You can't afford to stay out of your telephone company's Yellow Pages. This source alone can bring you three leads a week. No matter what it costs, it's an absolute necessity for any remodeler. If your competitors are there, you need to be there. If you doubt that, ask yourself these questions:

1) Do people who need a remodeling contractor look in the Yellow Pages?

2) Does your competition advertise in the Yellow Pages?

3) Do people who already know of your company use the Yellow Pages to find your phone number?

Deciding that you're going to be in the Yellow Pages is easy. Then the hard decisions begin. How large should the ad be? What's the most effective message? How much should you budget? If you're just starting out, here are my suggestions.

■ Order a quarter-page ad. A smaller ad tags you as a small operator. Use a smaller ad only if you want customers to think of your company as a small company.

■ Advertise in the Yellow Pages only in the areas you serve. Homeowners usually call local contractors to do their work.

■ Include your address in the ad, not just a telephone number. Including a street address gives your company more legitimacy.

■ Make your ad clear, simple, and clean. Spend a few dollars on a graphic artist, if necessary.

Notice that I'm referring here to the "official" Yellow Pages distributed by the phone company. There are others published by independent companies, but those are often limited in their distribution, and I've sometimes found them not as reliable. Since they usually cover much the same ground as the "official" Yellow Pages, using them is probably not as cost effective.

The primary purpose of a Yellow Pages ad is to generate leads. No ad can sell a remodeling job. The caller has to make the decision to remodel, and is shopping for a contractor. So write an ad that sets you apart from the competition. Use phrases like these: *Free Estimates . . . Low Monthly Payments . . . Licensed and Bonded.* These are strong selling points.

Direct Mail

Direct mail advertising is effective because it can be personal and highly selective.

Here are five principles for effective direct mail advertising:

1) Define your objective clearly. Give your ad a specific purpose. Aim it at a specific audience.

2) Select the right mailing list for your specific objectives and audience.

3) List the benefits for your customer.

- Promise a benefit

- Expand on that benefit

- Back up your offer with proof and endorsements

- Give a reason to "act now"

4) Make the graphics (layout and text) appropriate for the audience. Keep it consistent for easy recognition. That usually makes the difference between success and failure.

5) Encourage the prospect to respond — and then make the response easy. Here are some examples: *Phone 123-2468 now for a free estimate.* Or *Just check #1 or #2 on the prepaid reply card and mail today.*

After every batch of direct mail ads goes out, do some thinking about what worked and what didn't, and why. Take time to analyze the results. Ask yourself how you can improve the ad. Is the wording poor? Offer too weak? Timing wrong? These are all fixable.

Your volume of direct mail advertising will vary with the number of leads you need. Mail out 100 brochures a day — or 5,000 if you can handle it. But make sure you can follow up on inquiries when they start rolling in. It makes sense to build up your mailing volume slowly, as you acquire trained staff to handle the leads.

Direct mail experts generally expect a return of 2 to 4 percent. That's reasonable for lower-cost items, like clothing, books, or appliances. For high-ticket jobs like remodeling, you may be lucky to pull 1 percent. And those are leads, not jobs. Most of them won't bring in a dime.

Sounds like a small return, doesn't it? But it can pay off big. Let me share the experience of a prominent remodeler I know. His direct mail program keeps nine salespeople busy full time. Here's how he does it. He sends out 5,000 brochures twice a month, saturating a specific area. Each mailing pulls 60 to 100 qualified leads. He keeps the program going month after month, year after year, and makes money. Plenty of it.

Newspaper Advertising

Many remodeling contractors advertise in newspapers. Look through your local paper. If you see ads placed by remodeling contractors week after week, you know those ads are working. Maybe your ad should be in the same paper. Here's why newspaper ads work:

1) *Habit and tradition.* Most people read at least one newspaper regularly.

2) *Flexibility.* You can place or change ads on short notice.

3) *Ease.* Newspapers can make up ads complete with headlines, copy, and illustrations from the information you provide.

4) *Accountability.* You can know the results of the ad in a few days (or even hours).

5) *Effectiveness.* A good ad that costs about $250 should bring in two to four leads.

Guidelines for effective newspaper ads

Run your ad for several issues. Then, if it isn't working, try a different approach, a different illustration, or a different paper. Keep tinkering with the offer until you find one that works better than the rest. Then keep running that ad until results begin to drop off.

Your phone isn't going to ring off the hook after one or two ads. But just one good ad, repeated often enough, can help you build a good career in the remodeling business. Finding or developing an ad that works and works and works can put you on a gravy train.

A smaller ad once a week usually pulls better than a larger ad once a month. I've found that an ad two columns wide by 4 inches deep is a good size.

These are the essential *do's* for an effective newspaper ad:

- Make ads easily recognizable.

- Keep the layout simple.

- Use a dominant headline or illustration.

- Make generous use of white space.

- Write complete copy.

- State prices if appropriate.

- Give readers a reason to act *now.*

And just as important, here are the *don'ts:*

- Don't be too clever or cute.
- Don't omit your name, address, telephone number. (I've seen it happen.)
- Don't generalize. Be specific.
- Don't exaggerate.

Also, don't run ads in newspapers which have over 30 percent of their circulation outside the areas you serve. You're wasting that money, paying an extra 30 percent for the area you want covered.

Producing the graphics

There are several ways to design and do layouts for your ads:

1) *The newspaper can do it.* This is usually the least expensive. Most papers don't charge for the service. But your ads may look a lot like the other ads in the paper.

2) *Hire a free-lance graphic artist.* This can be expensive, but you should end up with a good ad.

3) *Use an advertising agency.* This is how big advertisers do it. With an agency, you're more likely to get professional-quality work. But few agencies will set type or prepare illustrations for free. They'll charge you extra for their "buy-outs" — any type, illustrations or design service they have to buy from others outside the agency. But the agency's basic fee is their commission, usually 15 percent of the ad cost. You pay the agency for the ad, they deduct 15 percent and send the remaining 85 percent to the newspaper.

4) *Do it yourself — if* you have some experience and skill in this area. If you're an amateur and produce amateur-looking ads, you'll waste a lot of money trying to save a few dollars. Remember, you're a business person first, and a remodeling contractor second. You don't have time to do all the detail work. Consider leaving this job to an advertising specialist.

Consistency is important

A good logo is your company's signature. If you don't have a logo yet, have one designed. Major companies spend thousands on a unique logo. But that's not necessary. Use a distinctive lettering style for your company name, or a graphic symbol or illustration. Design a logo that shows at a glance what your company does. Then use it wherever you advertise. It helps maintain the consistency that's so important in effective advertising.

Besides your logo, you can also use a special border on your advertising to give a characteristic, recognizable look. Once you've established a logo and border format, be consistent. Readers will come to identify that logo or border format with your company. Just drop in your new copy and illustration whenever you need to change your message.

Telemarketing

I'm including telemarketing here, although it's not actually a form of advertising. It's a way to get leads. And it can be an effective method — *if* you know what you're doing. Many remodeling contractors have tried and failed with telemarketing because they didn't understand the principles. They hired a couple of people, threw them a directory, pointed them at the telephones, and expected them to churn out stacks of leads. There's more to it than that.

Here are some tips on successful telemarketing for remodeling contractors:

- You need telemarketers with good verbal skills, people who can project warmth and sincerity.

- You need an organized telemarketing center, whether you have one caller with a desk and telephone or a sophisticated work space with many people making calls.

The best place to learn about telemarketing is from your telephone company. For reasons probably not entirely philanthropic, they're very anxious to help. They'll teach you how to make telemarketing a successful part of your sales efforts. Pacific Bell says of telemarketing, "The more you call, the more you'll earn." AT&T offers ". . . tips that can help your sales force open more doors, close more sales, and bring down the cost per sale." These phone companies offer comprehensive training seminars and workshops to teach your employees effective telephone techniques. They train people in sales, customer service, and collections. They'll even show you how to recruit and motivate telemarketing specialists. It's their business to keep close track of telemarketing successes — and failures. According to their findings, the script is the key. To help here, they'll give you tested guidelines to create an effective calling script so your telemarketing efforts produce the most possible leads.

Now let's work out some simple arithmetic. I've suggested that you start out with an advertising budget of about 5 percent of gross. If your average size job is $14,000, the budget per job sold would be $700. And if your closing ratio is one out of seven, the cost per lead should be no more than $100 each.

Hiring a telemarketer at $10 an hour for five four-hour days would cost $200 a week. Add the usual payroll deductions, phone costs and general overhead for the space used and the weekly total would be about $300. If your caller produced three leads a week, you'd be within your advertising budget. In theory, two operators should get you a $14,000 job each week if your aim is to do $750,000 a year. In theory. In actual practice, the number of jobs and the size of the jobs will vary from week to week.

One caller isn't likely to get more than one or two leads a week in the $14,000 range. But don't panic and don't be disappointed. The secret to success is patience. If you're willing to accept smaller jobs — say from $500 to $10,000 — you will probably get two to four leads per day from each caller. It's always easier to sell less expensive work.

Supervision and incentives

You'll need someone to supervise the telemarketers. Consider using an incentive system for the supervisor, maybe a $5 bonus for each lead over five for each operator each week and a $100 commission for each lead that results in a sale over $10,000.

Directories

Don't have your callers use an ordinary telephone book. Your salespeople will be chasing all over the city following up leads. A crisscross directory shows all listed phone numbers on both sides of every street in a community. That makes it easy to follow up on leads. Most large libraries have these directories. You may not be able to check out the directory you want, but you can copy a few pages to run a telemarketing test. If the test works, buy the directory you need. Buy just one and divide the pages among your operators.

Computers

Automatic calling machines can make a thousand calls a day and take messages from interested prospects. The quality of the leads may be very low, though. The advantage is no payroll, no deductions, and no operator fatigue. In some areas these machines are regulated or prohibited by law. In any event, consider an automatic calling system. Even if you get only one lead a day, that's still 200 to 300 a year. And even if your closing ratio is downright awful, you could still be money ahead.

Canvassers

Most contractors don't like canvassing — walking door to door, leaving a brochure at each residence. But I know some contractors who've been doing it successfully for years. It's probably a good method of finding prospects for less costly projects like sun decks, replacement windows, gutters, or roof and chimney repairs. Here's a money-saving hint: You might be able to find other companies using canvassers who could also drop off your brochures. Canvassers can solicit for leads and still deliver 30 to 40 brochures an hour. That may be less than the cost of mailing a brochure to each address. Be sure to offer canvassers a bonus for each lead they generate, or a convenient trash can may receive most of your advertising.

Of course, you can't even consider canvassing until you have an attractive brochure. But how do you get a brochure that will do the job?

Brochures and flyers

Your brochure is an important marketing tool. Make it consistent with your ads. Logo, type style and colors should be the same. Keep your message clear and concise, your design simple and eye-catching but not fancy or ornate. See what your competition is doing. Use a graphic artist if you're not good at layout and design. Most community newspapers can refer you to graphic artists who could help you. Some printers provide this service very reasonably if you're buying the printing job from them.

There are three elements to consider in putting together a flyer or brochure — its design, its message, and the cost. A well-designed brochure will pay for itself many times over. It's an effective tool for spreading a positive image of your business. Even if you don't do any canvassing, you need a brochure to give out at home shows and to prospects during sales calls.

No matter how much you budget for your brochure, make it attractive and full of useful information for prospective customers. Here's a short checklist of some things your brochure should include.

- Eye-catching pictures

- Short list of noteworthy projects

- List of services offered

- Testimonials

- Regions served

- Your qualifications

- Company philosophy

- Company history

Be sure to put in your address as well as your company name and telephone number. If you don't list an address, you'll look like a fly-by-nighter. Don't use dated material, such as prices, in your brochure. It can cost a significant amount to produce a brochure, so you want to be able to use it for a long time without major revisions. If you're offering a special discount to attract customers, be sure you put an expiration date on it. You don't want someone trying to take advantage of a special offer you made three years ago — back before lumber prices doubled.

Printing costs vary widely. Before you decide on design and artwork, get some bids on variables that affect the printing cost, especially paper quality and color. You can have anything from black ink on newsprint to high-gloss card stock in full color. The cost can range from $50 a thousand copies to several dollars each. Work up a budget with your printer and artist before you start work.

The State of California Department of Consumer Affairs and the Contractor's State License Board distribute free booklets to homeowners considering room additions, new kitchens, bathrooms, and other home improvements. Their *Blueprint for Building Quality* is considered a good consumer's guide to home improvement contracting. You can get a copy by writing to:

Department of Consumer Affairs
Contractor's State License Board
P.O. Box 26000
Sacramento, CA 95826

As a progressive remodeling contractor, you should support professionalism in the home improvement industry. Consider putting out your own brochure for consumers, something like the California booklet. You could distribute this booklet with some straight talk about what to expect during a remodeling job — a "Homeowner's Survival Manual." I've included copy for a booklet like this in Appendix A. Feel free to adapt it for your own use.

Radio

Radio advertising reaches a large audience with your personal message. A pleasant-sounding announcer on a popular radio station can be very effective in bringing in new leads. Some advantages of radio advertising are:

1) *Target marketing*. Most radio stations cater to a specific age group with their programming: news and public affairs, easy listening, rock, or country music. You can choose the audience most likely to respond to your message.

2) *Frequency and reach.* You control the time when your ad is on the air. And you know the areas covered by the broadcasts before you buy the time.

3) *Flexibility.* You can concentrate your ads in a particular time slot, vary the length of your messages, and choose the stations you want. It's all up to you.

4) *Intrusiveness.* Your advertising can penetrate right into the audience's living room, kitchen, office, automobile, and even their shower. No other medium gives you that.

As a remodeling contractor, you'll probably gear your ads to the more mature, middle/upper-income groups. You're not going to get a lot of response from a station whose listeners are mostly teenagers, even if it has the largest listening audience in the area. So you need to know what percentage of your prospects each station reaches. The radio stations can provide a media kit that shows information about their audience: age, sex, income level, etc.

The most expensive time slot for radio ads is during *drive time* (6:00 to 10:00 a.m. and 4:00 to 7:00 p.m.) when commuters provide a captive audience.

Cost per thousand (CPM)

There are two important questions: "How many people will I reach with my radio advertising dollars? And what's my cost per thousand?"

Calculate your CPM (cost per thousand) by dividing the cost of the ad by the number of target listeners. If you pay $100 for a radio commercial that reaches 10,000 middle/upper-income adults, your CPM would be $10.00.

As with all forms of advertising, frequency and repetition are the keys to a good radio ad campaign. One or two ads won't have customers lining up at your door. Repeat your ads to get your message across effectively. Your radio station's marketing representative can guide you into the best ad campaign for your budget.

Producing a spot ad

You can use an ad agency to produce your ad, or have the radio station do it for you. Most stations will include the cost of production if you buy their air time. Either way, you have to get your message across quickly to be effective. See what your competition is doing. Try to determine what it is about your company that stands out from the competition. Emphasize this in your ads.

Contact the radio stations for detailed information. They'll be more than willing to discuss what they can do for your business.

Television

Television is probably the most powerful of all the mass media. That makes TV an effective way to sell many products and services. But it's too expensive for most independent small- or medium-size contractors. It's out of reach for even some large developers. The air time is expensive and the cost of producing an ad may be prohibitive. Television stations won't produce your commercial free like radio stations will.

The cost of TV advertising depends on the size of the audience and the time period. If you want to try TV, use a media service or ad agency to help buy the appropriate times for your ads. They'll know how to reach the most desirable viewing audience for the lowest cost. To be effective, you'll have to budget for repeat ads, placed in the best time slots. Ads at 4 o'clock in the morning will be cheap, but probably useless.

You won't be doing any television advertising until your business has grown very large. Maybe not even then. But when you are large enough to afford TV, consider using it as one element in your ad mix. That just might offset some of the high TV costs and gain you name recognition as well. For instance, you could try using TV commercials for three months, then use other media for nine months, then back to three months of TV.

Showrooms

Many remodelers use a showroom with kitchen, bath, and family room displays. Here's why a showroom is so effective:

1) It sets you above 90 percent of your competitors, putting you in a more favorable selling position. Fly-by-night operators won't make this kind of investment. Its very presence should bring in a couple of leads a week.

2) It conveys an image to the prospective customer that your company is stable.

3) The customer is more likely to pay a higher price if they're confident of your stability and professionalism.

4) The customer can see and touch some of the items they're looking for. And they can examine the quality of workmanship and materials.

5) Your design department can give special attention to the customer's needs. That can reduce misunderstandings and increase your sales.

Most remodelers don't have display rooms. Small contractors and those who work directly with architects don't need them. But if a showroom sounds appealing, consider whether you can afford it and whether

prospective customers will expect it. If you do install a showroom, you need to choose the style and location, the kind of merchandise to display, and the staff you need to provide the service.

If you invest in a showroom, make it pay:

- Keep your display areas immaculately clean.

- Avoid high-fashion items and trendy colors.

- Encourage your sales staff to make use of the showroom and design department.

- Include the fact that you have a showroom in your advertising messages.

- Update your displays two or three times a year to avoid using discontinued or shopworn items.

- Make the displays reflect the class of work you do. Don't do second-class work from a first-class showroom or vice versa.

Showrooms can be an effective sales tool. They can also be very expensive. Only you can decide if the benefits are worth the cost. I recommend that you start modestly. It doesn't have to be huge and elaborate. A display of three or four kitchen vignettes, a couple of bathrooms, and a family room can be a good start.

Ask your suppliers and subcontractors to contribute to the cause. If they won't donate materials, ask for a substantial discount. After all, they stand to benefit along with you. I put up a showroom a few years back and it cost me practically nothing. But if you need financial help for your showroom, you might try borrowing under a long-term leasehold improvement loan.

An investment of $10,000 to $15,000 should get you an attractive showroom. Think of it this way: If you spent $10,000 for your showroom and amortized it over five years, your cost per year is $2,000. If your display attracted ten prospects from walk-in traffic each month, the cost is just $16.67 per lead. And walk-in leads usually produce a higher closing sales ratio than other leads — at least they did for me.

Signs

Here's another opportunity to get your name out to the public. Make sure you put up a sign at every job you're working on. If you run ten different jobs simultaneously, your name is displayed in ten different locations. Many remodelers get a sizable proportion of their customers from job signs. Your customers have neighbors who need work done, too.

What's the cost? About $30 to $50 each. If you remember to have someone retrieve every sign immediately after the job, each sign should last for six or more jobs. You can have signs mounted on a post for ground display, or taped in windows. Get the owner's permission, of course.

Company signs placed in strategic locations aren't only good for advertising, but also for easy identification of job sites for materials delivery people and subcontractors. That's a good argument to use when your customers don't want your sign on their property.

Signs on your trucks are an excellent way to get your name before the public. Your trucks travel all over the place and your signs enjoy high visibility. Don't miss out on this practically free advertising. But make sure that your trucks present a good image. An old junker billowing clouds of black smoke isn't going to make it.

Miscellaneous Advertising

There are literally hundreds of different types of advertising schemes, including some that are offbeat and of little benefit. Here's a short list. You be the judge — but I'll add my comments for what they're worth.

- Billboards, bench/bus/fence signs: Dubious value for the money.

- Premiums, incentives, and ad specialties: If inexpensive, may be a good way to make people aware of your business. Give them away to gain goodwill.

- Magazines (local and regional): Save your money.

■ Coupons: As in "Present this coupon for a 10 percent discount." Many prospects assume they're a hoax. They figure you probably just jacked your price up 10 percent, so the 10 percent discount is just a come-on. Don't do it.

■ Home shows: They're like a crap shoot. Some can bring in many leads while others are a complete waste of time. Participating in shows is time-consuming and expensive. You'd probably do better with another medium.

■ T-shirts: Many remodelers have their company name and logo printed on T-shirts. It may be a good idea. Your staff can wear these on the job like a uniform. You can give them to friends and family, and present them as gifts to customers. They're an inexpensive way to provide your company with high visibility.

A Note on Advertising Agencies

My feeling is that you're probably better off without them, unless you have a million dollar budget. But if you feel that you need their expertise, here are a few words of caution:

■ Don't contract on a retainer basis.

■ Treat them like you would a subcontractor.

■ Get bids for one program at a time.

■ Find out what services they provide and get an itemized list of charges. Contrary to what some agencies would have you believe, their services are not free. Advertising agencies get their fee (15 percent of your ad costs) from the media. Be alert for extra charges. Your local newspaper probably considers you a retail account. That means they don't allow a 15 percent discount for an ad agency. If your agency places newspaper ads for you, they may have to charge an additional 15 percent for their services.

Treat all media salespeople as if they were car salesmen. Just practice caution and remember — buyer beware.

It may be a little unfair of me to paint all advertising agencies with the same brush. Most are very professional and worth the cost — at least for some of their clients. I just don't feel that a remodeling contractor needs one.

Radio stations always provide full help in designing your ad messages and the "voicing." They do it for free, too (free, in the sense that it's included in the price of the ad, so you're paying for the help whether you use it or not). Radio stations do allow agencies a 15 percent discount for placing ads with them. That discount isn't available to you, unless you're a very good negotiator. Which brings up an interesting thought: If you start your own *in-house ad agency*, you'll qualify for these discounts. If your advertising budget runs more than about $100,000 a year, consider setting up your own in-house agency so you keep the commission.

Public Relations

Publicity releases may be the best marketing tool of all. And they're free — almost. Getting free publicity isn't too hard. If you have something that's newsworthy, someone is bound to be interested. Most local newspapers will print articles about grand openings, anniversaries and new branch businesses. They're always looking for informative articles for their real estate and home improvement sections.

Write up the articles yourself and include a photograph of your office, showroom, building, or truck. Don't send in your own picture, however — that makes it look like you're seeking personal publicity. If you're not a budding Hemingway, let someone who *is* help you with the writing.

There are many ways to get free publicity. Speaking to groups is just one. The Chamber of Commerce, service clubs, fraternal orders, senior organizations and schools are always on the lookout for speakers. If you don't have good public speaking skills, join the local Toastmasters Club. Or get someone capable and willing in your organization to do it. Before or after the talk, send a news release to the local newspapers.

Develop Your Company Image

Your *image* is how the public perceives your operation. It's an intangible that doesn't show up on your balance sheet. But it's a valuable asset. At least in part, your profits (or losses) reflect what the buying public thinks of your business.

Offer low, low prices, and people will peg your remodeling company as a cheap outfit. That image isn't the kind you want. But it is an image nevertheless. Stress high-quality workmanship and materials, and people will assume high prices and possibly unmet completion dates. That's image too — also not the kind you want.

Some remodelers have a better public image than others. And it probably took the good ones a long time to build up that reputation. It takes care and attention to maintain a desirable image in the marketplace. It takes even longer to turn a bad one around.

Live Up to Your Image

First you must determine the needs of the marketplace, then design your company image to support that need. Do you want a reputation for high-quality workmanship or for low, competitive prices? One-stop full service capability? Fast job completions? Liberal credit and terms? Whichever you choose, recognize that promotion sets your image as a professional remodeler.

Do you know what your public image is? You might think that you're known for high-quality workmanship when you're actually associated with liberal credit. Or maybe you think your business is increasing because you work fast, when actually increased volume is the result of low prices. It's hard to assess what the public thinks of your business.

How do you find out what the public thinks of your company? Conduct an informal survey. Ask your present customers, prospective customers and non-customers. Ask new customers why they chose your company. Ask current customers what they think about your company. Get answers to a few direct, open-ended questions. Also ask how they think your services can be improved. And don't forget about the opinions of your own key people.

What Do Your Key People Think?

Ask your key people — employees and friends — to take a few moments to fill out a simple survey. You fill one out as well. Compare your own perceptions with each of theirs. This will help you identify those areas that need improvement.

When you feel you've surveyed enough people, total the results of each question and divide by the number of people surveyed. This will give you the average opinion score for each question.

The results will show where the weaknesses are. They'll also show you where your strengths are.

Figure 1-2 is a suggested survey for your key people. You may want to reword it and add more questions that relate specifically to your operation. You can design a similar form to use for customers and prospective customers.

You'll probably get more honest responses if the surveys are anonymous. Otherwise employees will give answers they expect you'll

Opinion Survey

Rating: 10 = Excellent;   8 = Good;   5 = Average;   3 = Poor;   1 = Bad
Trend: NC = No Change;   + = Improving;   – = Deteriorating

Questions	Rating	Trend
1) The business in general		
2) Management overall		
3) Courtesy to customers		
4) Staff morale		
5) Pricing structure		
6) Salespeople		
7) Advertising		
8) Sales & promotional materials		
9) Management leadership		
10) Construction superintendents		

List our three strongest assets:

List our three weakest points:

Figure 1-2   *Opinion survey for key people*

want to hear, friends will avoid hurting your feelings, and customers will do what they can to earn a discount or better service.

To Sum It Up

A major cause of failure in the remodeling business is low volume or wide swings in volume. Some of that's to be expected, of course. But having too few customers is the direct result of poor marketing. You need a steady flow of new customers to be successful. Remember, if you have an adequate customer base, your business will survive in good times as well as bad. That's why marketing is so important. And it's also why marketing is the first chapter in this book.

Marketing includes advertising. Effective advertising requires promotional literature, handling sales leads, projecting advertising budgets, and much more. It's a huge subject, much too large to cover completely in one chapter. But if you've digested this chapter, you're several steps ahead of most remodeling contractors.

I'll end the chapter with this slogan that says it all: Take good care of marketing, and marketing will take good care of you.

2

Selling Your Market

Next to choosing your market, *selling* that market is your most important job. Everybody sells something to one degree or another. By definition, when you sell, you persuade people of the value of something and inspire them with a desire to have it.

Your employees have jobs because they *sold* you on hiring them. To be successful in remodeling, you have to be successful at *selling* your services. Just knowing how to estimate and how to do the work isn't enough. Selling is vital. When your business is too large for you to do all the selling yourself, you'll hire someone to help you. Then you have to manage your sales staff so that you're successful — and they are, too.

Understanding Sales Types

Professional salespeople are both valuable and vulnerable. Your success or failure depends largely on them. Learn to recognize and understand the three basic types:

1) *One-shot salespeople*: Because they close a sale on the first call, they're sometimes affectionately called "slamdunkers." They're usually in door-to-door sales or selling used cars or insurance. While it would be great to close every sale on the first call, that rarely happens in remodeling sales. There are just too many factors involved. Still, you'll find an occasional one-shot, hot-shot salesperson engaged in remodeling sales.

2) *Order takers*: Distributor's agents and people who "sell" industrial products fall into this category. They don't sell. They just make themselves available to take orders — if anyone is interested in buying. Don't hire this type. They'll be a handicap on your sales team. Order takers waste valuable leads.

"John is our top salesman. Maybe that's why we're going broke."

3) *Sales engineers*: These people *create* sales. They evaluate the customer's needs, customize your product and service to fit the needs, close the sale, and then provide after-sales service. Find a sales engineer to be your sales manager and you've got it made. Unfortunately, these people are hard to find and harder to keep once you've found them.

Your salespeople are the most important people in your company — after you, of course. Each one can bring in a million dollars' worth of sales a year. That means each one could bring you a gross profit close to half a million. Who else in your organization can do that?

A few good salespeople can make you a millionaire in just a few years — if you treat them with respect and make it worth their while. Otherwise they'll go to work for your competitors or go into business for themselves. Understand them, motivate them, and . . .

Treat Them Right

To hold onto outstanding salespeople, you have to know what makes them tick. Here are some common characteristics of sales types, and how you should respond to them:

1) *Most have extremely high drive and energy levels.* They'll put in long workdays for weeks on end, then suddenly short circuit. A some point, their tired body just can't keep up any longer. If you see this coming on, insist that they take some time off and relax — before the short circuit happens.

2) *They need to prove themselves by constantly selling.* Keep them supplied with sales leads. They'll give every one of those leads their very best closing effort.

3) *They need a lot of admiration and recognition.* Treat them with respect. Bolster their self confidence. Otherwise they'll likely drift to another job where their ego is better satisfied. If you can keep them happy, they'll stay with you.

4) *They need your full support.* They want to represent a reliable company that discharges its obligations honestly. No one likes to apologize for promises ignored and blunders committed. They might lie to a client once or twice to protect their reputation. But it won't go on forever. Don't drive your best salespeople into the arms of the competition.

5) *You hire a sales staff to sell.* Don't make them do other things. Their sales rhythm will suffer if they're running errands, making deliveries, collecting debts, or supervising jobs. Good salespeople can earn commissions of $50,000 to $100,000 a year. This means they must average $2,000 to $5,000 a day in sales. They can't do that if you steal even a little of their selling time for other duties.

6) *Good salespeople don't have time for paperwork.* Keep that to a minimum. You'll drive good people away if you force them to do too much record keeping, letter writing, or accounting.

7) *Guard against end-running your salespeople.* If you mail a quote to a prospect instead of letting the salesperson deliver it, that's an end-run. You took away their opportunity to close the sale.

8) *Abide by your employment agreement* — especially when dealing with commission payments. Pay your sales staff precisely the amount they earned when it's due.

If you're beginning to suspect that it takes tolerance and flexibility to deal with salespeople, you're right. And they're worth every effort you put into nurturing them. I'll summarize the key do's and don'ts for salespeople:

- Do hold on to your highballers, the cream of the cream.

- Do keep your promises: people have long memories for broken ones.

- Do establish a reputation for fair play and good pay.

- Don't nitpick their paychecks.

- Don't hold out on any of their commissions.

Observe these rules and the word will get around. Other crackerjacks will seek you out.

Remember, your sales department is your company's first line of offense (for profits) and best defense (for survival). Without healthy sales volume, you have nothing. Your equipment, organization, personnel, and experience won't mean a thing.

So tolerate some shortcomings in salespeople. Understand that they're specialists and require special handling. Help them improve their work habits and become more disciplined. But *never* fire a good producer just because he or she isn't as easy to get along with as other employees.

On the other hand, don't hesitate to fire a poor producer. A salesperson who blows just one lead a month can cost you dearly. If you have a sales staff of five, and each fumbles one lead a month, that's sixty leads lost in a year. What does that mean in dollars?

At a cost of $100 a lead, you've wasted $6,000. But let's look at it another way. Suppose your average job sells for $15,000. Your gross profit should be at least $5,000. If even one salesperson blows one lead a month, you've lost $60,000 in gross profits. Multiply that by five, and the loss is staggering.

How to Find Them

I've never found a foolproof way to identify good salespeople in advance. The most unlikely candidate may be a super producer. Look for people who are neat and well-spoken, friendly and attractive. It's true some people break all the rules and still write millions of dollars in sales year after year. What's their secret? I don't know. Of course, some remodelers use aptitude tests or personality tests and eliminate the obvious misfits. But my best guide is my intuition. I hire friendly, attractive people who make a good first impression.

Here's an approach that's worked for me: Interview ten to fifteen applicants. Pick two or three and put them on a probationary period, even though you need only one. That gives you a better chance of finding a winner. You may even get lucky and get two good people. If you get more good people than you expected, great! Keep them. Just step up your advertising program to bring in more leads to keep your sales staff busy.

Once you find likely candidates, protect yourself with an employment agreement.

Your Employment Contract

You can prevent most of the likely misunderstandings with salespeople by having each sign an employment contract. It should cover all the terms and conditions of employment. The agreement in Appendix B has saved me a lot of grief — and probably a few lawsuits. Use it as is or adapt it to suit your circumstances. Because it's such an important document, and because laws vary from state to state, have your lawyer review it before you use it. The important thing is to have a good agreement and use it consistently. You may not appreciate its value until you encounter a sticky situation — but believe me, it can save your hide.

How to Pay Them

You can base compensation for sales on salary, straight commission, or a combination of sales and commission. Salary alone doesn't seem to work for me. There's not enough incentive. The best salespeople will be underpaid and the worst will be overpaid. Neither will see the direct relation between production and compensation. In general, straight salary tends to attract an order taker instead of a sales engineer.

A small base salary plus a low commission rate isn't much better. I've interviewed a number of seasoned pros. They tell me they feel that an employer restricts their earning power with a base salary. They don't believe they're getting enough return on their investment of time and energy.

Straight Commissions Work Best

Put all your salespeople on a commission system. It's what professional salespeople want. The size of the paycheck should be directly proportional to effort and results. Stick with straight commission, even if your best sales engineer seems overpaid while the weakest link is starving. Payment proportional to production is the fairest system for remodelers and salespeople alike.

But make sure salespeople work only for you. Don't let anyone sell both your service and some other contractor's service on the same sales call. Include that in your employment agreement.

Commission Plus Bonus

A straight commission system that's enhanced with a bonus can be even more of an incentive than straight commission. Everybody wins. I'll explain.

Let's assume we're paying an 8 percent commission on the selling (or *book*) price. That's the going rate from many remodeling contractors. Remember, the book price is based on the unit price system. It's the *minimum* price your salespeople can work with.

If they make a sale at a price higher than the book price, they get a bonus. Let's look at an example based on a bonus of 50 percent of the difference.

Jake sold a room addition job. He calculated a price of $26,000 from the BP (book price) minimum. But he actually sold it for $30,000. How much did Jake earn? First, he made the 8 percent on the $26,000 book price, or $2,080. Then there's the 50 percent bonus on the $4,000 difference between book price and sale price. Half of $4,000 is $2,000. So Jake's total commission for that sale is $4,080. That's nothing to sneeze at.

But suppose Jake wrote up the contract for less than the book price. Then I'd use a *short-rated commission*, 6 percent or less instead of 8 percent. Of course, the sale isn't final until the company accepts the contract, so you could turn down the job at that price if you wanted to.

The job should have been sold for at least $26,000, but Jake just couldn't sell it at that price. Rather than lose the contract completely, he wrote up the sale anyway, fairly confident the company would approve it. He knew his commission would be less, but less is better than nothing.

If the owner isn't willing to pay a cent over $20,000, your company may not want the business. But Jake can't be certain of that. He should write it up anyway. If you need the work to bridge a cash flow problem, or

"Unfortunately, your policy doesn't cover arguing with housewives over remodeling kitchens."

have excess materials on hand, you may welcome even a low-profit job. Salespeople may not have that kind of information. So let them write up the contracts and leave it to you to accept or reject them.

Par Principle

The par principle is another payment method sometimes used by remodelers. The company sets the minimum (par) price for the job. Then it's up to the salesperson to sell at a price above par to earn his or her commission. It works this way. The par price is the company's estimated cost. The company's profit and the salesperson's commission come from the amount that the sales price exceeds the estimated cost of doing the job.

For example, Tony sells a kitchen remodeling job for $20,000. The par price set by the company is $14,000. The amount over par is shared on a prearranged percentage. It's often 50/50, but it could be 60/40, 40/60, 70/30, or whatever. In a 50/50 split, Tony makes $3,000 for the sale.

This method of payment can lead to some valid questions. How were the par prices calculated? Are the overhead figures accurate? How much is built in for executive salaries, contingencies and expenses? Is there some profit built into the par prices that the salespeople don't know about? What if the actual cost exceeds the par price?

That's why the par price system isn't used much any more by remodeling contractors.

How to Pay the Commissions

How and when you pay sales commissions should be clearly spelled out in the employment agreement. One common method is to pay half when the sale is closed (when all the contract documents are signed and financing is in place). The other half is due when construction starts. Make disbursements as soon as possible following the date the commissions are earned.

Another way is to pay on the *thirds principle*. Pay one-third after closing or the issuance of the building permit, one-third at the start of construction, and the final third on completion or when final payment is collected. Payments don't have to be in equal thirds. Many remodelers use 40:30:30 or 50:25:25.

Progress payments on sales commissions are often called *hold-out commissions*. It's a delayed payment commission scheme not generally favored by salespeople. So they may call it a *hold-up* commission, since the hold-out by the contractor is frequently unjustified. Even if the hold-out is justifiable, salespeople argue that delayed projects or delayed payments from the owners aren't their fault. They did their job, and that was to sell. And I'll admit that I have sympathy for these salespeople.

I don't recommend hold-out commissions. Sometimes they're used to cheat salespeople. Even when used honestly, it can lead to misunderstandings. That's a chance I wouldn't take.

Backcharges

Most contractors use a backcharge system. Just what is a backcharge? It's a charge imposed against a salesperson's commission to adjust for errors and omissions made by that salesperson. And some employers use it ruthlessly.

Should salespeople be responsible for errors and omissions in estimating, or for technical accuracy of the drawings and specifications? I don't think so. And yet backcharges are made every day against salespeople's earnings for just such things. I don't know why salespeople put up with it.

If you give your sales staff good training and have a system for reviewing every proposed contract, there should be little need for backcharges. Salespeople should be able to estimate, quote and write up contracts with very few errors. As far as I'm concerned, it's the contractor's fault if the salespeople don't know how to quote jobs correctly.

Set up checking systems to catch those inevitable errors and omissions before you accept the contract. That saves both you and your sales staff money and grief.

Now I'm not saying that backcharges are forbidden. Sometimes they're necessary. Here's an example. A homeowner claims that your salesperson promised to supply a lazy Susan in the kitchen cabinets. The salesperson forgot to specify it so you didn't do it. When asked, the salesperson admits to the oversight. In that case, a backcharge may be in order. Otherwise, the company absorbs the cost. It's your company. You make the decision.

Can You Use Independent Contractors?

Some home improvement contractors use independent contractors as salespeople. I don't recommend this. You have very little control. Independent contractors, by definition, work for themselves and may represent several companies. They're not putting their full effort into selling just for your company. They may know very little about your company, its products and capability. An independent may even shop your lead to another company that pays more or will take jobs at a lower price. All kinds of abuses are possible. Of course, not all independent contractors are unethical and dishonest. But can you tolerate even a single bad one?

Keeping Track of Commissions

It's good practice to keep accurate records of each salesperson's earnings. The form in Figure 2-1 is a weekly summary sheet for each sales rep's commissions. Use one sheet for each salesperson. It's worth the time to keep these forms up to date. They provide the kind of data you might need at a glance — including the job number, customer's name, contract amount, and commissions. This is confidential information, so keep the forms in a locked file cabinet.

How to Motivate Them

Salespeople dragging along in low gear can cost you a bundle. If someone is having a dry spell, give them some of your best leads. But also let them know that you expect top performance.

CONFIDENTIAL									Summary no.		

Sales Rep's Commissions (Weekly summary)

Date:

Sales rep:

Report by:

Week ending:

Job no.	Customer	Contract amount	Book price	Overbook price	Commission amounts		Manager's override	Total amount	Adjustments
					(book)	(overbook)			
		$	$	$	$	$	$	$	

Total

Figure 2-1 *Weekly commission summary*

Aggressive marketing + aggressive selling

Hold Contests

Contests between your salespeople can provide a reason to put out a little extra effort. If you run contests, make the rules clear. Post them for everyone to see. Make the contests short and award prizes promptly.

Consider setting monthly minimums tailored to each person's average volume. Joe, for instance, averages $60,000 a month. Set his contest goal at $72,000, a 20 percent increase. Tony, a new man, is averaging $30,000 a month. Set his at $36,000, also a 20 percent increase.

A sale brought in from a salesperson's own lead deserves a bonus. Pay an extra $100. Why not? It's good business. It encourages the sales staff to go after more business, rather than rely just on leads you supply.

Their Responsibilities — and Yours

The prime function of your salespeople is to sell. Their responsibilities should end when the sale is closed. You didn't train them to run your errands, or collect your debts, or supervise your jobs. Make sure they do only one thing and do it well — sell!

Salesperson's Responsibilities

Make clear to all sales personnel that you expect them to follow certain routines to the letter. Sales meetings, for instance. Expect everyone to attend. Sales calls which happen to conflict with meetings take priority, of course, but they'll be infrequent. On other days, have salespeople telephone or come in for their sales leads and messages — preferably during the morning. Discourage late afternoon call-ins. Leads that come in during the morning may have appointments set for the same afternoon. The salesperson who's on the ball will pick up the choice leads before noon.

The Cardinal Sin

The cardinal sin for any salesperson is to ignore sales leads. Qualified leads are hard to get, and expensive. A salesperson who makes a half-hearted presentation, then rushes off to a football game, is dropping the ball. I suppose every salesperson has done it at one time or another. But it sure hurts to know that a call was wasted. A salesperson who deliberately fumbles a lead deserves a reprimand.

Evening and weekend selling is the norm in the remodeling business. Make sure your salespeople know that when you hire them. They can't refuse or ignore evening or weekend sales appointments because they conflict with personal activities.

Site Surveys

Some remodelers require their salespeople to accompany the superintendent or designer when they examine and remeasure the project. I think that's a good practice. It reduces the likelihood of a misunderstanding about the job.

In general, I don't recommend having your sales staff do anything but sell. But I know some successful remodelers who train and require their salespeople to schedule and supervise their own jobs. Other remodelers try to keep salespeople off the site once work has begun. The salesperson isn't the owner's contact person in the company. Any complaints about construction should go through the job supervisor or person with authority to make changes in job specs.

Controlling Sales Records

Insist that all sales contracts and deposits be turned in to your sales offices without delay. Expect them the next morning at the latest. The sales manager should be briefed on all important facts of the sale. Also require this minimum paperwork:

- The contract form properly completed with all authorized signatures in place.

- The owner's signature on the acceptance of the specifications.

- The credit application and employment verification form completed and signed.

- The sketches with details and measurements.

- The book price worksheet.

The sales manager should be sure all documents are accurate and complete. This is the time to find any errors or omissions in the contract. Check to see if the job was sold short. (Selling short means selling below the book price or par price.) Calculate the sales commission and the gross margin, and evaluate the owner's ability to get financing. A lot of this checking can go on during the rescission period (three working days under federal law). But don't spend *too* much time at this stage; the owner can back out of the contract without any penalty up until the end of the three days.

You Provide Sales Tools

Your sales staff needs some support if they're going to get first-class results. Your responsibility is to provide the sales tools they need. Let's take a look at the most important tools.

Sales manual

Provide a three-ring binder with the company name, address, and logo screen printed on the cover. Number every manual, and have the salesperson sign for it. Remember, it's probably worth several hundred dollars. The manual should include:

- Color photographs of recent jobs

- Copy of contractor's license(s)

- Copy of business license

- Guarantee/warranty

- Bonds

- Evidence of liability insurance

- Contract forms

- Project survey

- Credit application form

- Employment verification form

- Business cards

- Brochures

Provide at least four pages of photos, either 5 x 7 or 8 x 10. Each salesperson will also need a ruled pad, graph paper, your confidential book price list, a tape measure, a Polaroid camera and film, a 6-inch scale rule and a pocket calculator with square root function. You might also want to provide premiums that the sales staff can give away when it's appropriate.

Just make sure that every salesperson accepts responsibility for all company property in his or her possession. Attach a $500 value to the sales kit simply to persuade the sales staff to return everything when asked to.

Leads Are Your Responsibility

Make sure that every salesperson is supplied with enough sales leads to fill most of their daily selling time. That's the only way they can earn a decent income and stay with your company.

What is an adequate supply of sales leads? If you specialize in room additions and second-story projects with a minimum job size of $10,000, about twenty leads a month for each salesperson would probably be enough. But there's no easy way to determine how many leads a salesperson can service in a week.

If you have a lower-cost specialty, like installing windows, siding, or gutters, you may have to furnish four or five leads a day to each salesperson. A salesperson for a handyman-type operation will probably need eight leads a day to keep busy and earn a good living.

It bears repeating: it's your responsibility to provide enough good leads. Remind your sales staff that it's their responsibility to give their best effort for each lead you provide — without exception.

The lead sheet

Train someone in your office to handle all incoming inquiries. Prepare your lead qualifier (or LQ, for short) to answer the questions they're sure to face, like these:

- What kind of work does your company do?

- Do you charge for estimates?

- How long would it take to get a quote?

- Is it necessary for both my spouse and me to be present?

- Is financing available?

- Can you give me a ballpark figure for my new bathroom?

- How much would a new bedroom cost?

Teach your LQ to be alert to clues which will help your sales staff. Make sure they write down comments like: "We have a few quotes already." or "My husband was a carpenter." Such comments should be recorded on a *lead sheet*. The LQ should also note the attitude of the prospect. Is he eager? Reluctant? Pugnacious? All of these things will be of immense value to the salesperson. Figure 2-2 is the lead sheet I use. Notice that fully one third of the form is used for these comments.

Always try to service leads within 24 hours, unless the prospect wants a later date. If you tell a prospect that someone will call later to set up an appointment, it could be days or even weeks before you make contact again. That prospect may be lost forever. So set up those appointments during the initial phone call. When a prospect is anxious to get a quote, don't disappoint. That's a buying signal you shouldn't let pass.

Here's an ideal conversation, from your point of view. Say it's Monday morning. The appointment book and lead sheet are sitting in front of the telephone. Your LQ says "We can see you tomorrow afternoon, or would the evening be better? How would 8 o'clock be? Good, we'll see you and your wife at eight then. We'll phone about six to reconfirm this appointment. My name is Kathy. Thank you for calling."

Name		Date:	
Address		Salesperson	
City		Appointment date:	
Telephone:	Home:	Day:	Time:
Requires the following:		Source:	By:

Requires the following:

- ☐ Kitchen
- ☐ Bathroom
- ☐ Family room
- ☐ Bedroom
- ☐ Laundry room

- ☐ Room addition
- ☐ 2nd story
- ☐ Garage
- ☐ Carport
- ☐ Fireplace

- ☐ Sun room
- ☐ Decks
- ☐ Staircase
- ☐ _____
- ☐ _____

- ☐ Residence
- ☐ Commercial
- ☐ Townhouse
- ☐ Apartment
- ☐ New   ☐ Old

- ☐ New work
- ☐ Remodel

- ☐ Financing required
- ☐ Equity: $ _____

- ☐ Yes
- ☐ No

Comments:

Price quoted:

Office: 01   02   03

Followup date:

Received:

Sales report:

Location:

Reviewed by:

Figure 2-2 *Lead sheet*

Remember to confirm each appointment one or two hours ahead. The LQ (like Kathy) or the salesperson can make the confirmation. Make it short. "Hello, Mr. Smith. This is Kathy from Goodguys Construction. I'm just calling to confirm our appointment for 8 o'clock this evening." That's about all you need.

Have your salespeople take the lead sheet along on the call. Use the form to describe the highlights of the presentation and the results. Train your sales staff to use certain standard descriptive words in their reports. Here are some sales terms and their definitions.

- *Sold* means you've received a deposit along with all completed and signed documents. It doesn't mean that the sale has been closed. You still need financing approval, final drawings, permits and passage of the rescission period.

- *Unqualified* means your salesperson didn't pursue the sale for some valid reason. Perhaps the job was too small to accept, illegal to build, or impossible to do. The owner may have been bid shopping, and the salesperson was the fifth one asked for a price quote. (Your salespeople shouldn't waste time on low-ball bid shoppers.)

- A *miss* is when you've measured, drawn sketches, quoted a price, made the presentation and asked for the job at least four times. But the sale may not be dead yet.

- *Call-back* means the salesperson will try again after a miss. There's still a chance to write up a sale.

- *Recall* means a lead appointment has been rescheduled before the original call is made.

How to Evaluate Your Sales Success

I've never met the perfect salesperson. You won't either. Everyone in sales has room for improvement. And everyone in sales should be working to improve their performance. Keep track of *sales ratios* (number of sales closed divided by the number of leads accepted).

I can't tell you how many sales you should expect from a given number of leads. It depends on where the leads come from, the type of work, the community where the work will be done and your prices. Your company's reputation in the community also has an impact on the closing ratio.

Lead source	Trainees			Sales Engineers		
	Min	Avg	Good	Min	Avg	Good
Newspapers	1:10	1:8	1:5	1:8	1:6	1:4
Yellow Pages	1:10	1:8	1:5	1:8	1:6	1:4
Direct mail	1:15	1:12	1:10	1:12	1:9	1:7
Telemarketing	1:9	1:7	1:5	1:8	1:6	1:4
Referrals	1:6	1:5	1:3	1:5	1:4	1:2
Radio/TV	1:10	1:8	1:6	1:8	1:6	1:4
Showroom: walk-in	1:8	1:6	1:4	1:8	1:6	1:4

Figure 2-3 *Sales ratio chart*

Of course, you'd expect a higher closing rate from referrals by satisfied customers than from telemarketing. If you have a twenty-year history of good performance, you'll be more successful than a company just starting out. And if you're operating with a low gross margin, your lower quotes will bring in more sales.

Sales Ratios

Sales ratios — and the way they're computed — vary from one company to another. But it doesn't matter what method you use as long as you're consistent. You need some valid way to measure the success or failure of your marketing efforts.

Use the sales ratio chart in Figure 2-3 as a guide. How do your salespeople compare? Use the chart as a guide for developing your own chart. Of course, your sales figures will probably be different. But it's important that you see what's happening to the sales ratio — and know the direction of change.

Assume the chart is for a typical small remodeling company. They've been in business for about three years, selling at a 70 percent markup. Their average job has a direct cost of $4,000 (labor and materials) and a selling price of $6,800. Their gross margin is 41 percent.

According to this chart, a sales trainee (one with less than six months' selling experience) should average one sale in every twelve direct mail leads. Selling one out of ten leads is pretty good. But one of the trainees, Jim, has gone through thirty leads and produced nothing. Something may be wrong. It's time for some analysis.

It may be that the direct mail campaign blanketed the wrong area, too many new houses and apartments. But it also may be that Jim's not effective at selling. Someone should identify the problem so you don't waste any more leads.

Your goal is to develop a team of professional, well-paid, very effective sales engineers. It's never easy. But many remodeling companies have done it. You can too.

The Follow-up Letter

Here's a good way to find out how your prospects view your salespeople. Use a follow-up letter like Figure 2-4. Of course, not everyone will reply, but the ones with strong impressions, either good or bad, will take the time to let you know. I've seen letters come back full of compliments, and I've seen letters that are anything but flattering. Either way, you need to know.

The letter is essentially a questionnaire asking about the salesperson's attitude and your company's performance on the job. It also asks for recommendations.

We've talked about identifying your market and described some techniques for building a team of salespeople to sell in that market. In the next chapter, I'll suggest ways to train your sales staff and describe what I feel is the best way to supervise salespeople.

Goodguys Construction Company

Date _____

Dear _____,

    The work we've been doing for you is now complete — except for one important detail. We want to thank you for your patience and understanding during the construction period. In case I don't get a chance to tell you in person, please accept my most sincere thanks. Of course, we're always trying to improve the work we do. I would appreciate receiving any comments you would like to make about the work we did. Please take a few minutes to tell us what we did well, and where you think we need to improve. Your comments and suggestions will be held in strictest confidence. No one except myself will see what you write. And I won't reveal your name or what you said to anyone. I've enclosed a stamped addressed business reply envelope for your convenience. Thank you for your help.

Circle Yes or No

1. Did we complete the job as promised?   Y   N

2. Was our salesperson courteous, helpful, and knowledgeable?   Y   N

3. Were the tradespeople who worked on your job neat and respectful of you and your property?   Y   N

4. Do you believe they were adequately trained and well supervised?   Y   N

5. On a satisfaction scale of 1 to 10, how would you rate our performance?
        Poor   1   2   3   4   5   6   7   8   9   10   Excellent

6. May we use you as a reference?   Y   N

7. Do you have another job that we could quote on?   Y   N

    If yes, when?   now____   3 months____   6 months____   9 months____   months____

Figure 2-4 *Follow-up letter*

8. Please list the names of those you would like to recommend us to:

Name _____

Address _____

City/State _____

Telephone _____

Name _____

Address _____

City/State _____

Telephone _____

Comments, if any: _____

_____

_____

_____

_____

_____

_____

Please use the reverse side for any additional comments. Thank you very much for selecting our company and for taking the time to complete this evaluation letter.

Sincerely yours,

Figure 2-4 (cont'd) Follow-up letter

3

Training Your Sales Staff

Your applicants for sales positions will range from rank amateurs to experienced salespeople. Of course, you'll hire (and pay for) experience, if it's available. But no matter how skilled they are, every new employee needs some training. That's the subject of this chapter.

Indoctrinating new salespeople wouldn't be so much of a burden if turnover weren't so high in sales jobs. But because it is, your training program should be trouble-free and nearly automatic. That's the only way to maintain high standards among your salespeople.

This chapter describes a complete training program for your sales staff. Naturally, every remodeling company is unique. What works for my company may not work for yours. But you shouldn't have any trouble adapting the training program I outline here to meet your needs. And that's exactly what I recommend. Use the ideas I offer to create an effective, simple, trouble-free, and custom-designed program to train your new sales professionals.

Training is very important in this business. In remodeling, more than in any other construction field, you need to know your product and how to sell it. Here's why:

1) You're dealing with homeowners, not professional purchasing agents. Your buyers don't necessarily know what's possible and probably don't understand what they need. You have to educate them.

2) People don't usually buy remodeling jobs on price alone. Subjective likes and dislikes may be more important. That means your margin is likely to be higher when you sell customer satisfaction, not just new kitchens or baths or siding or flooring.

3) Job requirements are infinitely flexible. There are at least a thousand ways you can do almost any multi-trade remodeling project. Your sales staff has to understand the possibilities.

So what should your training program include? I suggest you divide it into three sections. First, the *paperwork:* sales procedures, contract law, and financing. Second, *construction:* layout and design principles, estimating, and the building process. Finally, *practice:* customer psychology, making in-home presentations, maintaining self-discipline, and an analysis of the trainee's performance.

At the end of this chapter I describe the training program I've used. Use it as I wrote it or adapt it to your needs. In any case, don't let salespeople follow up on leads until you're satisfied that they're able and willing to represent your company as trained professionals.

Your training program should be mostly individual study — no instructor is needed for most lessons. Where an instructor *is* needed, he should just introduce the subject, assign outside work and answer questions. The trainees should work individually on the classroom phase. And don't assign your top producer to teach the class. That would be foolish. Your top salesperson should be selling in the field, not working in your office.

Move into field training only after a trainee has completed the individual study phase. The trainee should accompany one of your pros on several sales calls. Let the recruit watch how the experts do it. Better yet, have recruits accompany several different salespeople so they can see several different approaches.

Some top producers don't like to have amateurs along while they're selling. I can understand that. But I've never seen a sale lost because there were two salespeople on site. And the advantage of having new salespeople learn firsthand from experienced pros is too great an opportunity to miss. Consider including in your employment agreement or company policy statement a requirement that salespeople help train recruits when making sales calls.

The Training Agreement

If you're doing a good job of training, the most intense competition for customers will probably come from former salespeople you've trained. And ex-employees always seem to compete with you head-to-head on your turf instead of developing new territories. Just think of the advantage they have. They know your company's techniques, supply sources, philosophy, secrets, strengths, and weaknesses. And you don't know any of theirs.

While you can't deny anyone the right to move on, no one should take company documents when they leave. Make that clear in your training agreement. Your sales training course belongs to you and has to be returned to your office when training is complete. That should reduce the temptation salespeople have to start their own remodeling business or to join your competition.

Before anyone begins your training program, they should sign a training agreement. Be very specific about what your company will provide and what you expect from the trainees. How will you pay the trainee? Will there be a salary during training, or a draw against future commissions?

■ Include a non-competition clause. It may be difficult to enforce, but include it anyway. The words I use are: "*All information and data on sales and leads are for the exclusive benefit of the Company, and are to be kept confidential by the Salesperson during his/her term of employment and for a period of one year thereafter. The Salesperson shall not solicit or conduct sales or services of any sort on behalf of any other company, person, or entity, nor recommend any other company, person or entity to any of the Company's customers or prospective customers.*" The sample employment agreement for salespeople is included as Appendix B of this book.

■ How long will classroom training last? Field training? You may vary the schedule, depending on the caliber of your trainees. Some will have more experience than others, and some might just be brighter, more enthusiastic and come in with a better attitude. Expect to spend two to five days on the study phase, then have trainees accompany an experienced salesperson on calls for a couple of days. After that, they can call on their own prospects with an old hand along as an observer. They should share their commissions with the observer on a percentage basis.

■ Describe the circumstances that would lead to termination by the company during the training period. Will you expect the return of any salary advances or draws? Of course, you can discharge any employee when there's cause, but make it plain to sales trainees that they'll be judged more on their attitude and outlook than on their technical knowledge.

■ What will you require of a trainee who quits voluntarily during the training period? Be very specific about that in your training agreement, but above all, make sure they return all training materials.

You can make the training agreement a separate contract, or include it in the Employment Agreement for salespeople. Cover everything I've discussed here, and any other conditions you decide are suitable for your company.

Sales Meetings

Training is a continuing process, and regular sales meetings are an important part of that process. I like to hold sales meetings twice a week, at 10:00 a.m. on Tuesdays and Fridays. What do you do at the meetings? Review every customer call and discuss problems that crop up. Set goals. Use this time to introduce products, invite feedback from the field and provide some motivation. Announce a contest, perhaps. Finally, assign the new leads. Keep the meetings short, informal and light, but make sure your people know you're serious about the results.

Keep the discussion lively and interesting. This is no time for monologs or browbeating. Invite product reps to come in to spotlight new

products your salespeople could be promoting. Pass out product brochures and color or fabric samples your salespeople can include in their presentation folders. That's impressive stuff. Invite a loan officer to answer questions at one of your sales meetings. Ask your subcontractors to come, too. They can explain how they work and answer questions. Use sales meetings to update the training of everyone who makes sales for your company.

Policy Manual for Salespeople

Later in this book, we'll talk about general company policies. Here, we'll concentrate on those policies and procedures that apply to salespeople in particular. You should provide copies for your sales staff to include in their company manual.

Begin your sales manual with an introduction that sets the tone for what follows. Describe your operating philosophy and sell your company to your salespeople. Figure 3-1 is the introduction from my sales manual.

Why Stress Training?

I know that many remodeling companies (even successful ones) don't have a formal training program like I've outlined in this chapter. I think that's a mistake. The most successful sales organizations in the U.S. use programs very much like the one I've described here. If IBM and Ford and General Motors and every significant stock brokerage house and thousands of major companies have sales training programs (with training manuals and tests and homework), don't you think your company should too?

Most major sales organizations train new recruits for one simple reason: it pays. It's money well invested. You can't turn a fresh hireling loose on an unsuspecting public and expect good performance and high productivity. We're in a highly technical, very complex business. If your sales training program isn't up to the challenge, your results will be erratic, at best.

Here's my advice. No matter what you've been doing, try what I suggest. Create a training course for new recruits. Use as much of the training program in the rest of this chapter as you can. Adapt it to suit your style and operation. Then make completing the course your first assignment to new employees. See if you don't have 50 percent fewer problems and at least 25 percent better production from new salespeople. That's been my experience.

Goodguys Construction Company

SALES TRAINING MANUAL

Introduction

Salespeople are the very foundation of every business, including ours. No matter how well a company is organized, or how good their equipment is, none of that is worth anything without sales that lead to adequate profits. We welcome you to our sales team and look forward to a successful relationship for all of us.

You'll be expected to work without supervision. You'll need a high degree of self-discipline that comes from self-awareness. You'll need to know the soft spots in your character and reinforce them from the reserves of your inner strength.

To succeed, you'll have to work harder than your neighbors — long hours, and odd hours. You must be willing to make personal sacrifices for the sake of your career. You'll need a thorough knowledge of construction techniques, and the ability to engineer sales. You'll make good money for your efforts, and you'll be a welcome part of a winning team.

A sales career, then, is a profession that demands dedication, study, and high integrity. Selling offers both financial and spiritual rewards.

Why Sell for Goodguys Construction?

Goodguys is emerging as a leader in the remodeling industry in this part of the state. We control more than half of the market in this community and have the largest, most impressive showroom in this area. We've reached this impressive level of market penetration and performance after only three years of operation.

It took a highly professional sales force to get us to where we are today. And yet, very few of our salespeople had any experience selling remodeling before joining Goodguys. Much of the credit for our rapid growth goes to the sales training program we've used consistently since the company was founded. That's why we insist that you complete the training program before you begin selling for Goodguys Construction.

Another reason for our success is the bond protection we offer to every customer. Goodguys is among the rare few in this community who provide a bond on every job. This is a strong sales point.

Figure 3-1 *Introduction to sales training manual*

Goodguys also has the most efficient system to get sales leads. There are very few days when our sales staff does not have active leads from qualified prospects. No one has ever left Goodguys for lack of sales leads.

Goodguys salespeople earn well above the industry average. Typical earnings for full-time sales staff range upward from $4,000 to over $10,000 a month.

Training

Goodguys assumes all sales department recruits are inexperienced. We require everyone to complete our training program. The study phase includes design, construction methods and terminology, contract law, and sales techniques. This is the academic side to becoming a professional remodeling construction salesperson.

How long it takes you to complete the first part of your training is up to you. There will be both classroom study and individual study assignments to complete. The emphasis is on knowledge and understanding. Everyone who completes the work is certified as a Goodguys sales professional. While we expect you to absorb a lot of technical information, your instructor will decide when you're ready to sell effectively on your own, based on your performance during training, and on their observation of your overall attitude. Desire and attitude are the most important attributes of a good sales trainee.

Phase two, field training, starts after you've successfully completed the study phase. Field training will continue for at least one week, depending on the progress you make. During this time you'll meet our sales staff, attend sales meetings, be assigned leads, make presentations, prepare the required paperwork, practice closing methods, and sell your first job. Your sales trainer or sales manager will accompany you during part of this week.

What Goodguys Will Provide

1) Subsistence pay of $_____ a day during formal training. This pay is a draw against future commissions.

2) The finest and most informative training available.

3) A minimum of _____ qualified leads per month after you complete your training.

4) A sales kit containing: (Specify what your company will supply.)

What Goodguys Expects of You

1) Always represent the company in a dignified, fair, and honest manner.

2) Accept and follow up all sales leads and give them 100 percent of your effort.

3) Attend all sales meetings unless a sales call prevents you from doing so.

4) Observe all company policies and the terms of your Employment Agreement.

5) Maintain a minimum level of sales if you're on a draw system. *(Or meet the quota set by the sales manager.)*

Figure 3-1 (cont'd) *Introduction to sales training manual*

The Training Program Outline

Classroom and Individual Study

Use material from this book as a text, and refer to it for specifics about the following sections. Craftsman Book Company publishes several other books on remodeling and construction in general. Use the card in the back of this book to order them for your training library.

Use part of each classroom day to introduce the subject matter, review the previous day's work and answer questions, then distribute handouts and release trainees to study on their own.

The figures that follow are samples, intended to guide you as you design your own training manual. You're welcome to copy the parts that apply to your business, and use to rest to remind you of things you should cover. The italicized paragraphs in parentheses are notes to you, the reader, about additional things you can include in your own manual.

Day 1:

Company policies

Give each trainee a copy of your policy manual and briefly describe the high points — your company organization, personnel rules, and benefits.

Paperwork

In the packet for this lesson, include all the forms you use when you estimate and sell a job, along with detailed instructions about what goes in every blank line or space.

Provide trainees with a chart of symbols to use when they make sketches. Explain exactly how to take measurements — which ones have to be precise and to what degree.

Be sure trainees know who gets each piece of paper when they've completed it, and what happens to it once they turn it in. They'll need that information to expedite their jobs and answer questions from customers during the course of the job.

■ *Day 1 handouts*

1) Your company policy manual

2) Samples of all your company forms (except **estimating forms which** you'll cover on Day 4), with filled-out examples.

Day 2:

Contract law

Describe your contract requirements in detail. Explain the customer's rescission rights and your legal limits for deposits, down payments and progress payments.

How much authority will trainees have to make decisions on their own? Specify the dollar limit for contracts or specific operations that must be approved by others in your company before a salesperson can present a bid to the customer.

Financing

If you offer financing yourself, this will be a major part of the training program — how to qualify clients, what information you must have before you'll carry their job, and how to verify that information. Be sure the trainees understand how much of that is their responsibility, and what part will be handled by someone else in your company. Introduce your controller, credit or finance manager, and have that person tell trainees how to reduce the risk of writing bad loans.

If you work with a bank or loan company, invite their representative to attend this training session to describe their requirements and procedures.

■ *Day 2 handouts*

1) Your sales contract

2) Credit application

3) Forms for verifying employment and financial information

Day 3:

Building terminology

In the handouts for your class, include a glossary of construction terms that relate to your business specialty. Discuss them, and provide lots of pictures. Figure 3-2 is a sample.

Construction Terminology

Beam: A header more than 6" deep. See *Header.*

Bearing wall: A wall that supports weight on top of it. Only exterior walls are bearing walls in modern construction using engineered roof trusses.

Bottom plate: Treated lumber bolted to a footing, upon which studs are attached.

Cement: A component of concrete. Don't refer to the material in a driveway or foundation as cement when you really mean concrete.

Composition shingles: Roofing material, also called asphalt shingles.

Concrete: A mixture of sand, aggregate (gravel), cement and clean water.

Cripple: A short stud, such as above or below a window.

Curing time: The time it takes before you can walk on or frame over concrete, usually 2 to 5 days. Concrete cures to 90 percent strength in about a month. Concrete technologists claim that it takes about 40 years for concrete to reach maximum strength, after which it begins to deteriorate.

Drywall: Gypsum board interior wall finish used instead of plaster.

Expansion joints: A buffer, or a gap filled with a compressible material, in a concrete slab that prevents the slab from cracking with changes in temperature or moisture.

Expansive soil: Clay or adobe soils that lack proper drainage. Concrete has to be reinforced when placed on these soils.

Finish carpentry: Specialty that includes fine woodwork, mouldings, cabinets and doors.

Fire stops: 2 x 4 blocks fastened between studs.

Footing: A widening at the bottom of a wall that distributes the weight of the wall over a larger area of the ground.

GFCI: see *Ground fault circuit interrupter.*

Green concrete: Freshly placed concrete. Green or wet concrete sets up in a few hours. Allow two or three days curing time before putting any weight on new concrete.

Ground fault circuit interrupter (GFCI):   A device to instantly shut off electrical current in case of a short circuit to prevent fire or shock.

Gypsum board: see *Drywall*

Header: Support over a wall opening such as a window, doorway, or fireplace.

Figure 3-2   *Construction terminology*

Hot mop and rock: Roofing composed of rocks or colored gravel spread over hot asphalt that's mopped over felt paper fastened to plywood sheathing.

Jamb: The frame around a door or window.

Lintel: see *Header*

Monolithic pour: Concrete footing and slab poured in one operation, as opposed to separate pours, one for the footing and a later one for the slab.

Open sheathing: 1 x 4 lumber nailed to rafters 4" apart to form a base for wood shakes or shingles.

Plaster: see *Stucco*

Pony wall: A short wall, usually 3 or 4 feet high, that divides a room or defines a hallway.

Ridge cap: A layer of shingles placed over the ridge board of a roof to form a cap.

Rough electrical: Installation of circuit breakers, outlet, switch, and lighting boxes together with all necessary wiring.

Sheathing: Plywood nailed to rafters to form the base for composition shingles or a hot mop roof. Also, nailed to joists for raised floors or upper stories.

Slab on grade: A floor slab of concrete poured over compacted or firm bearing (soil, gravel or rock).

Sleeper floor: A floor that's built up with lumber and plywood to raise that floor to an existing floor level, or to line a concrete floor for warmth in cold climates.

Shear wall: A wall reinforced with plywood sheathing where braces can't be used because of space limitations.

Stem wall: The part of a foundation wall for a raised floor that shows above the ground.

Stucco: An exterior finishing material, made of *exterior* plaster, not to be confused with plaster, an interior wall finish.

Studs: Vertical 2 x 4s nailed on 16" centers between bottom and top plates of a wall. They're double at corners, and each side of windows, doors, and openings. Refer to Framing in your handout for Day 4.

Tapers: Extra long, machine-cut wooden shingles

Valley: The junction where two sloping roof surfaces meet.

Figure 3-2 (cont'd)   *Construction terminology*

Layout and design principles

Use lots of "before and after" sketches and pictures to illustrate the kinds of remodeling work your company specializes in. Figure 3-3 is a sample of some material you can use for your session on layout and design.

■ *Day 3 handouts*

1) A glossary of building terms

2) An illustrated design summary

Day 4:

Estimating and scheduling

Introduce your price book and show the students how to use it. They'll have a copy of this in their presentation kit, along with your estimating forms. But here's where you take them through a demo job and show them how you turn the raw measurements and your customer's requirements into a successful bid.

Put a marked-up copy of your price list with sample filled-out forms in the handout for this lesson, so trainees can refer back to it later if they forget what goes where, or where the information comes from.

Pay special attention here to things that *aren't* in the price book. Tell trainees where to find supplementary pricing information, and who in your company will help them with unusual situations.

Include a discussion of how to estimate how long a job will take, including time for concrete to cure, plaster and paint to dry, and other operations that require waiting time between steps. Remind trainees that jobs are sometimes held up while we wait for building inspectors. It's much better to leave some slack and finish a job ahead of schedule than to run late. Clients *hate* delayed completion dates. Figure 3-4 is a sample handout containing pricing information.

Planning the job

Here's where you cover the details of what it takes to get a job done. Your trainees may not have a strong background in construction, but that's OK. They don't have to know how to *build* a room addition or remodel a kitchen, but they *do* have to know about all the elements that go into the job so they can price it accurately. Figure 3-5 is a sample handout for this section.

Designing a Remodeling Project

One common problem with room additions is how to design access. Sometimes you have to create a new hallway, especially when you're adding a bedroom. Try using existing closet space.

That sometimes creates another problem though — nobody wants to give up closet space. See if you can increase the floor area of the addition to allow for more closet space between the existing and the new room. Illustration A shows one way to do this.

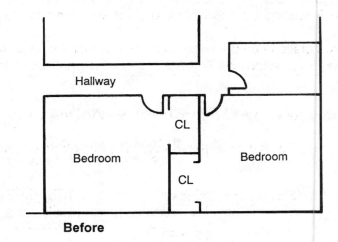

Before

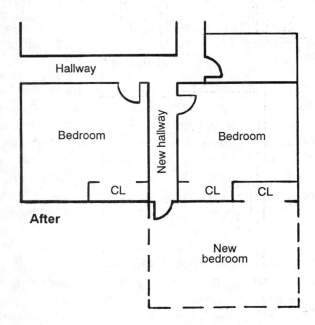

After

A Add a room and turn a closet into a hallway

Figure 3-3 *Designing a remodeling project*

Kitchens

Kitchens and baths provide unique remodeling challenges. Kitchens are food preparation and disposal areas, and often family rooms as well. Heavy appliances demand special electrical service and separate circuits. You have to consider traffic flow and convenience more carefully than in other areas of a home.

When you sell kitchen and bath remodels, especially in older homes, you probably have to allow for extensive relocation of electrical and plumbing services.

When you redesign a kitchen, pay primary attention to efficiency. Try to arrange the major work stations, cooking, food storage (including refrigeration) and cleanup in a triangle whose three sides total no more than 18 feet. Illustration B illustrates several common kitchen arrangements.

The cooking station can be a separate cooktop with the oven nearby, or a built-in or free-standing range. Remember, if you relocate the cooktop, you'll have to move the exhaust fan and electric service, and perhaps gas lines.

Try to locate counter space next to the refrigerator, and plan for a water line if the refrigerator has an ice maker.

When you help the customer select cabinets, don't forget to include drawer units.

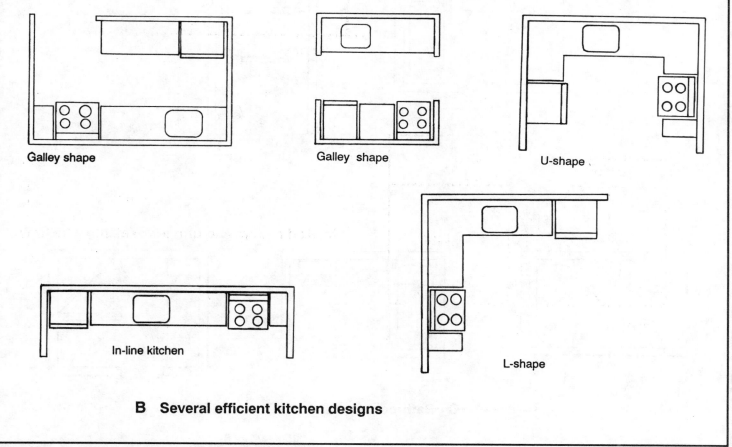

Galley shape

Galley shape

U-shape

In-line kitchen

L-shape

B   Several efficient kitchen designs

Figure 3-3 (cont'd)   *Designing a remodeling project*

Baths

Illustration C shows several typical bathroom layouts. Remember that the minimum clear size of a bathroom is about five by eight feet. Try to keep large-drain fixtures (bathtub and toilet) against a common wall to make plumbing less complicated.

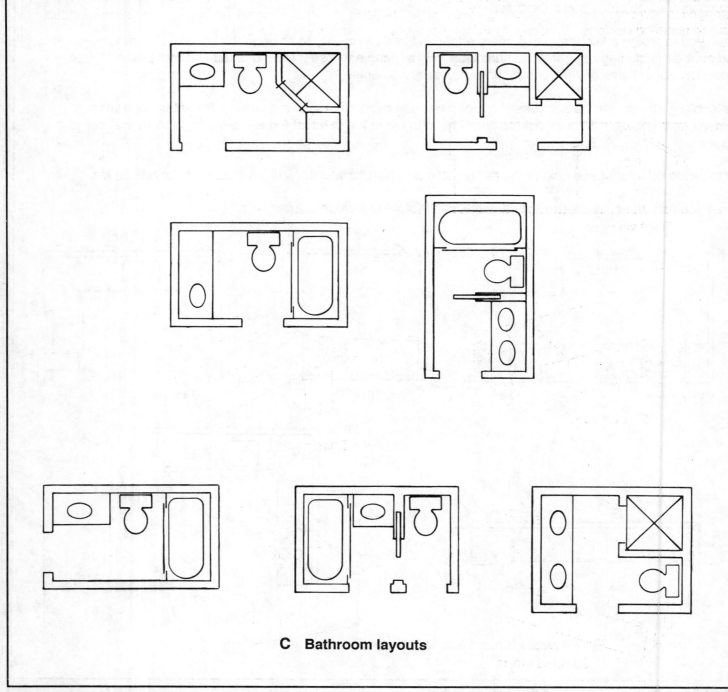

C Bathroom layouts

Figure 3-3 (cont'd)   *Designing a remodeling project*

Special Customer Requirements

Be sensitive to the special needs of your customers. Is the primary food preparer left-handed? They may prefer special placement of the dishwasher and garbage disposal. Are the owners especially tall (or short), visually or physically impaired? You may need to make special arrangements for cabinets or lighting.

You'll encounter all kinds of houses when you sell remodeling or room additions. The pictures in Illustrations D through L show some common housing styles. You may have to combine different roof styles to accommodate your remodeling designs, or modify an existing one like the example in Illustration M.

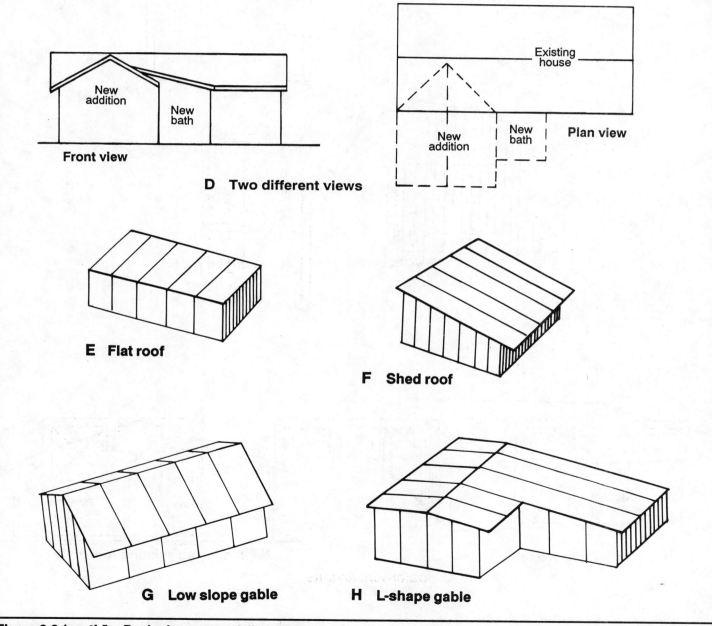

Figure 3-3 (cont'd)   *Designing a remodeling project*

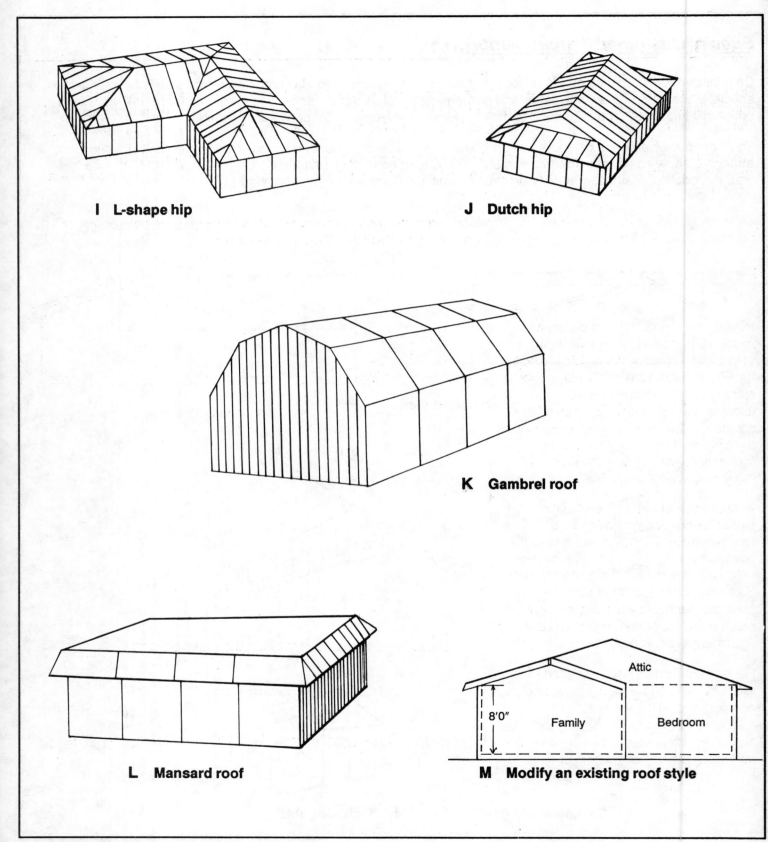

I   **L-shape hip**

J   **Dutch hip**

K   **Gambrel roof**

L   **Mansard roof**

M   **Modify an existing roof style**

Figure 3-3 (cont'd)   *The building process*

General Pricing Information

Our unit price list allows you to price jobs by the unit or square foot basis. These unit prices are *base prices* for normal or average situations. Unusual circumstances require additional charges. It's like buying a new car. You start with the base price, and then add to that for air conditioning, a turbocharger, a sun roof, or mag wheels.

Base prices include plans, permits, a slab floor, framing, composition shingles, stucco exterior, drywall interior, insulation, the standard (required by code) electrical outlets, and cleanup. It also includes stripping stucco where a room addition is attached to the existing house.

Base prices do *not* include demolition, plumbing, windows, doors, relocating or increasing electrical service, or decorating, such as painting, floor covering (including hardwood), or window treatments.

Pay Attention to Grading

Notice how your project is situated relative to the surrounding yard. If the yard slopes up from the building, you'll have to include additional charges for extra concrete, formwork and excavation, and drainage. Illustration A shows the ground sloping upward where a room addition will be built. The foundation wall has to be higher, and more excavation is required.

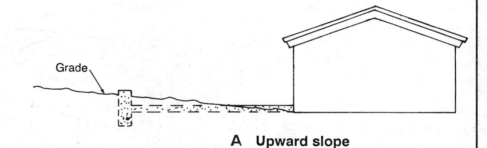

A   Upward slope

In Illustration B you can see that a higher foundation and extra fill is required even when the yard slopes downward. When you price these jobs, be sure to charge for the extra concrete. Your price book lists the cost for concrete per cubic yard. Figure how much extra concrete the job will take, and charge accordingly.

For example, if the book price for concrete is $150 per cubic yard, and you need an extra 16 cubic feet for a 16-foot-long foundation that's a foot higher than the base price allows, you'll have to charge an extra $88.89. (There are 27 cubic feet in a cubic yard, so 16/27ths of $150 is $88.89.)

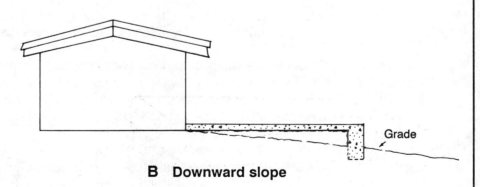

B   Downward slope

Figure 3-4   *General pricing information*

If you're adding a room with a slab floor to a house on a raised wood floor, the walls in the addition will be higher than the standard eight feet. (See Illustration C.) In this case, you'll have to allow for extra framing, drywall and stucco.

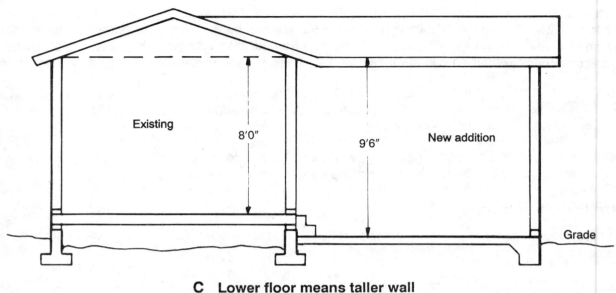

Existing   8'0"   9'6"   New addition   Grade

C   Lower floor means taller wall

When You Need Extra Stucco

We price stucco and plaster by the square yard. The exterior wall for a one-story house is about 8'6" high, so you can calculate one linear foot of wall equal to a square yard of stucco or plaster.

Plumbing

Prices in our book price list are for standard white, contractor's grade fixtures, including 15 feet of sewer line. You'll have to add for colors, deluxe fixtures, or a longer run to existing sewer lines.

If you're adding a gas fireplace in a room addition, first find the existing meter. It's against code to install gas lines inside a slab floor, so the line has to go outside the perimeter of the addition. Our book price allows for 30 linear feet of gas line. Charge $3.00 per foot for a line longer than 30 feet. If you must relocate a gas line for a clothes dryer, our book price covers the first 20 feet. Charge $3.00 per foot thereafter.

Our book price for relocating gas water heaters also allows for 20 feet of line and a $3.00 per foot surcharge. That's only for installation inside the building. If the heater will be relocated outside, add the charge for a cabinet enclosure.

Items Not on the Price List

Use your best judgment when pricing details not specifically covered in our price list. Try to give a firm price and walk away with a signed contract if you can. But if you're in doubt, it's better to check first. You don't want to quote a price so low we'll lose money on the deal. And if you quote too high we lose the customer. Always check when you're in doubt.

Figure 3-4 (cont'd)   *General pricing information*

The Building Process

Here's a mini construction primer — a brief explanation of the jobs we do most frequently at Goodguys Construction. They're arranged somewhat chronologically, beginning with demolition, then foundation, framing, roofing, plumbing, heating, electrical, interior finishing and cleanup. At the end are sections on special jobs like driveways and second-story additions, and a summary of inspection requirements.

Demolition

Demolition includes removing everything that's in the way of the proposed new construction. Here's what to look for:

Landings, stoops, stairs: Price for a jackhammer if the stairs are made of concrete. If they're wood, a laborer with a wrecking bar can usually do the job.

Trees and shrubs: Make that the owner's responsibility if you can. If we must remove them, charge accordingly, but never agree to replant *anything*. We're remodelers, not landscapers.

Concrete slabs: Don't plan to use an existing slab for the floor of an addition. They're usually sloped to allow water to run off. Pouring a new slab over an old one isn't a good idea either, because you still have to tear out a strip of the perimeter to place a new footing. We'll have to rip out the old one and start over.

Utility meters: Have the owner handle this directly with the utility company.

Sprinklers, water lines: Look out for water lines within your building envelope, especially if there's a pool.

Hose bibbs: See Illustration A. It's easy to relocate one that's not part of the main water line. It's much more expensive to move the main water line itself.

Aluminum patio roof: Include the cost to dismantle it and reassemble it in the new location, if that's what the owner wants.

Wood patio roof: Recommend demolishing it without considering salvage. It's cheaper to build a new one.

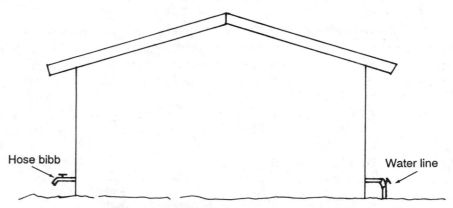

Hose bibb

Water line

A You can move a hose bibb easily if it's not part of the water main

Figure 3-5 *The building process*

Foundations and Footings

Floor slab levels must be at least 6" higher than the ground outside. Code requires 4"-thick concrete for slab floors, so we can use soil from the footing trenches to build the floor area up to bearing height. Forms for these foundations are 2 x 6 lumber braced vertically with stakes. See Illustration B. Forms are usually left in place for a few days, but sometimes we can remove them early to install drain tile or backfill.

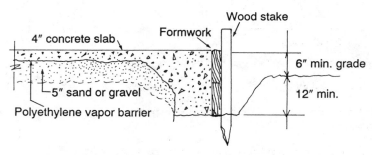

B   Foundation forms

Raised-floor Foundations

You can usually tell very easily whether a house has a raised floor or is built on a slab just by looking at the height of the front door in relation to ground level. A raised-floor house has a porch or stoop and a number of steps up. A house built on a slab has only a concrete landing and not more than two steps up. You'll also see vents in the stem wall on a raised-floor foundation. Illustration C shows you the difference.

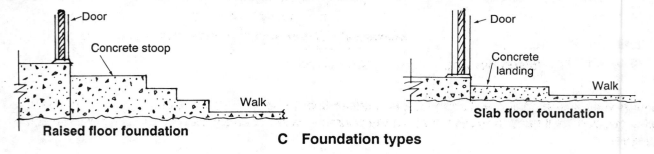

C   Foundation types

You can add a slab-on-grade room to a house that has a raised floor. The result is a sunken room, often desirable because of its character. However, it's best to avoid this if the addition requires connection to the sewer line. Illustration D shows the problem of connecting a new sewer line to an existing, higher one. It's possible, but usually expensive.

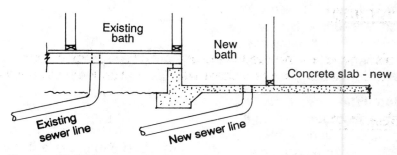

D   Problem sewer tie-ins

Figure 3-5 (cont'd)   *The building process*

Raised floors like the ones in Illustration E are made with floor joists and plywood sheathing. Make sure your client understands that a raised floor does *not* include a hardwood covering. That's a decorating accessory, just like carpet, tile or sheet flooring.

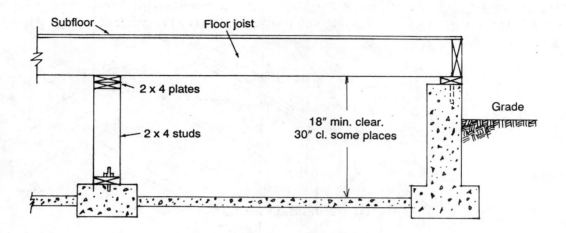

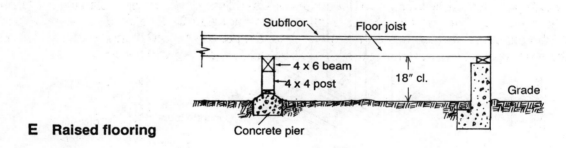

E Raised flooring

In older homes, inspect the crawl space under a raised floor to be sure it's up to code. In some cases, it will be too shallow, and we'll have to excavate within the perimeter walls of an addition so the floors will be at the same level.

Framing

This is generally included in the unit price for a room. If your design includes long windows, you may have to add for extra bracing or a shear wall. Illustration F identifies various parts of wood-frame construction.

Headers

Oversized headers are required over wide spans. The code for headers requires 4"-thick lumber that's 1" deep for each foot of clear span beneath it. Thus a header over a 6-foot sliding glass door must be 4 x 6, a header over a 10-foot opening must be 4 x 10, and a 4 x 20 beam would be required over a 20-foot opening.

Figure 3-5 (cont'd) *The building process*

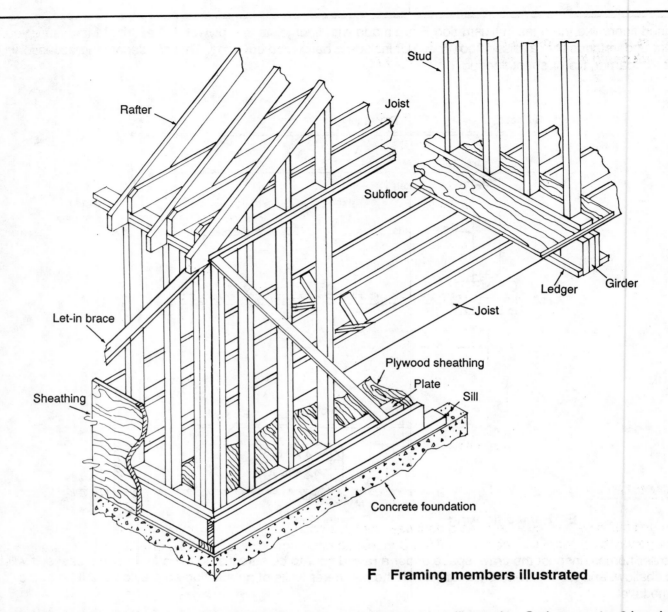

F Framing members illustrated

One way to avoid using oversize headers is to place posts in the opening. Illustration G shows a 4 x 6 header over a 15 foot opening.

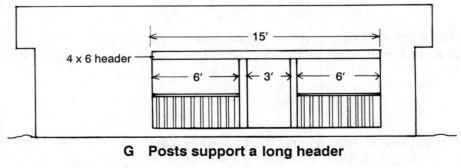

G Posts support a long header

Figure 3-5 (cont'd) *The building process*

(Discuss cut-out, dropped and flush headers and describe the extra framing and roofing charges that may be associated with them. Illustration H shows these.)

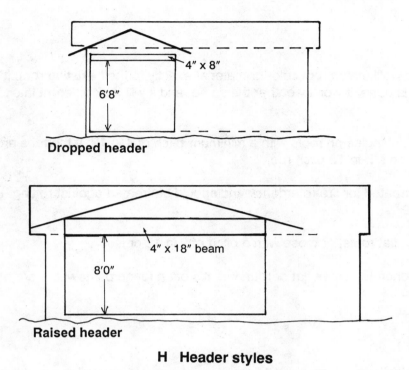

H   Header styles

Archways

You can't sell a semi-circular arch as a doorway, because code requires a minimum of three linear feet of passageway be at least 6'8" above the floor. Suggest an opening with rounded corners instead, like the one in Illustration I.

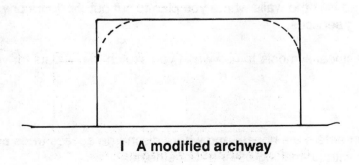

I   A modified archway

Figure 3-5 (cont'd)   *The building process*

Bearing Walls

These walls are designed to bear weight over them. Old houses with gable roofs usually have at least one interior bearing wall. If you're adding a second story, it must be supported by an existing or new bearing wall. All interior bearing walls must rest on a footing, or another bearing wall.

Roofs

Never promise an owner we'll match roof color or material exactly to their existing roof. It's impossible. Even if it matches when the job is done, it won't weather the same, and it will look different later. The same goes for exterior stucco.

You can use composition shingles on roofs with a minimum pitch of 4 in 12. If the tabs are fastened with tar gum, you can use these on a 3-in-12 pitch roof.

Wood shingles must be treated for fire retardancy and should be treated against rotting. Use them on a minimum slope of 4 in 12.

Use hot mop and rock on flat roofs, or those with a pitch of 2 in 12 or less.

Tile made from clay or concrete comes flat or rounded. It's often found on newer, more expensive homes, rarely on small, older ones.

Electrical

Code requires one electrical outlet for every 12 linear feet of wall. No point along a wall may be more than 6 feet from an outlet, and each habitable room must have at least 3 outlets. These minimum requirements are included in our book price list. Charge extra for additional outlets and for switched outlets.

Exterior doors must have an adjacent switch to a light that illuminates the area outside the door.

Check to see if the electrical service panel has to be moved, or if it's sufficient to accommodate new requirements. In older homes, the entire electrical system may need to be upgraded before the project will pass inspection.

Find out where existing wiring is in the walls where you plan to cut out for doors or windows. Extra charges may be involved in re-routing services.

Illustration J is a chart of electrical symbols to use when you sketch the layouts for your projects.

Plumbing

Notice where the water main enters the house, and where discharge access traps are. Don't plan a room addition that conceals them without making other arrangements.

Figure 3-5 (cont'd) *The building process*

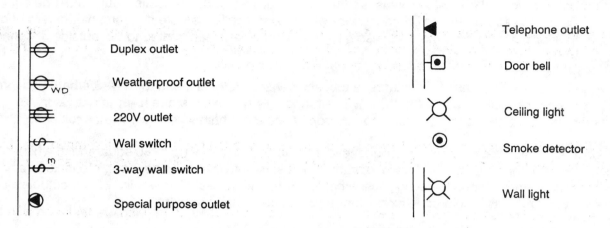

J   Electrical symbol chart

If you're moving the laundry service, you may have to provide a floor drain near the new location. And look out for water softeners. There's a significant difference in cost between moving one 5 feet, and moving it 50 feet to the other side of the house. If the softener is provided by a service, have the owner arrange with the supplier to have it moved.

When you add new plumbing fixtures (including wet bar sinks) to an existing house, locate them near an outside wall if you can. That way you minimize the cost of breaking up the slab to install new sewer lines.

Book price includes the valve and key, and 30 feet of piping when you connect a new gas fireplace to the existing gas lines in the house. Remember, you can't install gas pipe in a slab, so check to see how far it is from the meter to the new fireplace, measuring around the perimeter of the addition.

Heating

Indicate clearly on your sketches whether a wall heater is intended to heat just one room, or will be open to an adjacent room. There is an additional charge for the dual configuration.

If you're going to extend existing central unit heating ducts, make sure there's enough attic space to allow access.

Kitchens and Baths

These remodeling projects have special conditions that usually require charges not covered in the book price list. You need extra circuits (often 220 volt) for major appliances, and more than the minimum number of outlets, some of them located in unusual places.

Note the difference between charging to re-install the owner's garbage disposal or dishwasher, and installing new units. Don't forget to charge for the new ones, or for re-connecting the old ones.

Figure 3-5 (cont'd)   *The building process*

Bathrooms aren't considered habitable rooms, so they only require one duplex outlet. But it must be equipped with a GFI (ground fault interrupter) to prevent shock when using appliances like shavers, hair dryers and curling irons. Interior baths without windows also must have an exhaust fan vented to the outside. It cannot be vented to the attic.

By the way, a full (or 4/4 bath) has four fixtures, a tub, shower stall, lavatory, and toilet. A 3/4 bath has three, which includes a tub or shower, but not both. A 1/2 bath has only two fixtures, the toilet and lavatory. Be sure your customers understand those definitions so you don't price a 3/4 bath when they want a full one.

Our book price for a new bath includes a ground-level structural addition of up to 80 square feet, white toilet, white basin in a 36" vanity cabinet, and a white bathtub or shower stall with shower door. We include a medicine cabinet with mirror, one towel bar, tissue holder, GFI, and 15 feet of sewer line. Door cutouts, windows, exhaust fan, heater, colored fixtures, floor and wall coverings are extra.

To determine the total for a bath addition where most of the components are custom or non-standard, use the base price for an ordinary room addition, then price each individual item separately.

Be careful when you estimate a bathroom (or any room that discharges liquid waste) that's to be located lower than the floor level of the existing house. You have to maintain a slope of 1/4" per linear foot of sewer line between the house and the main, so be sure the existing sewer line is set deep enough. A new line may be needed. Look again at Illustration D.

Bathroom sewer lines are 4" in diameter, while kitchen drains are only 2", so you can't tie a bathroom line into the sewer line from the kitchen.

Cabinets

Our price book includes prices for several brands of factory-built cabinets. Price cabinets by linear foot of wall space. Notice that the price per linear foot for base cabinets is different from that of wall cabinets. Special cabinets (oven, pantry, utility) are priced separately, as are accessories such as lazy Susans, cutlery drawers, and free-standing island cabinets.

Floor Coverings

Carpeting and resilient floor covering is sold by the square yard and is supplied most commonly in 12-foot widths. A linear foot of this type flooring is 1.33 square yards, so you'd quote 24 yards for a 12 x 18 foot room. Pay attention to where seams will fall. You may have to allow for some waste. Don't forget to allow for underpad and installation when you sell carpet. You price hardwood and tile by the square foot.

Cleanup

- Will you need to rent a dumpster during remodeling? Or will you haul debris away as it accumulates?

- Charge extra if there's going to be an unusual amount of cleanup and debris, for instance if you have to rip out a driveway or clear many trees and shrubs.

Figure 3-5 (cont'd) *The building process*

Second Story Jobs, and Two-Story Additions

It's not hard to attach a new two-story structure to an existing single-story house. Basic construction is the same, except footings are larger in the addition, and the first floor ceiling joists have to be stronger to support the second floor.

Adding an upper floor to an existing building is more complicated. The roof has to be dismantled and major alterations must be made to the ceiling joist structure. You may have to provide additional bearing walls, or create bearing walls from existing non-bearing ones by adding footings.

In either case, you have to include stairways in the plan. Illustration K shows several typical staircase layouts.

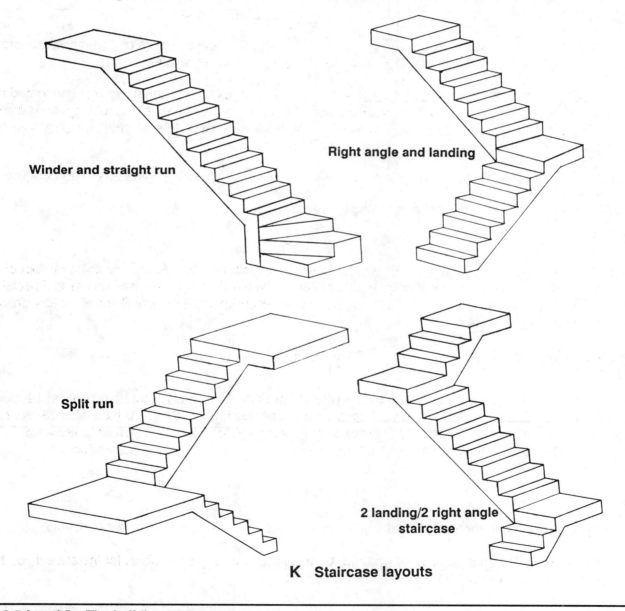

Winder and straight run

Right angle and landing

Split run

2 landing/2 right angle staircase

K   Staircase layouts

Figure 3-5 (cont'd)   *The building process*

(Expand on this so that it's appropriate for your operation. Explain how you price multiple stories or split levels, and how they relate to your base price list. Illustration L has some figures you can use.)

Two story, two living levels, varying roof and ceiling types

One story, pitched roof, flat ceiling

One story, pitched roof, sloped ceiling

One and a half story

L   Elevation drawings, multi-level housing styles and additions

Figure 3-5 (cont'd)   *The building process*

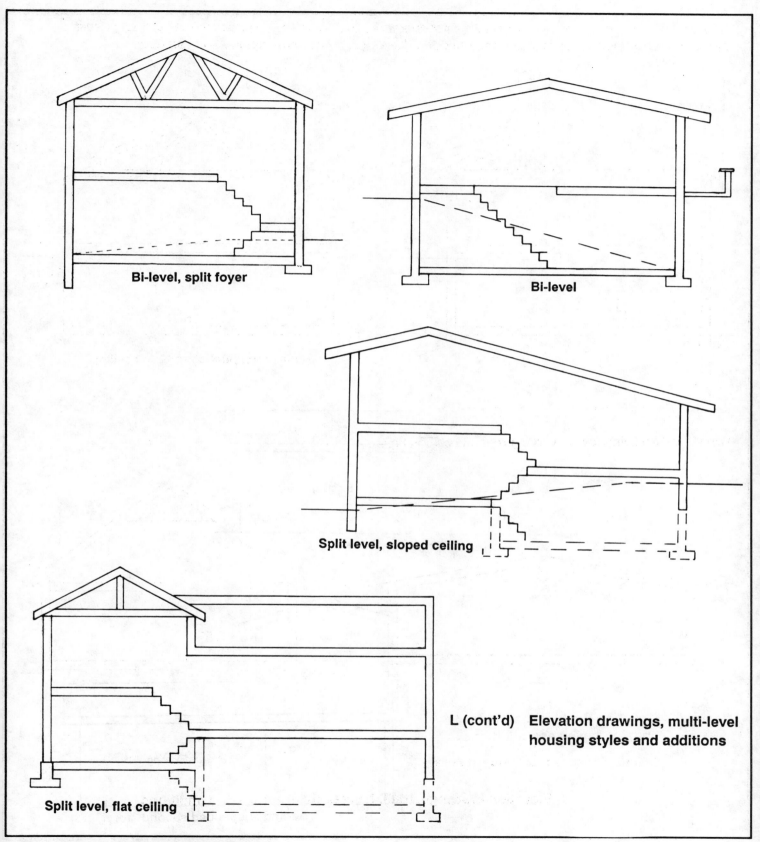

Bi-level, split foyer

Bi-level

Split level, sloped ceiling

Split level, flat ceiling

L (cont'd) Elevation drawings, multi-level housing styles and additions

Figure 3-5 (cont'd) *The building process*

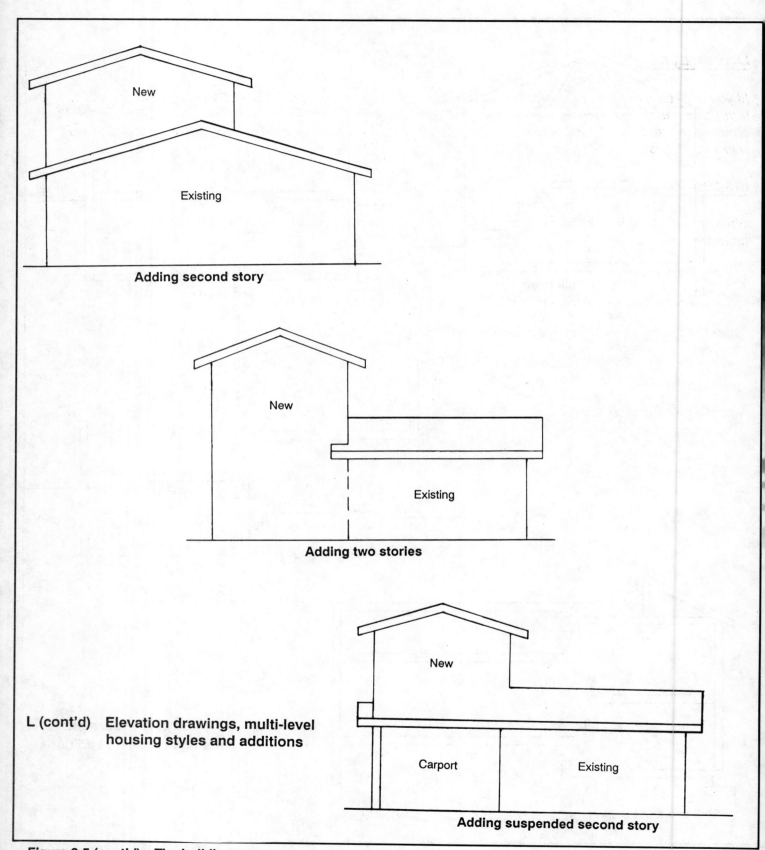

Adding second story

Adding two stories

L (cont'd)   Elevation drawings, multi-level
housing styles and additions

Adding suspended second story

Figure 3-5 (cont'd)   *The building process*

Driveways

(If you offer both asphalt and concrete, discuss the difference in cost and the benefits of one over the other in terms of durability, maintenance and attractiveness. Cover demolition, where an old driveway has to be removed to make way for a new addition. Explain your warranty restrictions regarding cracking of driveways, walks and slabs.)

Inspections

When you quote a completion date, be sure to allow for delays for inspections at the following points in the project:

- Excavation

- Formwork, reinforcement and placement of foundations or retaining walls

- Supporting members for second-story additions

- Plumbing — underground work, rough plumbing (vents, sewer tie-ins, and pipes to fixture locations), and fixture installation.

- Electrical

- Roofing

- Final

Figure 3-5 (cont'd) *The building process*

Have your instructor introduce the material, and then dismiss your trainees to study it on their own. Supply any other books and manuals they'll need for reference, such as cost manuals, construction dictionaries and code books.

■ *Day 4 handouts*

1)   A packet of estimating forms and price lists

2)   Some text to explain the forms and how to use them

3)   General pricing information

4)   A salesperson's primer of remodeling operations

Day 5:

Sales techniques and discipline

There are dozens of books, videos and audio tape programs on the market designed to train people in time management, goal setting, personal growth and sales. Supplement your own training program by making these available to your trainees, and require them to devote a certain minimum amount of time over several weeks to work with those resources. Provide an appointment book for trainees who don't already use one.

The presentation

Have someone from your sales staff give a demonstration with a trainee playing the part of the customer. Then set up several typical selling scenarios and have trainees practice on each other and on the instructor. Allow time for evaluation and discussion.

Make these role-playing sessions a mini-course in customer psychology. Describe ways to make a customer's mouth water over what you have to offer. Teach your trainees to recognize and deal with all kinds of sales resistance — objections, the timid buyer, "Your price is too high," and the guy who wants something for nothing. Emphasize closing techniques.

In the back of this book is an order form for a manual, *How to Sell Remodeling*. It may be worth your while to take a look at it. And libraries and bookstores are loaded with books on sales. Use them yourself and recommend your favorites to your trainees. If selling isn't *your* strongest suit, hire a professional sales consultant to lead this part of your training course.

At the end of your last classroom session, have a little "graduation ceremony." Pass out the sales presentation kits and assign each trainee to a seasoned salesperson for field training. Include some motivational inspiration (remind your trainees how much money they're going to make) and have a little party. Your trainees will end the day fired up, they'll spend the weekend studying, and they'll hardly be able to wait for Monday morning to get started making money for *you*.

■ *Day 5 handouts*

1) The sales presentation kit

2) Appointment books

3) A completion certificate

Field Training

If you have more than one full-time salesperson, have a trainee spend some time with two or three of them. Personalities vary, and every salesperson brings different talents and techniques to bear when they deal with customers. Trainees need to see that there's "more than one way to skin a cat." And each of your salespeople may be more informed and comfortable with one type of project than another. Expose trainees to as many different situations as possible during field training.

Questions for Classroom Discussion

Once you've written and perfected your training program, create a set of questions for trainees to answer afterws each day's lessons. Ask questions that are challenging enough to reinforce the most important points in your lesson plan. Make this an "open book" test — be sure everyone knows the right answers by the time the discussion is over.

So here you have it, a model you can follow to write your own manual to train a well-informed, productive sales staff. The following chapters contain the information and materials you'll need to complete this manual and build a successful and profitable business.

4

Estimating and Contracting

This chapter is intended as an overview of a very important topic: estimating and contract negotiation. I won't go into a lot of detail about contract clauses. And for a good reason: I'm a remodeler, not a lawyer. For the same reason I'm not going to cover mechanics' liens, waivers, stop notices, assignments, disclaimers, releases, demands or claims. The law varies from state to state. Anything I said about those subjects would be right for some states but wrong for others. But I will include copies of the standard contract forms I use. It's important that you have a good contract and use it on every significant job. Doing that is the best way I know to avoid the most common problems in this industry.

Nearly all of this chapter is devoted to the fundamentals of estimating and contracting. Think of this chapter as your introduction to the subject. In the next chapter we'll get into the details: estimating using the unit price system. That's how I estimate and it's the method I recommend you use. Once you've mastered the basics, you may want to use some estimating shortcuts on larger projects. We'll cover those in the next chapter too.

Estimating Fundamentals

When you estimate a job, you're dealing with probables. There's no certainty. That's what makes estimating so interesting — and so important to your survival. There are good estimates and bad estimates. Until the work's been done, it's hard to tell one from the other. This chapter will help you make just one kind of estimate: the best possible based on what you know about the job, site conditions and how the work will be done.

There are two parts to every estimate: *measurements* and *prices*. You measure (or calculate) the square feet of wall or floor or ceiling to be covered, the length of pipe or conduit to be installed, the linear feet of cabinet to be removed. That's usually the easiest part of every estimate. Of course, mistakes are possible. Maybe you didn't notice that a vent stack ran through a partition wall that has to be torn out. Maybe you didn't know that an old septic tank is right below where the plans show a new foundation wall. Those can be expensive mistakes — if your contract doesn't protect you.

After measurements are taken, you have to attach prices to each part of the job. Here's where many remodelers really get into the guesswork. How much is it going cost to install 15 linear feet of 8-foot partition, or to hang three new doors?

Estimating the material cost is the easy part. You know (or can find out very quickly) the delivered cost of lumber and nails and doors. But the cost of installation? That depends on your hourly labor cost and which carpenter is framing the wall or hanging the doors, and how many problems that worker has and how anxious he or she is to complete the job and a thousand other things that would make a list as long as your arm. But even listing them all wouldn't help much because you can't possibly know ahead of time which items on that list are important on this job and which items don't make any difference at all.

I hope I've made my point: There's no way to be sure exactly what your costs will be. But you want to make your estimates as accurate as possible. And to do that you've got to do a couple of things right.

First among those is to take estimating seriously. Adopt a professional attitude toward your estimates. Inform yourself. Collect a library of pricing information and estimating references that can help you do what needs to be done. Qualify yourself. Learn to work carefully and accurately. Save old estimates. Save cost records on completed jobs. When costs are much higher or lower than you estimated, find out why. If you make a mistake, it's no big deal. Every estimator makes mistakes. I'd guess that the most experienced estimators have made the most mistakes. But the best estimators don't *repeat* mistakes. That's the important point. And that's a good goal for you.

You Estimate from Experience

All estimates are based on knowledge about the job and knowledge about the cost of what's going to be done on that job. The plans and the contract will usually define the job. Your first task is to measure and count accurately.

Estimating costs is much harder. You have to anticipate every labor, material and equipment cost. Since no one carries thousands of labor, material and equipment costs around with them in their head, you'll have to rely on reference data when compiling cost estimates: catalogs, price sheets, manhour tables, old estimates and lots more. That's why most good estimators are good collectors. They keep files and files of cost information — and probably a good library of estimating reference manuals.

"Mr. Bigalow will not approve your remodeling estimates, but he'd like to buy the fiction rights"

Nearly all good estimates are based on experience. The best guess about costs on your next job will usually be based on the costs of your last job. Here's why. Every construction company is different. A good estimate for your company may be a bad estimate for the company across town. Work done yesterday by your crews, under your supervisor, using your equipment, and on your type of job will be the best guide when estimating tomorrow's job using the same crew, supervisor and equipment. Estimates for other companies or estimating information published in books and manuals is always a poor second choice if you have cost information from your own completed jobs.

What estimating manuals are good for is to double-check your estimate. After you've figured your costs from your records, figure the costs using the estimating manuals. If there's a big difference, check your estimate again. Maybe you forgot an item, or transposed a number, or misplaced a decimal. We've all done that. But a little mistake like that can cost you plenty.

Of course, everyone has to start somewhere. If you're new in the business, you don't have cost records from completed jobs. You have to rely on published cost information. There's no other choice. Even veteran estimators use reference manuals when nothing else is available. Several publishers offer estimating manuals. An order card at the back of this book lists titles available from Craftsman Book Company. But no reference manual is a substitute for your own experience. And none is a crutch that can save you the time and trouble of finding each cost item in a job.

Any time you use an estimating reference manual, remember that estimating is an art, not a science. Costs vary from job to job. No one cost fits all jobs. Productivity varies. Prices vary. You have to identify cost variables that make this particular work easier or harder than other jobs you've estimated. That's the key to compiling good estimates — your judgment. Because without judgment, no estimate is likely to be accurate.

Maybe that's why I don't believe computers will ever do all the estimating, especially not for remodeling work. Every estimate has to be custom made for a particular job and a particular set of conditions. Computers are very fast and usually very accurate. But I've never seen one that knows when the standard cost is either too high or too low for the given conditions. That's something experienced estimators will always do much better than any machine.

You Estimate from Cost History

Good cost records from past jobs are your best source for accurate estimating data. You need to collect information on:

- material costs
- labor costs
- equipment costs
- overhead costs
- profit margin

And here's the formula: cost = quantity times unit price

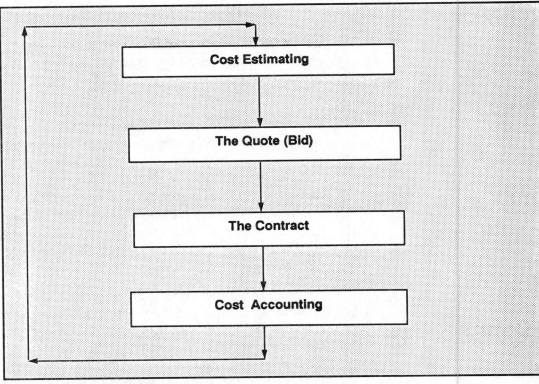

Figure 4-1   *The estimator*

There are several steps in the estimating process and each depends on the preceding steps:

1) First, you measure and price the work and prepare an estimate.

2) Then you submit a successful bid to the customer.

3) Next you get a signed contract and do the work.

4) While work is being done, you keep accurate cost and scheduling records for labor, material and equipment. (Order a copy of *Cost Records for Construction Estimating* on the order form in the back of the book.)

5) Finally, you use your experience and these records to make more estimates.

Figure 4-1 illustrates how this works.

The Estimator

Estimating costs on remodeling jobs tends to be very specialized, very demanding work. Contractors new in the remodeling business usually do nearly all of their own estimating. Larger companies usually have a professional estimator on staff. In either case the estimator has to have:

- a good knowledge of construction methods, materials and practices.

- some ability to sketch construction details, to communicate both on paper and verbally.

- basic proficiency in math and measuring techniques.

- a good knowledge of business and economics.

- imagination and an aptitude for visualizing and thinking in abstract terms.

- analytical skill and the courage to be critical and to make decisions in unclear situations.

Every estimator needs current labor and material costs. In the next chapter, we'll discuss in detail how to set prices and apply them to estimates.

Contract Basics

Every remodeling contractor needs to know about contracts. I won't talk about all the types of construction contracts here. You won't have to deal with most of them. But I'll cover the most common ones and explain how they work.

Contract law is basically the same throughout North America, although every state has its own statutes. Be sure you and your estimator are familiar with the laws that apply in the states where you do business. After all, you're a contractor. You should know enough about contracts to stay out of legal problems.

Contractual Relationships

Figure 4-2 shows some of the contractual relationships on most construction projects.

On larger jobs, the owner may select the designer. On many jobs your company will do the design work. The owner and local building department approve the design. On large new construction projects, the designer (usually an architectural firm) prepares the bidding documents and solicits bids from selected contractors. Sometimes the owner hires the designer to inspect and supervise construction. On smaller jobs the owner will deal directly with the general contractor.

Every step of the way, contracts are essential. One project, small or large, can involve many contracts: between owner and designer, designer and design consultants, owner and contractor, contractor and

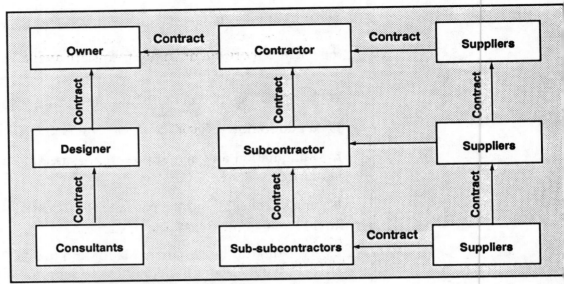

Figure 4-2 *Contractual relationships*

subcontractor, subcontractor and tradesmen, subcontractor and supplier, sub-subcontractor and supplier, and so on.

Making the Contract

What's the difference between a contract and an agreement? None, usually. Every contract is an agreement but every agreement isn't a contract. If I agree to meet you in church next Sunday, that's an agreement. But no court would enforce it. Only common courtesy requires that I be there as promised.

A contract requires agreement. Without it there's no contract. But a contract is legally enforceable. A court will award damages for non-performance and may even order one party to perform as promised.

Is a contract any less valid because it isn't written? Suppose a contractor does work for an owner under an oral agreement. Everything is done as planned but the owner won't pay because the contract wasn't in writing. Will the contractor collect? He should collect in full. But I wouldn't recommend building under an oral contract. If something goes wrong, proving the terms of the contract may be a real problem. It's your word against the owner's.

When I was new in this business, I completed a 12,000 square foot custom house on a handshake. It was one of the best jobs I've ever had, a real pleasure. But it could have been a severe headache — or worse. Too many jobs go sour. A falling-out with the owner can make your life miserable. Play it safe. *Put it in writing.*

Fortunately, it's easy to get good construction contract forms today. Many larger stationery stores offer standard construction contracts. Better, usually more evenhanded forms are available from:

American Institute of Architects
1735 New York Avenue, N.W.
Washington, D.C. 20006

American Building Contractors Association
11100 Valley Blvd., Suite 120
El Monte, CA 91731

Royal Architectural Institute of Canada
151 Slater Street
Ottawa, Ontario

Royal Institute of British Architects
66 Portland Place
London, WIN 4AD, England

Most states have what is usually called the *Statute of Frauds*. Any agreement that concerns title to real estate won't be enforced unless the terms are in writing. Contracts valued over a certain amount or that can't be performed within a year may also have to be in writing. But in practically all other cases, there's no requirement for a signed contract.

To be valid, a contract must meet these conditions:

■ There must be mutual agreement between the parties. An offer is made by one party and accepted by the other. All conditions have to be agreed to by both parties within the contract or there's no agreement at all. Beware including such phrases as "terms to be agreed." An "agreement to agree" is no agreement at all.

■ There is "consideration" or a promise to do something in exchange for something of value, such as money. A promise to do something a contractor or an owner is already required to do is not consideration; neither is a promise to do something that's already been done. The *amount* of the consideration isn't an issue with the courts. But there is no contract without consideration.

■ It can't be changed except by formal change order which constitutes another contract. Your contract should explain how changes will be made and specify how to adjust prices.

■ Both parties must show "capability." Capability means neither party is prohibited from entering into a contract. For example, you can't require someone to work for you if they don't want to, and minors usually can't enter into contracts.

■ Both parties must be sincerely willing to enter into a binding contract. If either party's intent isn't genuine, the contract is invalid. An error like mistaken identity, unintentional misrepresentation of facts, or intentional fraud will invalidate the contract. One party can't threaten the other or put the other under any kind of duress. There's no contract when an illiterate person signs a contract without knowing what they're signing, for example.

Withdrawing the offer

You have the right to withdraw an offer, bid, or tender — all three words mean the same thing — any time before it's accepted. But you must give notice of withdrawal before acceptance, not after you're notified of acceptance.

If you make an offer that's accepted and later discover that your price was too low, you're probably stuck. You can't just abandon the contract. That's why accuracy in estimating is so important.

Be Careful with Wording

Pay careful attention to the wording of your contracts. If there's a dispute, the arbitrator or judge will interpret the contract by what it says, not what you meant it to say. Write in plain English that leaves no room for argument about what the words mean.

Consult your lawyer and design a contract form that lets you cover all the following conditions:

1) Verify that you're properly licensed, if that's required in your state.

2) Have the owner certify that they in fact own the property in question, and that your company has permission to enter the property to do the required work. Ask for a legal survey of the property and a warranty as to the accuracy of corner markers, easements and restrictions before you start work.

3) Describe the job in detail and refer to the applicable specifications and plans.

4) Indicate that all work will be done according to code and will comply with all pertinent laws.

5) Specify that the owner pays for variances, assessments, zoning changes, engineering, and soil tests, unless otherwise specified. If you're responsible for any grading or drainage, make it a detail of the contract.

6) Promise to supply all labor, materials, permits, applications and fees necessary to complete the job in a workmanlike manner, and state how much time you expect the project to take.

7) Require the owner to pay for toilet facilities and drinking water for your crews if those aren't already available on the job site.

8) Show a payment schedule, including total price and a breakdown. How much for the down payment? List the details of required progress payments: when, or at what state of construction, will they be due? If the owner has the right to withhold a portion of the payments until completion, specify exactly what that portion is, and when final payment is due.

9) List any penalties, service charges or interest rate due on late payments.

10) Cover the issue of extra work: Who can authorize it? How will extra charges be determined? When is payment due?

11) Specify when the work will be considered complete or substantially complete, and when the final inspection will occur.

12) State that the proceeds of any third party financing will be paid directly to you. If you help the owner get financing, specify that the owner pays all lender's fees and loan costs.

13) Describe under what circumstances you'll stop work if the owner defaults on payments. How will any remaining outstanding money be paid? Will there be interest or penalties imposed?

14) Describe the procedure for arbitration in case of a dispute.

15) Declare that the owner is financially responsible for all fees, permits, documents and legal costs relating to the project.

16) Note that the job is based on information concerning subsurface conditions furnished by the owners. If conditions aren't as stated, any additional charges are the responsibility of the owner, including any damages your company suffers as a result.

17) State what will happen if you're prevented from working for a period of time because of bad weather, a disaster, permit or loan delays, or the customer's convenience. Include a statement in your contract that if you cease work for any of these reasons, you won't supply further materials or services, and you're entitled to full payment for all work completed to date, plus payment for damages or loss of profit the customer causes.

18)   Declare the owner responsible to remove or protect personal property, and state that you won't be liable to damage that occurs during the course of construction to property that remains in place, or other damage beyond your control.

19)   Require the owner to provide insurance for you against fire and vandalism and to protect you against liability claims connected with the project.

20)   Declare your complete control over the job and personnel, and that you're solely responsible for construction methods, techniques, sequences and procedures.

21)   State under what conditions written communications will be considered received by either party, and specify where they should be sent.

22)   Say that no part of the contract can be waived under any circumstances, expect as specifically agreed to by all parties, in writing.

23)   Note that if any part of the contract is unenforceable, the rest of the contract remains in effect.

24)   State which government entity has jurisdiction over the effect and interpretation of this contract.

25)   Specify that the contract is binding on the owner and any heirs, legal representatives, or successors.

Warranties

Warranties are related to contracts and in fact are sometimes part of the contract itself. Take the same precautions you do when writing a contract. Don't make any promises you're not prepared to keep. And be sure your customer understands and acknowledges the terms of the warranty.

Figure 4-3 is a form I've used.

Stock Printed Forms

Printed contract forms are popular. But before you use one, be sure you understand what it says — and what it *doesn't* say. If you stick in your own favorite clauses, test and examine them for conflicts and contradictions that could affect other clauses. It's possible for you to end up with a worthless piece of paper. You can't imply things that are omitted, and you can't ignore terms that are included.

Some contractors use virtually blank contract forms like the one in Figure 4-4. I don't think these forms are explicit enough. But many

COMPANY NAME

CONTRACTOR'S WARRANTY

Issued to: _____ Date: _____
OWNER

For work performed at: _____
ADDRESS   CITY   STATE

COMPANY NAME , contractor, hereby warrants that the construction work performed at the above location is free from defects in materials and workmanship for a period of one year from the date of substantial completion, date of commencement of use, or date of notice of completion, whichever occurs first.

This limited warranty is subject to the following conditions:

•   This warranty covers the property described above for as long as the said property remains in the possession of the owner named above.

•   The construction work has not been subject to misuse, abuse, accident, or neglect.

•   The construction work has not been modified, altered, defaced, worked on or repaired in any way by others.

•   The owner will notify the contractor of any defect within 10 days of discovery of that defect.

•   The owner shall give the contractor the first opportunity to:

    1)   inspect the defect claimed; and

    2)   to effect the repair, replacement, or correction.

•   Under no circumstances shall the contractor be held liable by virtue of this warranty or otherwise, for damage to a person, or property for whatever reason, whether from direct, indirect, special, secondary, or consequential cause(s) arising from the use or inability to use the property because of a construction defect.

•   Excluded from this warranty are those items not manufactured by the contractor, and which may carry individual warranties.

REGISTRATION No _____

Figure 4-3   *Contractor's warranty*

Proposal

Goodguys Construction Company

Telephone: 876-1773

Proposal Submitted to: _____ Telephone _____ Date _____

Address _____ Project Name _____

_____ Project Location _____

Designer _____ Plans _____

We hereby submit specifications for and offer to furnish all materials and labor necessary to complete the following:

_____

_____

_____

_____

_____

All work to be completed in a substantial and workmanlike manner in accordance with standard practices for the sum of_____($_____)Dollars.

Payments to be made as follows: on acceptance $_____._____

_____ _____

_____ _____

_____ _____

All material is guaranteed to be as specified. Changes or additions to the above involving extra costs will be supplied only upon written orders signed by both Owner and Contractor. This proposal is made on the basis of current material and labor costs and may be withdrawn if not accepted within 30 days.

Authorized Signature _____Contractor

===

Acceptance

I/we, the undersigned, understand that acceptance of the above proposal constitutes a binding contract. I/we hereby accept your proposal and authorize you to supply all materials and labor as described above. I/we agree to pay you, the Contractor, the amounts as set out above and the terms described thereof.

Signature_____

Date of Acceptance _____ Signature_____

Figure 4-4   *Blank contract form*

builders I've interviewed use them for nearly all work with never a hint of a problem. All I can say is, some people are very lucky. If there are no surprises and no problems on a job, it doesn't matter much what the agreement says. Like I said, once I built a 12,000 square foot home on a handshake. What goes well, goes well. But when there's a problem, you need a good agreement.

I believe all contracts should contain a clause such as, "This agreement shall constitute the entire agreement between the Contractor and the Owner, and there is no representation, warranty, collateral agreement, or condition affecting this agreement other than as expressed in writing herein." Or at least this: "This contract constitutes the whole agreement between the parties and supersedes any previous discussions, correspondence, or agreements." Words like that tend to keep an owner from insisting "But you promised this . . ." or "You promised that . . . ." The only promise is what's in the contract — and nothing else.

Contract Types

I'll discuss three major types of construction contracts in some detail.

1)   The usual contract forms, including fixed sum, cost plus fee, and unit price contracts.

2)   Modified contracts such as cost plus fee contracts limited by a "not to exceed" clause, and contracts that include a management fee.

3)   Home improvement contracts that include special conditions and restrictions required by state and federal law.

Fixed Sum Contract

The fixed sum contract is the most common of the basic contracts. The customer pays the contractor a set price for completing the work. The contract usually requires partial payment after a specified portion of the work is completed.

First, the builder makes an offer to the owner. The offer is worded something like this: "We propose to supply all labor and materials to perform the work described and shown in the specifications and drawings for the sum of $_____."

A fixed sum contract isn't very flexible. Most don't anticipate changes and may not work very well if there are a lot of changes. The contract terms allow the contractor little room to maneuver. You have to follow all conditions of the contract. But there are advantages for both the contractor and the owner.

The contractor's advantage is independence. You can demand to be left alone to do the work without interference from the owner. The contract may even contain a clause to that effect.

The fixed price is the owners' advantage. They know the final cost of the project. At least, that's the theory. An owner or designer who makes changes after the agreement is signed forfeits the advantage. Costs for changes are usually set by the contractor and bound by a written change order.

Most owners will get bids from several contractors. They'll usually choose the best price, all other things being equal. It's up to you to be sure that your price is accurate, based on current cost information and your past experience. If you pad your price to protect yourself against estimating errors, you'll probably lose the job to a lower bidder. No one ever said the construction business was easy money.

But don't try to be the lowest bidder on every job. If you sell your services solely on low, lower, or lowest price, you'll be vulnerable to every lowball, cut-throat operator in town. No matter how low your price, someone will be willing to do it for less. Or worse, you'll get the job and lose your shirt.

If you can't estimate costs accurately, don't give a firm price. Here are some reasons to avoid a firm price contract:

■ unstable soil conditions

■ incomplete design information

■ component prices not available

■ time of construction not set

If you offer a firm price in these cases, you'll have to include a contingency allowance or inflate your gross margin to cover errors.

The Design-Build Proposal

If you agree to draw plans for the job, protect yourself. Use a form like Figure 4-5. If the owner uses your plans but has another builder do the work, at least you'll get paid for the design.

The Cost Plus Fee Contract

In this type of contract, the contractor agrees to do a job for actual cost plus a fee. The owner pays for all labor, materials, equipment, rentals,

Company Name
Address
City

Date:_____

Owner's Name_____Phone_____

Address _____ Office_____

City_____State_____Zip_____

The Company named above hereby submits a design-build proposal ordered by the Owner, for plans and specifications for work to be performed according to the following terms:

1) The Company agrees to provide working drawings and specifications for the Owner's project, namely:

_____

Project_____Address_____

2) Working Drawings shall include:_____

3) Proposed budget range for project: $_____to $_____

4) Changes to the design after drawings are started or have been finished, whether affecting the budget range or not, shall be charged as an extra cost. Engineering work, if required, shall be charged as an extra cost.

5) Changes will be made only upon notice in writing from the Owner to the Company.

6) The design, drawings, and specifications are intended for construction by the Company. The Company shall not be held liable nor responsible in any manner whatsoever for the use of its design, drawings, and specifications if used by others.

7) Title of the drawings and specifications shall become the property of the Owner, upon full payment to the Company of the fees under this agreement.

8) The design work shall begin not later than_____ 19____, with substantial completion on or before _____19____. Owner agrees to make payment in full upon execution of this agreement.

The Company proposes to furnish the design drawings according to the terms and conditions of this agreement for the sum of $ _____. The Owner agrees to make payments in full upon execution of this agreement.

ACCEPTANCE

Contractor   Owner

_____   _____

_____   _____

Figure 4-5   *Design-build contract*

and other costs directly chargeable to the project. The fee is either a flat amount or a percentage of the costs. You quote only the fee, not the costs. The owner assumes most of the risk and doesn't know the job's final cost until the work is done.

The cost plus fee contract is more flexible than the fixed sum contract. Owners can make changes to suit themselves practically any time during the course of the job. Of course, they must be prepared to pay the extra for the changes. For the contractor, there's no incentive to be economical or efficient. The owner may end up paying more than under a fixed sum contract. That isn't always the case, but it happens often enough to make informed owners wary.

You may be asked to bid on a cost plus fixed fee contract. For example, you might offer to do the job for cost plus 12 percent, while another contractor bids at cost plus 10 percent.

Be careful to define and list exactly what's included in the definition of cost. Job overhead is usually part of job cost. On some jobs you may include it in the fee along with general overhead and profit.

The fee is most commonly a percentage of cost. Sometimes the formula varies. You might decrease the percentage once costs exceed a certain amount. Either way, the customer pays the costs as scheduled in the contract, along with the prorated fees.

If you bid on cost plus fee contracts, be sure your fee fits the particular situation. Decide at the outset what your absolute minimum fee must be to cover expenses and overhead. Beyond that, you have some flexibility in deciding how much your net profit should be.

There are circumstances that make a cost plus fee contract advisable. A project with tight time limits might have to be started immediately. If the roof's blown off and a storm is due tomorrow, start work now (under a set fee) and settle up on labor and material costs when the work's done. In this case, the owner and contractor will be working together and planning the job as work proceeds.

Unit Price Contracts

There are two parts to an estimate for a unit price contract:

1) Quantities and measurements

2) Prices

Under unit price contracts you bid only the cost per unit, not the cost to complete the entire job. Some designers prepare a schedule (list) that shows the measured quantities for all items of work. That way you don't have to make your own take-off. Just apply your unit prices to the quantities listed and extend the totals. Other designers leave the quantity estimating to the contractors. Your unit price bid will probably include both overhead and profit, though these are sometimes listed separately in the schedule.

Unit price contracts are good when you can't determine exactly how much work it will take to complete the job. For instance, you don't know exactly how much excavation or fill is necessary until work is under way. On a job like this, the owners have better control over costs with a unit price contract than they would with a cost plus fee contract.

When the job is under way, the contractor measures and records quantities and confirms them with the owner or designer. The owner then pays for the actual work done at the price per unit agreed to in the contract. The contract should specify how measurements and quantities are determined.

I'll define *unit price* as the average price for each unit of measure. *Unit of measure* might refer to a yard of concrete, a thousand board feet of lumber or a square of shingles. But in remodeling, the contractor often calculates unit prices on a larger unit. You could have a unit price for a wall system, for example, including studs, drywall, insulation, sheathing, siding and fasteners. You'd quote the unit price as so much per linear foot of wall.

Some builders take this further and use unit prices for even larger chunks of work. Your price book might list shell room additions at so much per square foot of floor.

Modified Contracts

The fixed sum contract and the cost plus fee contract are the two extremes. In between, there are modifications that distribute risk between the customer and the contractor in varying proportions. We'll look at three modified contracts: the modified cost plus fee, the cost sharing, and the management fee.

Modified cost plus fee

This is a cost plus fee contract that can't exceed a fixed sum. They're also known as *maximum cost plus fee*, or *guaranteed maximum cost* contracts. They can control the maximum cost or the builder's fee.

Cost sharing

The contractor and the owner share any cost savings below the contract price. They divide the savings 50/50, 60/40, or whatever proportion they agree to in the contract. However, if costs exceed the fixed sum,

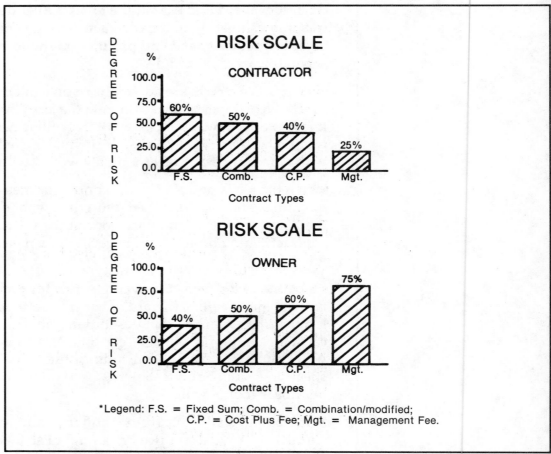

Figure 4-6 *Shared risk in different contracts*

they come out of the contractor's pocket. The owner pays only the fixed sum (after adjustments for changes).

The cost-sharing agreement encourages the contractor to be efficient and economical. A 30 to 40 percent share of any savings is a pretty good incentive to most contractors.

■ As you can see in Figure 4-6, this modified contract spreads risk equally between the owner and the contractor. You'd think this type of contract would be most popular since it seems the fairest of all. But for some reason, you'll seldom see them. Contractors either don't know about them, or they feel these contracts complicate their bookkeeping too much.

Management fee

Some projects are so complex that it's impractical to hold the general contractor or the designer responsible for all the work involved. For instance, most general contractors don't know much about elevators or stair lifts. They can't take responsibility for the work of an elevator contractor. In this case it would be better for the elevator contractor to be directly responsible to the owner.

When the owner doesn't have the time or the knowledge to oversee every part of a complex project, a management fee contract might be appropriate. There are two types of management fee contracts:

1) Some or all subcontractors on the project contract directly with the owner. These might include the designer and project manager. Each contractor may have subcontractors, who may have subcontractors of their own.

2) The owner has only one contract with the manager that includes both design and construction. The contract may also cover land sale or lease. These are turnkey projects, also known as design-build projects. The contractor's or project manager's prime responsibility is to organize and manage the job at the site in the owner's best interest.

In each case, the manager monitors work in progress to see that work is finished on time and within budget. The management contractor acts as the owner's agent when dealing with other contractors. The management contractor might also act as general contractor where site improvements are part of the contract.

It's better if the project manager doesn't have a financial interest in the project. That way responsibilities are clearly defined, and the manager can act impartially as the owner's agent.

Local conditions set the precedent for pricing management contracts. You might charge a percentage of the total job cost, a flat fee, or an hourly rate — whatever you and the owner agree upon.

As you see in Figure 4-6, this type of contract carries more risk for owners, because they must pay for cost overruns, just as they would with a cost-plus contract.

Figure 4-7 shows some sample terms that might be included in a typical management contract.

Home Improvement Contracts

I consider home improvement contracts a separate category because the federal government and several states have laws that apply specifically to this type of work. California, for example, has very tough laws that affect home improvement contractors.

Legislatures have passed laws protecting the public from abuses by some home improvement contractors. Why? Because that's where the complaints are. One construction industry spokesperson has been

CONSTRUCTION MANAGEMENT CONTRACT

This AGREEMENT made this _____ day of _____ 19_____

Between:_____, Owner, And_____, Manager

WHEREAS the Owner intends to erect _____

and related facilities at _____ known as the Project, as set out in the designs and specifications of

_____, known as the Designer.

1) The Owner hereby retains the Manager to perform for the Project, management services as set forth below and for the consideration and fee determined.

2) The Manager hereby agrees to perform the Management Services as described in Appendix "A" of this document.

3) The Owner hereby agrees to and appoints the Manager his authorized limited agent to award contracts (with the Owner's approval as to forms and terms of contracts and bonding arrangements, if required), for the Owner's account covering the furnishing of materials and labor by subcontractors and suppliers for various parts of the Project, and to purchase and/or rent for the Owner's account, the necessary tools, materials, equipment, and supplies for the work, (provided that no purchase or rental costing more than _____($_____) dollars, shall be made without the Owner's approval). All contracts for labor, materials, supplies and rentals shall be awarded in the name of the Owner.

4) Preconstruction work such as surveys, soil tests, etc., shall be undertaken by the Manager unless already done or supplied by the Owner. The Owner shall pay for all necessary preconstruction costs required for the proper performance of the work as well as advertising incidental to soliciting bids, applying for permits and licenses, and legal work.

5) The Owner shall be responsible for costs, delays, or damages caused by delays or errors in providing information or decisions to the Manager.

6) The Owner may, upon 30 days' written notice, terminate the services of the Manager by paying the Manager a fee of ____% of the total estimated cost of the Project at termination.

7) The Manager may, upon 10 days written notice, terminate his services if the Owner fails to make timely payments, or if work ceases under court order or other public authority through no fault of the Manager. The Owner shall pay the Manager within five days of the termination notice, ___% of the total fee paid to date.

8) The Manager shall certify for the Owner, within five days after the end of each month, the amount due to be paid to each contractor for work performed in the previous month, and the amount due to each supplier for materials delivered during the previous month. The Owner shall pay the amounts as certified by the Manager within seven calendar days, subject to the holdback amounts as required by the Mechanic's Lien Act.

9) The Owner shall pay the Manager for the preconstruction phase the sum of ($ _____) Dollars, at the execution of this agreement. During the construction phase, the Manager shall submit to the Owner a statement with certified invoices, the amounts due to contractors and suppliers, and include an invoice for the management fee for the current month at the rate of _____(____ %) percent of the total sum of the certified amounts payable for the current month.

Figure 4-7 *Construction management contract*

10)   All communications in writing shall be considered received by the addressee if sent by certified mail, or delivered by hand, to an authorized officer of the Company, or to an official of the Owner.

11)   The provisions of this agreement shall inure to the benefit of and be binding upon the parties hereto, their respective heirs, legal representatives, successors, and assigns.

Appendix A
Management Services

1)   The Manager shall act as agent of the Owner and shall make all agreements necessary for the performance of the work and for the supply of materials, and for all other matters which may be required for the completion of the Project.

2)   The Manager shall be responsible for the supervision and coordination of the work.

3)   The Designer shall be permitted free access on the work site for the purpose of carrying out inspections on behalf of the Owner or the Owner's mortgagors.

4)   The Manager shall carry out all written instructions from the Designer. If the Manager considers the instructions to be counterproductive, improper, or against the interest of the Owner, the Manager shall promptly notify the Owner. Such information to the Owner shall not relieve the Manager of the obligation to carry out the written instructions of the Designer unless instructed in writing by the Owner to do otherwise.

5)   Each month the Manager shall certify for the Owner all amounts due to be paid to contractors, suppliers, and others, in accordance with respective agreements.

6)   The Owner shall pay the certified amounts by the due dates.

7)   The Manager shall use his best efforts to complete the Project by the target date, namely _____ 19____, and to complete the Project at minimum reasonable cost.

8)   If written instruction from the Designer will, in the opinion of the Manager, require substantial additional cost or delay in completion of the Project, the Manager will promptly notify the Owner with a written estimate of the cost increase and/or delay.

9)   If the Manager considers changes in the work necessary or advantageous, written notice of such changes with details and cost estimates shall be provided the Owner. The Manager shall not proceed with such changes unless written authority is given from the Owner.

10)   Additional provisos or conditions waived:

_____

_____

_____

_____

IN WITNESS WHEREOF the parties have executed this agreement by their respective signatures and seals as of the day and year first above written.

Owner_____

Signature_____

Manager_____

Signature_____

Figure 4-7 (cont'd)   *Construction management contract*

quoted as saying remodelers are, "the culprits who give us the black eye and force the legislators to tighten up on loose behavior." Don't be one of the bad apples that spoils the barrel for everyone.

Of course, remodelers have to comply with all laws, not just those written to control the remodeling industry. Here are some examples:

■ The Federal Truth in Lending Law

■ The Federal New Consumer Product Warranty Act

■ Unruh Act (If you do business in California)

■ The Commercial Code (of your state)

■ The Civil Code (of your state)

■ Business and Professions Code (of your state)

■ Contractor's License Law (if your state has one)

■ Health and Safety Code (of your state)

As if that weren't enough, there are even laws for governing your salespeople. Welcome to the home improvement business!

Special home improvement contract forms

Figure 4-8 is a home improvement contract I've used in California. State law requires that it include the following key elements:

■ The mechanic's lien law Notice to Owner

■ Notice of Right to Cancel, and the cancellation form

■ Notice of Right of Rescission.

You also have to use a Home Improvement Installment Contract whenever you sell a job that's to be paid for by installments.

Change Orders and Extra Work

A *change order* is a written direction to the contractor from the owner or designer that alters the basic contract. Use it whenever there's a change to the plans or specifications, even if the price stays the same. Any changes must be mutually acceptable to both the contractor and owner. In spite of what a layman might expect from the name, change orders

Proposal and Contract

For Residential Building Construction and Alteration

Date_____19____

To _____

Dear Sir:

We propose to furnish all material and perform all labor necessary to complete the following:

_____

_____

_____

_____

_____

Job Location:

All of the above work to be completed in a substantial and workmanlike manner according to the drawings, job specifications, and terms and conditions on the back of this form for the sum of

Dollars ($_____)

Payments to be made as the work progresses as follows:_____

_____

_____

the entire amount of the contract to be paid within_____days after substantial completion and acceptance by the owner. The price quoted is for immediate acceptance only. Delay in acceptance will require a verification of prevailing labor and material costs. This offer becomes a contract upon acceptance by contractor but shall be null and void if not executed within 5 days from the date above.

By_____

"YOU, THE BUYER, MAY CANCEL THIS TRANSACTION AT ANY TIME PRIOR TO MIDNIGHT OF THE THIRD BUSINESS DAY AFTER THE DATE OF THIS TRANSACTION. SEE THE ATTACHED NOTICE OF CANCELLATION FORM FOR AN EXPLANATION OF THIS RIGHT."

You are hereby authorized to furnish all materials and labor required to complete the work according to the drawings, job specifications, and terms and conditions on the back of this proposal, for which we agree to pay the amounts itemized above

Owner _____

Owner _____ Date_____

Accepted by Contractor_____ Date_____

Figure 4-8 *Home improvement contract*

TERMS & CONDITIONS OF CONTRACT

1. The Contractor agrees to commence work hereunder within ten (10) days after the last to occur ot the following, (1) receipt of written notice from the Lien Holder, if any, to the effect that all documents required to be recorded prior to the commencement of construction have been properly recorded: (2) the building site has been properly prepared for construction by the Owner, and (3) a building permit has been issued. Contractor agrees to prosecute work thereafter to completion, and to complete the work within a reasonable time, subject to such delays as are permissable under this contract. If no first Lien Holder exists, all references to Lien Holder are to be disregarded.

2. Contractor shall pay all valid bills and charge for material and labor arising out of the construction of the structure and will hold Owner of the property free and harmless against all liens and claims of lien for labor and material against the property.

3. No payment under this contract shall be construed as an acceptance of any work done up to the time of such payment, except as to such items as are plainly evident to anyone not experienced in construction work, but the entire work is to be subject to the inspection and approval of the inspector for the Public Authority at the time when it shall be claimed by the Contractor that the work has been completed. At the completion of the work, acceptance by the Public Authority shall entitle Contractor to receive all progress payments according to the schedule set forth.

4. The drawings and specifications are intended to supplement each other, so that any works exhibited in either and not mentioned in the other are to be executed the same as if they were mentioned and set forth in both. In the event that any conflict exists between any estimate of costs of construction and the terms of this Contract, this Contract shall be controlling. The Contractor may substitute materials that are equal in quality to those specified if the Contractor deems it advisable to do so.

5. Owner agrees to pay Contractor its normal selling price for all additions, alterations or deviations. No additional work shall be done without the prior written authorization of Owner. Any such authorization shall be on a change-order form, approved by both parties, which shall become a part of this Contract. Where such additional work is added to this Contract, it is agreed that all terms and conditions of this Contract shall apply equally to such additional work. Any change in specifications or construction necessary to conform to existing or future building codes, zoning laws, or regulations of inspecting Public Authorities shall be considered additional work to be paid for by Owner as additional work. If the quantity of materials required under this Contract are so altered as to create a hardship on the Contractor, the owner shall be obligated to reimburse Contractor for additional expenses incurred. It is understood and agreed that if Contractor finds that extra concrete is required he is authorized by the Owner to pour the amount of concrete that is required by the building code or site conditions and shall promptly notify Owner of such extra concrete. Owner shall promptly deposit the cost of the required extra concrete with the Contractor. Any changes made under this Contract will not affect the validity of this document.

6. The Contractor shall not be responsible for any damage occasioned by the Owner or Owner's agent, Acts of God, earthquake, or other causes beyond the control of Contractor, unless otherwise herein provided or unless he is obligated by the terms hereof to provide insurance against such hazards. Contractor shall not be liable for damages or defects resulting from work done by subcontractors. In the event Owner authorizes access through adjacent properties for Contractor's use during construction Owner is required to obtain permission from the owner(s) of the adjacent properties for such. Owner agrees to be responsible and to hold Contractor harmless and accept any risks resulting from access through adjacent properties.

7. The time during which the Contractor is delayed in his work by (a) the acts of Owner or his agents or employees or those claiming under agreement with or grant from Owner, including any notice to the Lien Holder to withhold progress payments, or (b) any acts or delays occasioned by the Lien Holder, or by (c) the Acts of God which Contractor could not have reasonably forseen and provided against, or by (d) stormy or inclement weather which necessarily delays the work, or by (e) any strikes, boycotts or like obstructive actions by employees or labor organizations and which are beyond the control of Contractor and which he cannot reasonably overcome, or by (f) extra work requested by the Owner, or by (g) failure of Owner to promptly pay for any extra work as authorized, shall be added to the time for completion by a fair and reasonable allowance. Should work be stopped for more than 30 days by any or all of (a) through (g) above, the Contractor may terminate this Contract and collect for all work completed plus a reasonable profit.

8. Contractor shall at his own expense carry all workers' compensation insurance and public liability insurance necessary for the full protection of Contractor and Owner during the progress of the work. Certificates of such insurance shall be filed with Owner and with said Lien Holder if Owner and Lien Holder so required. Owner agrees to procure at his own expense, prior to the commencement of any work, fire insurance with Course of Construction, All Physical Loss and Vandalism and Malicious Mischief clauses attached in a sum equal to the total cost of the improvements. Such insurance shall be written to protect the Owner and Contractor, and Lien Holder, as their interests may appear. Should Owner fail to do so, Contractor may procure such insurance as agent for Owner, but is not required to do so, and Owner agrees on demand to reimburse Contractor in cash for the cost thereof.

9. Where materials are to be matched, Contractor shall make every reasonable effort to do so using standard materials, but does not guarantee a perfect match.

10. Owner agrees to sign and file for record within five days after the completion and acceptance of work a notice of completion. Contractor agrees upon receipt of final payment to release the property from any and all claims that may have accrued by reason of the construction. If the Contractor faithfully performs the obligations of this part to be performed, he shall have the right to refuse to permit occupancy or use of the structure by the Owner or anyone claiming through the Owner until Contractor has received the payment due at completion of construction.

11. Any controversy or claim arising out of or relating to this contract, shall be settled by arbitration in accordance with the Rules of the American Arbitration Association, and judgment upon the award rendered by the Arbitrator(s) may be entered in any Court having jurisdiction.

12. Should either party hereto bring suit in court to enforce the terms of this agreement, any judgment awarded shall include court costs and reasonable attorney's fees to the successful party plus interest at the legal rate.

13. Unless otherwise specified, the contract price is based upon Owner's representation that site is level and cleared and is not filled ground or hard rock and that there are no conditions preventing Contractor from proceeding with usual construction procedures and that all existing electrical and plumbing facilities are capable of carrying the extra load caused by the work to be performed by Contractor. Any electrical meter charges required by Public Authorities or utility companies are not included in the price of this Contract, unless included in specifications. If existing conditions are not as represented thereby necessitating additional excavation, blasting, plumbing, electrical, curbing, concrete or other work, the same shall be paid for by Owner as additional work.

14. The Owner is solely responsible for providing Contractor prior to the commencing of construction with such water, electricity and refuse removal service at the job site as may be required by Contractor to effect the construction of the improvement covered by this Contract. Owner shall provide a toilet during the course of construction when required by law.

15. The Contractor shall not be responsible for damage to existing walks, curbs, driveways, cesspools, septic tanks, sewer lines, water or gas lines, arches, shrubs, lawn, trees, clotheslines, telephone and electric lines, etc., by the Contractor, sub-contractor, or supplier incurred in the performance of work or in the delivery of materials for the job. Owner hereby warrants and represents that he shall be solely responsible for the condition of the building site with respect to finish grading, moisture, drainage, alkali content, soil slippage and sinking or any other site condition that may exist over which the Contractor has no control and subsequently results in damage to the building.

16. The Owner is solely responsible for the location of all lot lines and shall identify all corner posts of his lot for the Contractor. If any doubt exists as to the location of such lot lines, the Owner shall at his own cost, order and pay for a survey. If the Owner shall wrongly identify the location of the lot lines of the property, any changes required by the Contractor shall be at Owner's expense. This cost shall be paid by Owner to Contractor in cash prior to continuation of work.

17. Contractor has the right to sub-contract any part, or all, of the work herein agreed to be performed.

18. Owner agrees to install and connect at owner's cost, such utilities and make such improvements in addition to work covered by this contract as may be required by Lien Holder or Public Authority prior to completion of work of Contractor.

19. Contractor shall not be responsible for any damages occasioned by plumbing leaks unless water service is connected to the plumbing facilities prior to the time of rough inspection.

20. The Owner is solely responsible for all charges incurred for grading of lot for level building site, removing all trees, debris, and other obstructions prior to start of construction.

21. Owner hereby grants to Contractor the right to display signs and advertise at the building site.

22. Contractor shall have the right to stop work and keep the job idle if payments are not made to him when due. If any payments are not made to Contractor when due, Owner shall pay to Contractor an additional charge of 10% of the amount of such payment. If the work shall be stopped by the Owner for a period of sixty days, then the Contractor may, at Contractor's option, upon five days written notice, demand and receive payment for all work executed and materials ordered or supplied and any other loss sustained, including a profit of 10% of the contract price. In the event of work stoppage for any reason, Owner shall provide for protection of, and be responsible for any damage, warpage, racking, or loss of material on the premises.

23. Within ten days after execution of this Contract, Contractor shall have the right to cancel this Contract should he determine that there is any uncertainty that all payments due under this Contract will be made when due or that an error has been made in computing the cost of completing the work.

24. This agreement constitutes the entire contract and the parties are not bound by oral expression or representation by any party or agent of either party. All changes to the work approved by Owner and accepted by Contractor become part of this contract.

25. The price quoted for completion of the structure is subject to change to the extent of any difference in cost of labor and materials as of this date and the actual cost to Contractor at the time materials are purchased and work is done.

26. The Contractor is not responsible for labor or materials furnished by Owner or anyone working under the direction of the Owner and any loss or additional work that results therefrom shall be the responsibility of the Owner.

27. No action arising from or related to the contract, or the performance thereof, shall be commenced by either party against the other more than two years after the completion or cessation of work under this contract. This limitation applies to all actions of any character, whether at law or in equity, and whether sounding in contract, tort, or otherwise. This limitation shall not be extended by any negligent misrepresentation or unintentional concealment, but shall be extended as provided by law for willful fraud, concealment, or misrepresentation.

28. All taxes and special assessments levied against the property shall be paid by the Owner.

29. Contractor agrees to complete the work in a substantial and workmanlike manner but is not responsible for failures or defects that result from work done by others prior, at the time of or subsequent to work done under this agreement, failure to keep guttes, downspouts and valleys reasonably clear of leaves or obstructions, failure of the Owner to authorize Contractor to undertake needed repairs or replacement of fascia, vents, defective or deteriorated roofing or roofing felt, trim, sheathing, rafters, structural members, siding, masonry, caulking, metal edging, or flashing of any type, or any act of negligence or misuse by the Owner or any other party.

30. Contractor makes no warranty, express or implied (including warranty of fitness for purpose and merchantability). Any warranty or limited warranty shall be as provided by the manufacturer of the products and materials used in construction.

31. The owner shall assume full responsibility for the project and the site beginning on the date the Certificate of Substantial Completion is issued.

32. Any conflict between plans, specifications, and this contract, this contract shall prevail.

Figure 4-8 (cont'd) ***Home improvement contract***

Notice To Customer Required By Federal Law

You have entered into a transaction on_____ _____which may result in a lien, mortgage, or other security interest on your home. You have a legal right under federal law to cancel this transaction, if you desire to do so, without any penalty or obligation within three business days from the above date or any later date on which all material disclosures required under the Truth in Lending Act have been given to you. If you so cancel the transaction, any lien, mortgage, or other security interest on your home arising from this transaction is automatically void. You are also entitled to receive a refund of any down payment or other consideration if you cancel. If you decide to cancel this transaction, you may do so by notifying

_____
(Name of Creditor)

at_____
(Address of Creditor's Place of Business)

by mail or telegram sent not later than midnight of_____. You may also use any other form

of written notice identifying the transaction if it is delivered to the above address not later than that

time. This notice may be used for the purpose by dating and signing below.

I hereby cancel this transaction.

_____   _____
(Date)   (Customer's Signature)

Effect of rescission. When a customer exercises his right to rescind under paragraph (a) of this section, he is not liable for any finance or other charge, and any security interest becomes void upon such a rescission. Within 10 days after receipt of a notice of rescission, the creditor shall return to the customer any money or property given as earnest money, downpayment, or otherwise, and shall take any action necessary or appropriate to reflect the termination of any security interest created under the transaction. If the creditor has delivered any property to the customer, the customer may retain possession of it. Upon the performance of the creditor's obligations under this section, the customer shall tender the property to the creditor, except that if return of the property in kind would be impracticable or inequitable, the customer shall tender its reasonable value. Tender shall be made at the location of the property or at the residence of the customer, at the option of the customer. If the creditor does not take possession of the property within 10 days after tender by the customer, ownership of the property vests in the customer without obligation on his part to pay for it.

Figure 4-8 (cont'd)   *Home improvement contract*

protect the contractor more than they gratify the owner. Don't make changes in what you've agreed to do under the contract until the owner agrees that it is a change and agrees on the additional charge.

Extra work means work that's independent of the contract. It could be something not required under the contract, or something omitted from the contract because of an oversight. An extra work order can come in various forms, sometimes in writing, sometimes not.

Extra work orders are often issued after the work is done. Change orders may be made before the work begins but are usually made while work is under way.

There's a typical extra work and change order in Chapter 11. An order like this may be used between all parties under contract — owner and contractor, contractor and subcontractor, or subcontractor and sub-subcontractor.

You're in a somewhat different position if your company is a subcontractor. You'll be presented with subcontracts prepared by the owner, designer, manager, or general contractor. These subcontracts are often weighted heavily in favor of the party that offers the contract. As a sub, if you want the work, you accept the conditions as they're written.

If you take subcontract work, examine the general contractor's prime contract. Think about how that contract will affect your performance. Note any conditions in the contract that affect your payments, especially what happens if the owner fails to pay the prime contractor (whether you've completed your portion of the work or not). What are the insurance or bond requirements, penalties for delays, and the procedure for changes or extra work orders?

So Sue Me

Even under the best conditions, and with a contract that seems airtight, there can still be problems. As contractors, we have to be tough negotiators when we hammer out the terms of our contracts. Starting construction without a written contract, or without understanding the contract you've signed, is usually an invitation to disaster.

Unfortunately, the contractor is usually the loser when customers threaten suit. Even if you "win," there's usually no real winner in most legal quarrels — except maybe the lawyers. When your dispute ends up in the lap of two law firms, both your bank account and your reputation are likely to suffer. And the dice are heavily loaded against the

"....MMM, can't remember agreeing to that, can you?"

contractor in many states. My advice? Easy. Find some way to avoid disputes, even if you have to suffer some "loss of face" to do it.

But What About Me?

The public may believe that the Yellow Pages are full of unscrupulous remodeling contractors. But we all know there are good and bad operators in every business. Maybe it's just that people seem to holler louder when they discover a bad apple in the remodeling business.

When contractors come out on the short end, no one hears about that. Why? Because there are no agencies for them to complain to. There's no Contractor Protection Agency to protect us from the deceitful homeowner. That means legitimate remodeling contractors must be much more careful to survive in this business — to keep their contractor's license and bond untarnished.

Of course, the vast majority of remodeling work is done without incident. But when something goes wrong, very wrong, it's the lawyers who get the complaints first.

Your Lawyer Can Help

Verbal construction agreements are especially problem-prone. Remember, a contract doesn't have to be written to be enforced. Of course, no one wants to get in a dispute about a verbal contract. But it happens often enough.

What most lawyers do best is practice preventive law. It's easier to describe what you should do than it is to fix what you've done. But that doesn't help if you're being sued now.

If you're in a dispute that involves a relatively small sum, say under $2,000, there's usually not much a lawyer can do for you. Litigation may cost more than the amount you stand to recover. Small claims court may be a better choice.

So how do you avoid problems — and avoid lawyers? Before you enter into any contract, read the contract. Try to anticipate the problems. Check the job site, the specifications and drawings, and the details of the contract itself. Owners and contractor get into disputes because of surprises, things neither expected would happen. Avoid surprises and you avoid most disputes.

Here's what I mean: You've remodeled a living room and added an entry. The building inspector refuses to sign off because there's not safety glass next to the front door. If you had checked the codes carefully, you would have anticipated that, and included it in the original contract. Now, the owner is surprised and annoyed about the added cost, and might try to get out of paying you to replace the glass.

Too Late?

I've gone to a lawyer hoping to find a loophole or technicality to get me out of a bad contract. Sometimes it works and sometimes it doesn't. Here's every contractor's nightmare: You jump for joy when your company is announced as the winning bidder on a major rehab project. But then your estimator checks his bid. *Whoops!* He forgot to include the cost of the whole second floor on one building. Now you want out, but the owner says no dice. You made your bed, now lie in it. No changes.

Sometimes a lawyer can find a loophole, sometimes he can't. Either way, the process is expensive and risky. The lawyer will search for a slipup by the owner in preparing documents or awarding the bid. Even then, a court might be reluctant to set aside the award because of an irrelevant technicality. Everyone knows the real reason you want out. You made a mistake. So triple check before you make your offer. Make sure you know exactly what you'll be giving and getting.

An Agreement Is an Agreement Is an Agreement

Verbal agreements are legal, but they're hard to enforce because they're hard to prove. It's your word against the other guy's. A written contract protects you if the other side doesn't live up to their commitments. Review the contract carefully. Make sure it says exactly what you intend. Even when your lawyer draws a contract, the terms may not be just what you want. Lawyers get paid to know the law. But none understands your business as well as you do.

Most contracts favor the side that drew it up. If you draw up the contract, consider including an escape clause that lets you back out. If you don't draw the contract, take time to read it. Question what you don't understand. Don't rely on the owner's lawyer for advice. Your interest and their interest don't coincide. Be sure the agreement includes all the other side's obligations as well as your own.

Finally, make certain that all parties properly sign and date the contract.

Preventive Legal Advice

If you face a complicated or high stakes job, consult a lawyer who's an expert in that field. You need a specialist in construction law, not a divorce lawyer. Preventive advice at this stage — whatever its cost — may be justified. The time, money and aggravation you save will probably be worth more than the fee.

Keep Good Records

If you're in a dispute, good records and notes about transactions will probably help you win the argument. Keep notes on meetings you have with the owner, understandings you reach, changes that are requested, invoices, change orders, drawings, and P.O.'s. To protect yourself, write up a summary of meetings or conversations and send a copy of that summary to the owner in a letter. If the owner doesn't complain that your summary is inaccurate, your summary has probably been accepted as correct.

Most people don't want trouble. You can often avoid a lawsuit if you can produce documents showing that your actions were correct, proper, and according to the agreement. But cases are lost every day when remodelers can't back up their recollection with written proof.

Settle If You Can

Try to resolve problems without a lawyer, especially if you want to maintain friendly relations with the other party. Deal with your opponent on a one-to-one basis, or suggest arbitration. Call in your lawyer only as a last resort.

If you've gone this far, have your lawyer judge the strength of your case. Consider the cost of litigation and the amount of time involved. Then you can decide whether it's worthwhile to proceed. Lawyers negotiate all the time. Yours may suggest creative ways to arrive at a settlement that might not have occurred to you.

Sometimes avoiding court action means eating crow, or giving up something to the other side that they're not really entitled to, for the sake of settling. No doubt about it, you lose something. But probably less than you'd lose in time and peace of mind if you went to court. So in that respect, you win. Treat the matter gracefully, like losing to an ace high flush.

Avoid the Problem

Like defensive driving, claims consciousness must always be in your mind. You could be processing jobs carefully and professionally, but watch out. There's always someone willing to pounce on you at the slightest excuse. It can happen unexpectedly, although certain clues often signal muddy waters ahead. When an owner expects you to supply work not included in your contract, when complaints about quality become unreasonable, when interference affects job progress, look out. Like a good scout, *be prepared*.

Besides keeping good records, be sensitive to your customer's attitudes. If the owner is interrupting the normal work progress, keep notes on his behavior. If the owner complains, you or your manager should visit the job site and air out differences, minor or otherwise. Resolve them to the owner's satisfaction even if it costs more money. Then record the event in detail in the customer's file in the office. Be specific. Your logbook records should contain:

■ The date and time of any conversation, by phone or in person

■ Names of individuals involved

■ Nature of the complaint

■ The results of any inspection

■ The details of any agreement

That Uneasy Feeling

Ever have that sixth sense that you're sure you're going to be sued? Every contractor has felt that at one time or another. How should you react to it? When that feeling gets intense, launch a last ditch effort to resolve the problem and avoid a suit. Try to arrange one more meeting at the job site. Have another contractor go with you. If the dispute involves a trade you subcontract, also take a subcontractor who specializes in the same kind of work, but not the same one who did the job for you.

What if the owner complains of poor workmanship on a concrete slab and wants it redone even though framing is fairly advanced? If your contractor and subcontractor friends tell you confidentially that the slab was poorly done, you'd better dismantle and break up the concrete and do it over. Quietly, of course.

On the other hand, if they find no fault with the slab — that it's satisfactory in every way — you have two good independent authorities to back you up. But you can assume the owner has his own experts advising him. So what do you do next?

Let your concrete sub know of the complaint or claim and have him re-inspect his own work. Tell him that if the case goes to court and the job is proven defective, you'll have to recover against him for costs and damages. Of course, this example oversimplifies the situation. The mechanic's lien and holdback under the contract have a bearing on your strategy.

Many cases are settled on the courthouse stairs the day of the trial. Be receptive to an offer or initiate your own if necessary. The worst thing to do is get angry and treat your opponent vindictively. No one's going to win any big award. Everyone involved will be a loser — except the lawyers.

Here's another suggestion. The moment you suspect a suit is coming, meet with everyone involved in the job to review and record everything that's happened so far. This is important. By the time the case gets to court, some of these people may no longer be available to remember the events.

You'll also be astounded at people's inability to remember details months or years later. Why was there a delay in starting the job? Did the owner extend his vacation? Last minute changes? Rained two weeks solid? Strike at the concrete supplier's? It's very hard to remember accurately all the details of a job months, or even weeks after they happen.

In summary, the easiest way to avoid legal hassles is to prevent problems in the first place. Investigate before you plunge into anything. Enter into a written contract only after you've reviewed it and found it acceptable. Keep good and complete records. Try to satisfy your opponent before a suit is filed. Settle out of court if you can. Above all, if problems come up, don't spin your wheels — *act*.

Arbitration

Arbitration is an alternative to our system of law courts. The hope is that you can get a decision faster and cheaper through arbitration than you could using our legal system. Of course, arbitration is always voluntary. No one can force you into arbitration. But you may have agreed to arbitrate in a contract. If you have, courts will usually require arbitration before any suit can be brought.

The arbitration process begins with selection of one or more arbitrators. Sometimes both parties select a qualified, neutral arbitrator. The Better Business Bureau or the American Arbitration Association can usually suggest the names of arbitrators willing to serve.

Usually you'll want to select an arbitrator who's experienced in the remodeling business. Your nominee should know something about contract law, construction liens, holdbacks, and construction methods in general. Find someone with a reputation for successful arbitration, neutrality and strength of character.

The arbitrator's personal experience shouldn't influence his or her decision. It's up to the disputants to prove the facts they present. Then the arbitrator interprets those facts and decides which side made the best case.

As in a court of law, arbitrators will usually base their decisions on legal precedent. But unlike a formal trial, an owner and contractor can agree ahead of time to let the arbitrator decide the case on the basis of fairness rather than strictly according to the law.

Arbitration hearings are usually less formal than court hearings. Rules of evidence don't have to apply. The arbitrator has sole discretion on evaluating witnesses and weighing evidence.

Either party can be represented by a lawyer. But costs are usually lower than for a court trial because arbitration can be set up in a very short time — days or weeks instead of months or years. And arbitration hearings usually take far less time than a court trial.

The parties to an arbitration usually agree that the arbitrator's decision will be final. It can be entered in a court of law and enforced by the remedies given to any legal decision. Owners and contractors who agree to the process do so with that in mind. Most courts are willing to reconsider an arbitrator's decision only if there was a major error in law.

So, compared to a lawsuit, arbitration normally offers the advantage of lower cost, speed, privacy, and informality. In addition, the parties get to choose the arbitrator or arbitrators.

There Are Disadvantages

Arbitrators usually aren't as well qualified as judges to decide important legal issues. And arbitration panels seldom provide for juries. If you want a qualified legal expert to make decisions and feel a jury is needed to decide issues of fact, maybe arbitration isn't the best choice.

Consider carefully the advantages and disadvantages of arbitration whenever it's proposed. Odds are high that you'll get into a dispute sooner or later that will put you into an arbitration meeting. Everyone who's in the remodeling business for more than a few years will probably have an opportunity to try arbitration.

How Is Remodeling Contracting Different?

The remodeling business is more like a retail business than a general contracting company. I think that's because remodelers deal directly with the homeowner. Making the sale is the key to success in remodeling construction.

All contractors have to price their jobs competitively. Home improvement and remodeling contractors have an additional burden. They have to sell their professionalism: service, workmanship and quality. Price usually takes a back seat.

Sometimes you can bid low and still make good money. Here are some situations where I'd lower my profit goal to get some extra work:

You have surplus materials left over from a previous job.

You don't have enough work and want to cover overhead and avoid laying off key employees. This is a tough situation to be in, but everyone goes through periods like this sooner or later.

So there are times when it makes good business sense to lower your profit goals. Here's what happened to me once. We were invited by the city to bid a small job which they wanted done in a hurry. We hadn't done much city work because competition was as heavy as the red tape. Also, the city always awarded work to the low bidder. But I thought we were in a good position to get the work. Other contractors that could do the work were busy and wouldn't be bidding. An official in the planning office told me confidentially that we would probably get the job if we submitted a bid.

Okay. We decided to tackle it. Our estimated labor and material cost was $12,000. The usual gross margin for my company is about 50% (a 100% markup on labor and material costs). We decided to shave our margin a little and be content with half our usual profit — especially since we were nearly guaranteed the job. So we entered a bid of $18,000. *Surprise*! Six bidders popped up against us — $16,900, $14,400, $14,190, $13,650, $13,450, and $10,940. *The lowest bidder was $1,060 below our bare labor and material cost!* On top of that, we heard that the lowest bidder tromped into the planning office and demanded the award on the spot.

This exercise taught us several things. One is not to believe what an official tells you in confidence. Another is not to offer special treatment to government. And most important, not to change our bidding policy. We wasted time and money filling out forms — getting ready for what we thought was a sure thing. Our only consolation? Knowledge that the low bidder must have lost much more than we did.

That concludes what I intend to say in this introduction to estimating and contracting. In the next chapter we'll get down to the details of creating good estimates.

5

Setting Prices

Sales are the key to growth in the remodeling business. Without aggressive selling, you're stuck with small pickup jobs at low margin — the type of work nearly anyone can do. That's no way to build a career.

If you agree with me that every remodeling company needs a sales staff, you arrive at the next hurdle: Few salespeople are as good at estimating as they are at selling. Salespeople are specialists — selling experts. But every salesperson needs to quote prices and discuss costs. No owner's going to close a deal without a full discussion of the cost.

That's where your unit price system comes in. It's fast, so it helps your sales staff concentrate on *selling*. At the same time, they can make sure the jobs they sell will make you money, not cost you money.

When you start in the remodeling business, you'll probably do your own selling and estimating. But as business grows, you can add salespeople to help carry the selling load.

Chapter one covered my views on hiring salespeople. As I said, you can't just hire them — you have to teach them to do the job the way *you* want it done. And an important part of that training will be on estimating and quoting prices. That means you need a system that's easy to teach, and easy for your sales staff to learn. That's what you'll find in this chapter.

What Do I Mean by Unit Prices?

The unit price is, in simplest terms, the average price for each unit installed. We'll be a little more specific than that, though.

General contractors who handle new construction see the two steps in developing unit prices: measuring quantities and setting prices. For example, suppose the labor cost to place 50 cubic yards of concrete required for a particular job is $1,000. That's the total cost of placement. To find the unit cost, we divide $1,000 by 50 cubic yards. The answer is $20 per cubic yard.

The unit cost for placing one cubic yard of concrete is $20. But notice I said unit *cost*. That's not your selling price. It's your cost. The term *unit price* is your selling price and includes your overhead and profit.

Most remodelers let their sales staff quote unit prices from a company price book. How accurate are these unit prices? We know it's unlikely that any two jobs will have exactly the same costs. So it's unlikely that prices in a price book will be exactly right for every job. In fact, your unit prices may not be exactly right for any job. So why use them? Easy! Your unit prices should be an average of what that item can be expected to cost on all jobs. Sometimes it's too high and sometimes it's too low. But on average, it should be a good selling price. If you have enough jobs that include that item, you'll end up with the markup you expect.

To be accurate, your standard unit prices should be based on the cost of similar items installed on previous jobs. That means the accuracy of your standard unit prices depends on the accuracy of your cost records for past jobs.

But why calculate unit prices at all? Why not just estimate the actual cost for each job from a take-off? Why bother to divide costs by quantity to get unit prices when all you really need is the total cost? Here's why. It's the most convenient way to keep track of cost data from past jobs so you can apply it to present and future jobs. And unit prices make estimating super fast.

Remodeling salespeople need to estimate and give out quotes quickly — sometimes on the very first sales call. So they need a way to make fast, accurate estimates. This system of standard unit prices is the best I've ever found for closing deals quickly and profitably with very little time wasted in pricing and estimating.

Computing Unit Prices for Remodeling Sales

Here's how to establish unit prices for your company. First, account for all the materials (and waste) needed to complete each common item that's included in most of your jobs. Then add the cost of labor. That gives you the *unit cost*. Now, add the gross margin (overhead and profit) to arrive at the *unit price*.

For example, most jobs require interior walls. They're 8 feet high, with lengths running from 6 feet to 24 feet. The typical wall has 1/2-inch drywall on both sides, 2 x 4 construction grade hemfir studs 16 inches on center, a 2 x 4 sill plate, two 2 x 4 top plates, fasteners, filler and tape, and so on.

Begin by doing an accurate material take-off for this typical wall. Do it for your three most common lengths — 6, 12 and 24 feet. Add the labor, handling, freight, taxes, and other miscellaneous costs for each size. Finally, average them on the basis of cost per linear foot. The result is the *unit cost* for interior walls. Now add the gross margin to get the *unit price* for quoting purposes.

Do the same for exterior walls, foundation walls, footings, decks, slabs, floors, ceilings, roofs, doors, windows, demolition, — everything your crews are likely to do.

But your price book isn't finished yet. What about the work your crews *don't* do? Find unit prices for all your subtrades and materials suppliers.

For example, ask your electrical contractor to give you a list of prices he charges you. Get your cost for each wall switch, light switch, outlet, 100 amp service, GFCI, home run, and so on. From your concrete contractor, get the price per square foot for a 4-inch concrete slab without mesh and with mesh, and any other work he does for you. And don't forget to collect information on other charges, like minimum charges and callback costs. Take your time and do a good job of it.

Establish a clear understanding with all your trades and suppliers that they *must* give you at least 30 days' notice before hitting you with any price increase. (Price decreases take effect immediately, of course.)

Take the time to develop costs of the most common subcontract items. It can save hours of your time getting sub bids. In fact, you'll seldom have to ask for quotes from your subs.

Compare Your Costs to Your Subcontractors'

If you're going to do some of the work with your own crew — carpentry, roofing, drywall or concrete — keep an accurate accounting of your true costs. Convert the figures into unit costs and periodically compare your costs with the cost of hiring a subcontractor. Don't forget to add the overhead costs and profit to your unit costs. Otherwise you won't be comparing prices on an equal basis with your subtrades.

If you find that doing your own work isn't cost effective for some trades, either find a way to make your crews more efficient or give more work to subcontractors. Many subs provide excellent service at low costs. It isn't easy to improve on the performance of a specialist's specialty.

What Is Your Product Worth?

Deciding how to set your prices is important and sometimes tricky. Many successful contractors try to set their prices either lower or higher than the mid-range competition. One marketing researcher says, "High prices can actually mean an increase in the market share, while prices more in line with competition do not necessarily result in higher sales." I subscribe to this belief. Higher prices can set you apart from the "rest-of-the-pack" contractors. Some people equate higher prices with higher quality. So be the high-quality contractor. Just be careful that you don't price yourself out of the market.

So what does that mean to you? For one thing, it means that finding your upper price limit isn't just a matter of deciding what your customers are willing to pay. If one competitor already has a big slice of the remodeling market, you might have to match their prices and service. On the other hand, cutting prices is dangerous if you're already running on short margin.

How do your prices compare to prices quoted by the competition? Answer that question and you're beginning to develop a company marketing strategy. The most successful companies I know started out with high quality and moderate prices. Once their business was established, they raised prices by up to 50 percent without substantial loss of business.

You may be able to command premium prices if your advertising emphasizes broad and fast service with high-quality materials. And careful discounting can sometimes pay off. If your competitors charge high prices, you may have room to discount their prices and still harvest reasonable profits.

Should You Slash Prices?

You're thinking of lowering prices. Your sales just aren't as healthy as you'd hoped. So you wonder if cutting prices would help.

You might be surprised at how much more you have to sell to maintain your profit margin at lower prices. Don't cut your prices until you know exactly how it will affect your cash flow.

For instance, if your gross margin is 40 percent, (which is already too low) and you cut prices by 20 percent, you'll have to double your sales volume to maintain that margin. Will you be able to do that? Do some analysis before slashing prices.

Look at Figure 5-1. It's a U.S. Small Business Administration chart that shows the percentage you'll have to increase sales in order to earn the same gross profit whenever you cut prices.

Gross Margin

Gross profit margin, gross margin or just gross profit all mean the same thing. But it's not all profit. In fact, it can end up as a loss. But it is gross and it is a margin, so I'll call it gross margin. It's what you make *before* you deduct the cost of doing business, which is called "overhead." If your overhead is more than the gross margin, you're losing money on every job. So knowing your overhead cost is the first step in building a profitable business.

Find Your Overhead

Every remodeling company, no matter how small, has overhead expense: phone, car or truck, supplies, etc. You have to add an overhead percentage to each job to cover operating expenses. Look to your profit and loss (income) statement to decide how much to add. You can find your overhead costs in your financial statement, if it's accurate. Then convert that overhead figure into a percent figure by dividing total overhead by total sales and multiplying by 100.

For example, suppose your company's volume is $1,000,000 for the year and your overhead (rent, phone, office staff, etc.) is $100,000. Dividing $100,000 by $1,000,000 we get 10 percent. That means 10 percent of the contract price is needed to cover your overhead.

Job cost includes the direct cost (labor and materials) and overhead (all other expenses). We haven't touched on contingencies and profits yet. They're coming up.

Percent Gross Profit

Amount cut	10%	15%	20%	25%	30%	35%	40%
1%	11.1	7.1	5.3	4.2	3.4	2.0	2.6
2	25.0	15.4	11.1	8.7	7.1	6.1	5.3
3	42.8	25.0	17.6	13.6	11.1	9.4	8.1
4	66.6	36.4	25.0	19.0	15.4	12.9	11.1
5	100.0	50.0	33.3	25.0	20.0	16.7	14.3
6	150.0	66.7	42.9	31.6	25.0	20.7	17.6
7	233.3	87.5	53.8	53.8	38.9	30.4	21.2
8	400.0	114.3	66.7	47.1	36.4	29.6	25.0
9	1000.0	150.0	81.8	56.3	42.9	34.6	29.0
10		200.0	100.0	66.7	50.0	40.0	33.3
11		275.0	122.2	78.6	57.9	45.8	37.9
12		400.0	150.0	92.3	66.7	52.2	42.0
13		650.0	185.7	108.3	76.5	59.1	48.1
14		1400.0	233.3	127.3	87.5	66.7	53.8
15			300.0	150.0	100.0	76.0	60.0
16			400.0	177.8	114.3	87.5	66.7
17			566.7	212.5	130.8	94.4	73.9
18			900.0	257.1	150.0	105.9	81.8
19			1900.0	316.7	172.7	118.8	90.5
20				400.0	200.0	133.3	100.0
21				525.0	233.3	150.0	110.5
22				733.3	275.0	169.2	122.2
23				1115.0	328.6	191.7	135.3
24				2400.0	400.0	218.2	150.0
25					500.0	250.0	166.7

Figure 5-1 *Sales increase vs. price slash chart*

Without accurate overhead figures, accurate pricing is nearly impossible. If you aren't covering your overhead expense on every job, your losses increase as your volume goes up. That's a disaster. It's also why you need an accurate profit and loss statement every month, if possible, or at least every other month. You also need to know if your overhead is constant, or if it varies during the year.

Most remodeling contractors I know don't keep accurate records on overhead costs. That's a mistake. Too many think they have little or no overhead because their business is small. Overhead is what the big guys have. Not me! Right? That seems logical. They're working out of their home, doing their own bookkeeping — cutting back everywhere they can. But in spite of that, overhead for many small remodeling contractors is a higher percentage of gross sales than for their larger cousins. In general, as sales volume increases from $100,000 to $5,000,000, the overhead percentage decreases. That's a fact of business life.

Calculate Your Markup

Here's how to decide how much to add to job costs to cover overhead:

Goodguys Remodeler's financial statement for the last 12 months show sales to be $200,000, with overhead expenses at $50,000. Most of that $50,000 was Mr. Goodguys' salary. Applying my formula, you see that overhead is 25 percent of sales.

Now Goodguys can compute a selling price that will cover overhead and yield the profit they want.

Suppose Mr. Goodguys estimates direct cost on a job (labor, materials, subcontracts, supervision, etc.) at $10,000. We know his overhead is 25 percent of gross. And he wants to make a profit of 20 percent on the job. Adding overhead (25 percent) and profit (20 percent), we get 45 percent. Can Mr. Goodguys multiply $10,000 (the direct job cost) by 45 percent to find the amount to add for overhead and profit? Is the bid price $14,500? That's $10,000 for direct cost, $2,500 for overhead and $2,000 for profit. Isn't that right?

The answer is clearly *NO!*

The correct bid price is $18,181.82 if Mr. Goodguys wants to cover overhead at 25 percent and earn a profit of 20 percent. Follow me through on the math and you'll understand why.

Overhead and profit together have to be 45 percent of the selling price to have 25 percent of gross to cover overhead and another 20 percent available for profit. That's easy to understand. Let's go one step further.

If overhead and profit are 45 percent of gross, direct cost (mostly labor and material) must be 55 percent of gross (100 percent minus 45 percent is 55 percent). So far so good?

O.K. Now, if direct cost is $10,000 and that's 55 percent of the selling price, how much is the selling price? Easy, just divide $10,000 by 0.55. The answer is $18,181.82, just like I insisted two paragraphs back. Maybe you didn't believe it then. But I hope you do now. There's a big difference between $14,500 and $18,181.

Let's check our math and prove that my method is accurate. If the selling price is $18,181.82, 20 percent for profit would be 0.20 times $18,181.82. Use your calculator to get $3,636.36. Twenty-five percent for overhead would be 0.25 times $18,181.82 or $4,545.46. Adding direct cost ($10,000), overhead ($4,545.46) and profit ($3,636.36) gives you $18,181,82. It works!

Overhead is usually quite high in the remodeling business. The 25 percent figure we've used in the above example isn't uncommon, but yours could be quite different. The point is, be sure to allow enough. If you don't, the difference will come out of your profit.

Most profitable remodeling contractors aim for gross margins between 60 percent to 120 percent, depending on their overhead. In our example, Goodguys' margin was 82 percent (markup divided by cost.) This may be a surprise, especially if you've been figuring markup at 5 to 8 percent. It doesn't work in the remodeling business.

Remodeler getting ticket for not charging enough!

If you're still adding 10 percent to your bids for overhead and another 10 percent for profit, take a vow now to change your ways. Start making a reasonable return on your money invested and your effort. On many jobs, all you have to do to get a good markup is ask for it.

I know what you're thinking. You'd never get any work at 50 percent margin. Don't believe it. Not for a minute. Many successful remodelers use a markup of 100 percent or more. My own company uses 110 percent. It's no coincidence that the big, successful remodeling companies get the highest prices. Competing on price alone can do more harm to your company than just about anything I can think of.

Contingencies

Some people, and this includes contractors and accountants alike, treat contingencies as an afterthought. But contingency is an important direct cost.

You've heard the old cliche, "If anything can go wrong, it will." A remodeler probably said that first. Hidden problems, unknowns, errors, omissions, accidents, misunderstandings, customer demands, new codes . . . anything can happen on a job. And surprises in the remodeling industry very rarely make the job cheaper. They make it more expensive. Contingency is intended to cover these unpleasant little surprises.

How much should you allow for contingency? On most jobs 8 percent is probably enough. But sometimes even 12 percent may not be enough. If you can't accurately estimate some part of a job (excavation for instance), you'd better allow a hefty sum for contingency on this part of your bid. Better yet, put this part of the job on a cost plus basis, if you can.

But don't let contingency become an excuse for poor estimating and pricing. Contingency should cover events you can't foresee, not costs you're too lazy to determine.

Pricing Design Services

Never give your design sketches away! Your salespeople will probably make sketches as part of their sales pitch. They'll use them during the presentation, before quoting the price. Even if the sale is closed and a contract signed, the salesperson keeps the sketches. The next step is to get the preliminary design drawings done and approved by the owner. Then you'll prepare the final working drawings. All these steps cost you money.

If you're asked to provide design services without a firm construction contract, be sure to use a design-build contract like the one mentioned in the last chapter.

Drawing costs can range from 3 to 10 percent of the price of the job. But keep your design cost modest. Otherwise you risk losing the contract before it's signed. For instance, you wouldn't charge 10 percent on a $50,000 project. Neither would you charge 5 percent on a $2,000 project.

Never let the owner have preliminary drawings before the final contract is "in the bag." You'd only be giving the client permission to shop for prices elsewhere — from someone who won't have to pay for design or drafting time.

Markup on Small Jobs

For jobs under $5,000, use at least a 100 percent markup on direct costs. That's the only way to make a reasonable net profit. The amount of effort required to sell, set up, and produce the job is about the same as for a large job. The smaller the job, the higher your overhead and your gross margin. Very small jobs may have a gross margin of twice the direct cost. Otherwise, a single call-back wipes out your entire profit.

In most communities, one-man construction companies compete fiercely for small jobs. These contractors usually work out of a panel truck. They usually price the job at an hourly wage plus materials. Owners who hire these small contractors usually don't demand high quality materials and workmanship and don't need any design work.

Some larger contractors will take on small jobs. Others won't touch anything below $5,000, or even $10,000. Those willing to accept the smaller jobs do so knowing the profit may be small or nonexistent. Maybe they're hoping that small jobs will lead to larger ones. They do small jobs at a loss and consider the time and money spent as good advertising. Such jobs are called *loss leaders*.

In my opinion, taking any job at a loss is foolish. There's no benefit from selling your skills for peanuts. It cheapens the market price for what you do. Worse, you can get bogged down in a handful of loss leader projects so you won't be able to take some really good work when it comes along. Finally, it's hard to do your best on any job where you're losing money. I wouldn't do it. Do top quality professional work and expect a good price for what you do.

Large Jobs

Don't slash your percentage of gross margin just because a job is larger. Not even for jobs in the $100,000-plus range. You're even more vulnerable on large jobs. Opportunities for hidden problems and mistakes are compounded on larger jobs, and will be more expensive when they happen.

The Unit Price System

The unit price system makes it easier for salespeople to quote prices and make estimates. Here's how the system works in many of the remodeling companies that use standard unit prices:

1) The salesman does a complete quantity take-off, listing everything that has to be removed, replaced and installed and the quantity of each. Whether your company will do the actual work or subcontract it out, you have to know what materials are involved and how much.

2) Measurements should be in the units commonly used in the construction industry: lumber in board feet, brick in thousands, carpet in square yards, concrete in cubic yards, etc.

3) The salesperson quotes unit prices for the job from the price book. To make this quick and easy, standard unit prices should be as complete as possible, including all the labor and material usually associated with installing the item priced. For example, the price for 1/2-inch drywall should include both labor and material for installing board, screws, tape, beading, filler, sanding, texturing, delivery, tax, and the usual waste. The price for a door should include all labor, material, and taxes for installing the door, hinges, lockset, casing, jambs, fasteners, shims, filler, and delivery.

4) Every job is unique in this business. No two are the same. That's why judgment is essential when estimating. When you (or your salesperson) expects that the job will be either more or less difficult than the typical job, a productivity multiplier should be used. For example, your productivity multiplier is 1.00 on the average wallboard job. It might be 1.10 (10 percent more) in a small room where more cutting and fitting is needed and where waste is higher. Productivity multipliers can be built into every item in a bid to adjust for down time, inefficiency, higher costs or a more demanding owner. You determine the factor to be used based on your own judgment and experience.

5) For subcontracted items, negotiate prices with your subs. Get typical unit prices from your plumber for basins, tubs, faucets, stacks, etc. Your cabinet manufacturer should supply prices for wall and base cabinets and countertops. These prices would include everything — materials,

labor, delivery, and the subcontractor's overhead, incidental costs and profit.

The subcontractors you use regularly should be willing to provide typical unit prices. Using standard unit prices saves them as much time as it saves you. They're saved from bidding small jobs the remodeling contractor doesn't have in the bag.

Monitor your costs and keep your unit prices up to date. Your cost book will be of little value if the prices are stale.

A Sample Unit Price Book

Here's a unit price system one successful remodeling contractor uses. They've asked us not to use their name, but we thank them for letting us reprint their material. These are the instructions they give their sales people for using the price list.

Book Price List Instructions

The Goodguys Construction Company developed this Book Price List for use of our salespeople. All salespeople are authorized to quote jobs based on these prices.

1)   The list is organized in the same order in which most construction projects are built.

2)   The Index Number (IN) is listed in the first column beside each item. This IN corresponds to the IN on the Project Survey form.

3)   To estimate a project, determine which items will be needed and the quantity. Enter the units needed for each IN. Then find the bid price by multiplying the quantity needed by the unit price.

4)   This Price List is accurate for most jobs but will need adjustment when other than standard grade labor or materials are required, when access to the work area is limited, or when working conditions slow productivity.

5)   Notice that some items carry a minimum price as well as a price per unit. The higher of the two will apply in all cases.

6)   Add 5 percent to the total of every job for permit fees and job cleanup. (Items 1.15 and 2.20.)

7)   Include the $400 charge for plans and specifications on all jobs. (Item 1.01.)

8)   Further, add an 8 percent contingency fee to each estimate.

9)   For unlisted items and those without prices, get a current price quote from our local sources. Verify these prices by checking them against estimating handbooks in our library.

Book Price List

Index No.	Category	Unit Price
1.00	**GENERAL**	
1.01	Plans & specifications	400.00 each
1.03	Models, renderings	400.00 each
1.05	Engineering	_____ /Bid
	(For 2nd floor, add $500-750)	_____ /Bid
1.10	Soil testing	_____ /Bid
1.15	Building permits	2 percent of project
1.16	Special permits	2 percent
1.26	Rentals — pumps, scaffolding, etc.	300.00 min
1.32	Insurance — liability	2.5 percent
2.00	**DEMOLITION**	
2.01	Roof tearoff	2.00 psf
	- to ceiling line & cleanup	
2.04	Roof stripping (shingles only)	.50 psf
2.06	Removal — Concrete slab, 4" thick	1.80 psf
2.08	Removal — Exterior wall, masonry	45.00 plf
2.10	Removal — Exterior wall, frame/stucco	35.00 plf
	- (add beam removal @ $8.00 plf)	_____ plf
2.12	Removal — Interior wall, bearing	35.00 plf
2.14	Removal — Interior wall, nonbearing	33.00 plf
2.16	Removal — Stucco, plaster	.80 psf
2.20	Site cleanup	3 percent of project

Figure 5-2 *Partial book price list*

Goodguys' full price list is reproduced in Appendix C. Figure 5-2 is a copy of the first few sections of that price list. These prices were accurate for the time and place where they were used but won't necessarily be accurate for the jobs you're bidding now.

The Goodguys price book is based on a gross margin of 50 percent (100 percent markup). But the company pays a sales commission of 8 percent, and their sales manager gets a 5 percent override on gross sales. So their selling cost is 14 percent of the contract price.

You're welcome to adapt the Book Price List for your own operation.

Project Survey

You'll need something like Figure 5-3, the Project Survey form, to list each work item on the job. Figure 5-3 shows the first part of a survey form. Your salesperson completes the form during the sales interview. Back at the office, you'll use it as the basis for checking the estimate on the estimating form I'll describe in Chapter 11. All three forms, the Book

Project Survey

Index No.		Exc.	H.O.	Cont.
1.00	**GENERAL**			
1.01	Plans & specifications			
1.03	Models, renderings			
1.05	Engineering			
1.10	Soil testing			
1.15	Building permits			
1.16	Special permits			
1.20	Survey			
1.22	Renderings & blueprints			
1.26	Rentals — pumps, scaffolding, etc.			
1.32	Insurances			
1.33	Temporary facilities			
1.34	Hoarding			
1.36	Sidewalk crossing			
2.00	**DEMOLITION**			
2.01	Roof tearoff			
2.04	Stripping-shingles only			
2.06	Removal — Concrete, 4" thick			
2.07	Removal — Riprap, 4 x 4			
2.08	Removal — Exterior wall, masonry			
2.10	Removal — Exterior wall, frame/stucco			

Figure 5-3   *Project survey*

Price List, the Project Survey and the estimating form, use the same Index Numbers. That makes it simple to refer to the information from one form to the other.

The three columns — "Exc.," "H.O.," and "Cont." stand for excluded, by homeowner, and by contractor, respectively. You put a check mark in the proper column for each item you'll need for the job. That way you'll have a record of everything you're responsible for, and everything that's to be supplied by others. You'll avoid problems later, and won't hear your customer say, ". . . but I'm sure that was included in the contract." It was, and you can respond, "Yes, and you agreed to supply it."

Notice that the survey list contains more items than are in the Book Price List. You need space to list items that only come up occasionally or whose prices vary by job. They also make the list look more impressive to your customer when you're hovering over it at their kitchen table. They'll see how thorough and efficient you are.

Unusual Pricing Factors

Every job has special problems that have to be considered in the estimate: Unusual conditions, access problems, code limitations, extraordinary customer requirements and the like. All these and more make it harder to quote a job. For instance:

■ Access to upper floors or basements. Passageways may be inadequate to transport materials — damage to walls and stairwells will probably occur. Salespeople can easily miss this.

■ Rare or valuable landscaping might be in your way. Will workers have to use special care to work around plants, or will you have to protect them, or even move them? Either will increase the cost.

■ You may have to replace fascia, soffit or gutters. Will you need to rent scaffolding or oversize ladders?

■ Roofing problems. Do you have to join the roof of the new addition to one that's badly deteriorated and uneven? Is repair of the old roof part of your job?

■ Access from the street. What if there's no parking allowed in front of the job site? And maybe the nearest legal parking space is half a block away and can only be used between 10:00 A.M. and 3:00 P.M.

■ Concealed wiring and plumbing can be a crapshoot. Where is it and where does it have to be moved? Does it comply with the code? Will the building department require that all wiring in the building be brought up to code?

I guess there are at least a thousand places where you can get into trouble on a remodeling job. If you or your salespeople don't recognize the potential problems that require special treatment and allowances, you're likely to end up in a dispute with the owner. But use the contracts I've recommended and the price system described in this chapter and you're protected — at least legally. When the carpenter opens up the wall and discovers five rotten studs that have to be torn out, you're protected. Your bid and the contract includes removing and replacing only ten studs. If 15 have to be taken out and reinstalled, you'll get paid extra for the five extra studs.

That's why your bid has to list each item of work in the job. If, after work begins, you discover that more work's needed, you'll get paid extra for doing it. The risk of unknowns is with the owner, not you, the contractor. After all, they're his rotten studs, not yours. That's a very important point and something both you and the owner should understand clearly before work begins.

That nearly finishes what I wanted to say about using standard prices to sell a job. But there's one more point I want to make. If you're one of the many remodeling contractors who does most work on a cost plus fee basis, you probably skimmed right through this chapter. It doesn't apply to you. You don't have to quote prices. Right? Well, maybe so and maybe not. I'll explain.

Pricing "Cost Plus" Jobs

Cost plus fee contracts aren't necessarily a gravy train. Making money on these isn't a sure thing. You can still lose money if something goes wrong that's your fault. And the profit can be quite skimpy. The fee is often 10 and 10. The first 10 percent is supposed to cover your overhead. The second 10 percent is your profit. This 10 and 10 is cumulative. That is, the total direct cost is multiplied by the overhead, then the total is multiplied by the profit. That way you make a 10 percent profit on the 10 percent overhead. But even that may not be enough if your overhead is 25 percent. The key is defining exactly what's included in the term "cost."

I'm not necessarily recommending them, but here are some ways to sweeten the deal on cost plus fee contracts:

■ You might bill labor at a higher rate than you actually pay. You could justify the surcharge as labor overhead.

■ Charge for site supervision. This is generally accepted in the industry on the basis of one hour of supervision for every eight hours of direct labor. The charge is legitimate only if you actually have a superintendent on your payroll. If you do the supervising yourself, supervision expense should be included as an overhead charge.

■ Don't overlook equipment charges. If you had to rent a pump or radial arm saw for the job, you'd include that cost as a charge to be reimbursed. You're entitled to do the same reimbursement for use of your own equipment. I recommend you use a rate schedule published by a local equipment rental yard. Some remodelers apply a flat percentage for use of tools and equipment. I don't like that. The owner is likely to squawk. Use the correct daily or weekly rate for each piece of equipment.

Cost plus fee work isn't a picnic. Some owners don't understand why they have to pay for workers who aren't physically on site, such as when they're picking up materials, for instance. Or they might accuse you of removing materials to another job site. You usually won't have these problems on commercial work, where the owner is a little more sophisticated about work force requirements and construction practice.

Never — Well, Maybe Not *Never*

The biggest argument against accepting cost plus fee work is that you can't get more than 10 percent for overhead. Owners won't pay more. If your actual overhead is close to 25 percent, recovering 10 percent for overhead just won't do. Unless . . .

If the income from your other work is already enough to cover your overhead, it could make good sense to accept a cost plus contract. It's extra work and may not add much to your actual overhead expense.

If you don't have *any* work, a cost plus fee contract can seem like it came from heaven. It'll at least reduce your overhead loss. So grab it.

Summing Up

It bears repeating. Make estimating easy, even if you sacrifice some accuracy. Keep the most accurate price book you can. Make sure prices are current and that they include enough markup to guarantee a decent profit. Don't overlook contingencies and special cases. And don't sell your time too cheap. You're a skilled professional remodeler doing nothing but quality work.

Up until now, we've talked about your company's relationship to your customers. In the next several chapters, we'll concentrate on things that go on behind-the-scenes inside your company — how to manage your money and personnel and run your jobs efficiently.

6

Planning for Success

If you're really serious about thriving in the remodeling business, I'd advise you to develop a written business plan. Running a remodeling business without a business plan is like driving without a roadmap. You can get around the neighborhood OK. But travel very far and you're likely to lose your way. A business plan is the same. It helps keep you on track and moving toward your goal.

I think everyone in business does at least have *some* business planning. If you're like me, you have your day pretty well planned out in your head before leaving home in the morning. That's one type of planning. Most of us also have longer range goals — what we want to be doing next week, next month and for the rest of our career. But these are just dreams until we decide how we're going to reach these goals and start taking steps to get there. That's what this chapter is about. Taking steps to make your dreams come true.

Even if you know exactly where you're going, there's another reason for drafting a formal business plan. If you've ever applied for a management level job with a big company, you know how important it is to have a very professional-looking, very well-written resume. Job interviewers judge applicants by their appearance and their resume. They have to. That's all they've got to work with.

Having a good business plan is, in some ways, like having a good resume. It's a good introduction to your company and what the company will become. It helps inspire trust and confidence in prospective lenders, investors and anyone you want to have a favorable impression of you and your remodeling business.

"Mr. Barnes said that I might as well pick up a hamburger for him while getting the coffee, Mr. Pedersen thought he would like a hamburger too, and Mr. Thorburgh said that sounded like a darn good idea."

I know it takes time to develop a good business plan, time away from your work or family. But once a plan is completed, bringing it up to date occasionally is relatively easy. I know some remodelers who have been keeping up and revising their business plan for many years. Why do they do it? Because it pays. It puts them a step ahead of remodelers who are less professional — less prepared to deal with other business managers who consider planning an essential part of every well-run business.

Very few of the remodelers I know understand the importance of business planning. Unless you have a degree in business administration, you probably haven't studied business planning and strategy. Most contractors haven't. So I'm going to show you how to prepare a business plan, and explain why it's so important. This chapter is a simplified guide to creating your own business plan.

In the past, accountants and financial advisors produced most business plans. The plans were limited to a company's financial affairs and didn't address the overall operation. They were accounting documents, not true business plans as I'm going to discuss.

Today, many contractors develop their own business plans. And why not? No one knows the remodeling business better than the owner. It's usually easier for an owner to learn business planning than it is for a business planner to learn construction contracting.

Many plans are written because a loan officer requires it as part of the loan application process. A plan is essential if you're raising money from investors to start a business. But those aren't the only reasons to write a business plan. Planning is just as important when you're trying to update, review or change the focus of your company.

What Is a Business Plan?

Simply stated, it's a written summary of what you hope to do, what you need to get it done and how you intend to do it. A plan identifies your goal and explains how you're going to meet that goal. Once completed, the plan becomes a yardstick for measuring your progress toward the goal.

This chapter includes some worksheets you can fill out as you gather planning information. Be conscientious as you complete these worksheets. Don't leave anything out. A sloppy plan is probably worse than no plan at all.

Why Is Planning So Important?

- It forces you to look at matters realistically.

- It helps you identify your customers, market area, pricing strategy, and competition. With any luck it will help you discover a competitive advantage or new opportunities. It can also reveal deficiencies in your company.

- Putting your plan in writing helps focus your thoughts on what's right and what's wrong with your company. It also helps you see deviations from your plan before they become major problems.

- You'll be able to predict how much financing you need, and when you'll need it.

■ Your lender or investor can judge the potential success of your business, and your skill as a manager.

Recommended Format

1) Begin with an introduction. This should be a one or two page summary of your plan. Even though you'll describe the entire business in detail later, this "teaser" helps get the attention of a potential lender or investor. Include a table of contents and show page numbers for major subjects.

2) Describe your business concept. Use this section to identify your market potential and your plan for the coming year. Specify your goals and be sure they're compatible with your personal goals, management ability, and family considerations.

Your monthly sales forecast for the coming year is the heart of the business concept. It's your statement of confidence in your marketing strategy. And it forms the basis for your cash flow forecast and projected income statement.

The business concept also contains the assessment of business risks and a contingency plan. Be truly honest about your risks and how you plan to deal with them.

3) Present a detailed financial plan. Show how much you owe and how much more you need. Be concise, but be prepared to supply supporting material when it's requested.

Your Cash Flow Projection

No business plan is complete without a cash flow chart. It's a forecast of when you expect to receive cash from your sales and when you expect to pay your bills.

■ It's a guide for planning the most effective use of your cash.

■ You can see at a glance when money is due in and when it's due out.

■ You can compare actual performance to predictions. You'll see the significance of any changes right away. If sales drop off, you'll know immediately when the cash crunch is due and how bad it will be.

■ It promotes peace of mind. Don't let uncertainty about available cash keep you awake at night. A cash flow projection isn't an instant cure for sleeplessness, but it certainly helps. It also clears your mind for more productive thinking.

■ You'll know how much money to borrow to meet day-to-day needs. This may be the most important advantage of a completed cash flow projection.

■ It will show a lender that you have enough cash to make loan payments if you're planning to borrow money on a term basis.

The cash flow projection lets you forecast receipts, schedule payments, and predict how you'll use your operating funds and line of credit. You'll see how much cash you'll need, and when. It also shows when your receipts will reduce or eliminate the need for borrowed money.

Updates — How Often?

You'll probably want to revise your cash flow plan each month and make up a new plan each year. Most lines of credit are renewed annually. An annual cash flow projection will help create an effective presentation for your lender.

Cash flow planning should be an ongoing activity. So don't put your projection away and forget it after you've got your loan. If you don't meet your sales objective or you have a sudden unexpected payment to make, take the cash flow out and work through it again. When you know the effect of the change on your cash position, you can make revisions as needed.

Where Do I Start?

The first step in preparing a cash flow plan is to estimate sales month by month. Use your record of monthly sales from the previous year to forecast the coming year.

There are many ways to estimate sales. I feel more comfortable with a relatively conservative sales estimate. It's nice to be optimistic. But a high sales forecast puts more strain on your working capital. With high sales you'll probably have more money tied up in work in progress, materials, equipment and receivables. A lower forecast reduces the need for working capital proportionately. In addition to a conservative forecast, I'll sometimes make both a more optimistic forecast and then a "most probable" forecast that's somewhere between optimistic and pessimistic. This middle forecast may be the best anchor point about which plans are made.

Forecast how many jobs you'll have each month and estimate about when you'll receive payment for each. Now, forecast accounts payable each month. Payables, receivables and sales usually run parallel. If you pay bills "net 30," you'll pay for January's deliveries in February.

Cash Flow Worksheet

Once you've estimated income and expenses for each month, use the cash flow worksheet to list your actual cash transactions for the month. Do this at the end of every month. If there's a big variation between your planned and actual figures, you may have to revise your figures for succeeding months. If the difference between planned and actual cash available is too large, you'll have to make some adjustments to operations.

Figure 6-1 is a sample cash flow projection worksheet. This one shows only three months, so you'd need to use four sheets to show your projections for the full year. Use worksheets like the ones in Figures 6-2 and 6-3 to collect the amounts for lines 1, 2, and 22 of the cash flow worksheet.

How Good Is Your Plan?

It takes a lot of thought (and a lot of paper) to prepare a business plan. Have your key employees and a few impartial outsiders review your plan in detail. And judge it carefully yourself to make sure it's workable. Satisfy yourself that the plan is sound before you invest money and time trying to carry it out.

But even the best plan is useless until you put it into action. Sitting on a shelf, all it does in collect dust. Here's how the Small Business Administration puts it in their brochure "Business Planning for Small Construction Firms" (Management Aids, No. 2008): "When your plan is as near on target as possible, you are ready to put it into action. Keep in mind that action is the difference between a plan and a dream. If a plan is not acted upon, it is of no more value than a pleasant dream that evaporates over the breakfast coffee." How true it is.

Income (Cash only)	January		February		March	
	Planned	**Actual**	**Planned**	**Actual**	**Planned**	**Actual**
1. Cash sales						
2. Collection from accounts receivable						
3. Loan proceeds						
4. Sale of fixed assets						
5. Other cash received						
6. **Total cash in**						
7. Rent (for premises, equipment, etc.)						
8. Management salaries						
9. Other salaries and wages						
10. Legal and audit fees						
11. Utilities (heat, light and water)						
12. Telephone						
13. Repairs and maintenance						
14. Licenses and municipal taxes						
15. Insurance						
16. Other operating expenses						
17. Payments on purchase of fixed assets						
18. Interest paid on loans (short term loans, lines of credit, overdrafts)						
19. Payments on mortgages/term loans						
20. Income tax payments						
21. Cash dividends paid						
22. Payments on accounts payable						
23. Other cash expenses						
24. **Total cash out**						
25. Surplus or deficit (subtract cash in minus cash out)						
26. Opening cash balance						
27. **Closing cash balance**						

Figure 6-1 *Cash flow worksheet*

	JAN	FEB	MAR	APR	MAY	JUN	JUL	AUG	SEP	OCT	NOV	DEC
Projected sales												
Cash sales (line 1)												
Collection of previous month's sales												
Collection of sales from two months previous												
Collection of sales from more than two months previous												
Collection from accounts receivable (line 2)												

Figure 6-2 *Projected cash sales and accounts receivable*

	JAN	FEB	MAR	APR	MAY	JUN	JUL	AUG	SEP	OCT	NOV	DEC
Planned purchases												
Payments on current month's purchases												
Payments on previous month's purchases												
Payments on purchases from two months previous												
Payments on purchases from more than two months previous												
Payments on accounts payable (line 22)												

Figure 6-3 *Projected accounts payable*

Contents of Your Business Plan

Title Page

Compose an introductory page with the following:

- Company name, address, phone number and your name.

- A description of your company, the type of work you do and your market area.

- If you are seeking investors, describe the type of securities offered, such as promissory notes, shares, debentures, or stock.

- Tell whether you're applying for any loans or line of credit. Give the term of any existing loan.

Summary

Next, write a one page summary of your plan. Describe your goal, your competitive advantage and how you're going to use that advantage to reach that goal.

Table of Contents

List the sections and their page numbers.

Part I: Business Concept

- **Description of the Industry**

Outlook and growth potential. Describe industry trends, new products, and developments. Give your sources of information.

Markets and customers. Estimate the size of your total market. Describe what that market needs and how it's changing.

Competition. What do you expect your market share to be? Describe your strengths and weaknesses compared to the competition. How profitable will your business be?

National and economic trends. Discuss population shifts, consumer trends, relative economic indicators.

■ **Description of Your Remodeling Business**

Products and services. Use photographs and drawings to show your specialty. Emphasize the quality of your work.

Rights. List any trade marks, franchise rights, or copyrights your company holds.

Market target. Describe your potential customers' buying patterns, average purchase amounts, wants and needs. Identify typical customers by groups.

Competitive advantage of your plan. Tell why your company is unique.

Estimating, bidding, bonding. Describe your estimating method, the number of bids you put out, and the amount of coverage and type of bonding you carry.

Location and size. Where is your office/showroom in relation to the market you intend to serve? How much space does your office occupy?

Staff and equipment. How many employees do you have? What are their job titles and duties? Describe your office furniture, fixtures and equipment.

Brief history. When was your company founded. What work has it done? Show how the company has grown over the years.

■ **Business Goals**

Identify your goal for the next year: Gross sales, profit margins, share of market, hiring of additional staff, etc. What are your goals for the longer term: return on investment, net worth, additional offices, etc.

■ **Marketing Plan**

Sales strategy. How many salespeople will you have? Describe their commission rate and their training.

Pricing policies. Discuss markups, margins and your anticipated break-even point.

Promotional. Describe the scope of your advertising. What kind of promotion will you do? How will you attract prospective customers?

Warranties. How long and what kind?

Tracking methods. Explain how you determine which types of promotion are effective and which types are ineffective.

■ **Sales Forecast**

Make a month-by-month forecast for the coming year. Project annual sales each year for the next four or five years. Explain the assumptions you made to develop the forecast. Notice that the sales forecast is the starting point for your projected income statement and cash flow forecast in Part II.

■ **Production Plan**

How do you schedule work on your jobs?

Who are your suppliers and where are they located? What discounts are available? How do you control quality on your jobs?

■ **Company Structure**

Legal form. Is your company a proprietorship, partnership, corporation? And who are the owners?

List any key contracts in force. Include here any management contracts, shareholder or partnership agreements, franchisor agreement, or service contracts.

Directors and officers. Include names and addresses and describe each one's role in the company.

Background of key management personnel. Give brief resumes of active owners and key employees.

Contract professionals and consultants. Who can you call on for outside help if you need it?

Organization chart. Show who's in charge of each function.

Duties and responsibilities of key personnel. Include brief job descriptions.

■ **Risk Assessment**

Competition. Can the competition beat you on prices? On quality? On name recognition? On referrals or tie-ins with manufacturers or distributors?

What if. . . Evaluate the risk to your company from things you can't control: strikes, recession, weather, new competition, supplier or subcontractor problems.

What if. . . Describe what you'll do if sales drop off by 25 percent, if sales double, if a key staff member quits, etc.

■ **Action Plan**

Steps you're going to take to reach this year's goal. List what you'll do each month. Describe who's responsible for what.

Checkpoints to measure results. Identify significant dates, sales levels and decision points.

Part II: Financial Plan

■ **Financial Statements**

Start with last year's closing balance sheet and income statement. Include the past two or three years' statements if you have them.

Projected income statements. Make a detailed operating forecast for the next year, and a less detailed forecast for the following two years. Use your sales forecast as the starting point for these statements.

Cash flow forecast. Detail your income and expense budget for the coming year.

■ **Financing and Capitalization**

Loans. Identify any loans you've applied for. How long are they for? How much? What are the terms? When will you draw on loan proceeds?

Purpose of loans outstanding or applied for. Are they for particular projects or just to pay bills? Attach a list of property that secures these loans. What's the interest rate on each?

Owner's equity. How much money have you and other owners put into the business?

Operating loan. If you've applied for a line of credit, specify if it's a new loan or an increase of an existing one.

■ **References**

Name and address of present lender(s). Specify type of account. Name an individual bank officer if you can.

Attorney's name, address, and phone number.

Accountant's name, address, and phone number.

■ **Appendix**

Your lender or potential investor may also want to see the following:

Personal net worth statement, including personal property values, investments, cash on hand, bank loans, charge accounts, mortgages, and other liabilities. This will substantiate the value of your personal guarantee if required for security.

Letters of intent. Customer commitments. Letters of support.

List of leasehold improvements. Show date and description.

List of fixed assets, vehicles, equipment and tools. Include serial numbers, the date acquired and the estimated present value.

Your *current book price list* showing your standard selling prices.

Insurance. Describe the coverage and policy limits.

Aged accounts receivable summary. How much are you owed and for how long?

Copies of legal agreements, contracts, leases, franchise agreements, mortgages, and debentures.

As you can see, the business plan is a very detailed, comprehensive document. Once you've made the effort to complete it, you'll know exactly where you're going. And so will your banker.

For a complete, step-by-step coverage of every aspect of business planning, including a sample plan, order a copy of *Contractor's Growth and Profit Guide.* There's an order form in the back of this book.

In the next chapter, we'll talk specifically about borrowing money to make your plan work, and how to increase business by making money available to your customers.

7

Money for Everyone

Few remodeling contractors are as good at managing their business as they are at building. That's too bad. When you select a career in remodeling you're selecting a career in business above all. And that means you have to understand financial matters.

In this chapter, we'll cover the subject of money in four areas:

1) Borrowing money to operate your business

2) Helping your customers borrow money so they can afford your services

3) Advancing credit to customers

4) Collecting from customers once the job is done

You have to know something about accounting, law and economics to be successful in the remodeling business. If you don't learn at least a little about these subjects, you'll be left far behind.

Wouldn't It Be Nice!

Now and then I meet someone who's thinking of going into the remodeling business. They have enough money to buy a little equipment, some supplies, and to cover the payroll for a few weeks. The first month's sales should bring in enough money to pay for the second month's operating expenses, the second for the third, and so forth. So profits will gradually build into a comfortable amount of working capital. Well, that's a nice dream — but it just doesn't work that way.

There's a delay between the time you buy materials and pay your workers and the time you bill your customer. Then there's often a further delay before you finally collect the money. This delay can be days or weeks. In the meantime, you still have to pay your overhead and finance new work.

Figure 7-1 shows a sample budget projection for a new remodeling business.

Cash receipts	
Capital	$10,000
Bank loan	10,000
Equipment loan	20,000
Sales	20,000
	$60,000
Cash disbursements	
Equipment	$30,000
Supplies	1,000
Labor and materials	14,000
Overhead – 2 months	4,000
Equipment loan payment	1,000
	$50,000
Cash surplus	$10,000

Figure 7-1   *Cash budget projections*

This projection shows $10,000 cash-on-hand surplus at the end of two months' operations. That would be enough to retire the bank loan. But Figure 7-2 shows you how it *really* turned out.

	First month	Second month
Opening cash	$ -0-	$ 1,000
Cash receipts		-0-
Capital	10,000	-0-
Bank loan	10,000	-0-
Equipment loan	20,000	-0-
Sales	2,000	10,000
	$42,000	$11,000
Cash disbursements		
Equipment	$30,000	$ 1,000
Supplies	1,000	1,000
Labor & materials	6,000	12,000
Overhead (rent, utilities)	2,000	2,000
Deposits (rent, utilities)	2,000	-0-
Miscellaneous	-0-	1,000
Loan payments (equipment)	-0-	1,000
Licenses, legal, accounting	-0-	1,000
	$41,000	$19,000
Cash-on-hand	$ 1,000	$<8,000>

Figure 7-2 *Actual cash receipts and disbursements*

The contractor had projected a $10,000 cash surplus at the end of the first two months. But there's actually a shortfall of $8,000. Now look more closely at what happened. The contractor made a profit of $6,000. How come there's no money in the bank? Let's look at the income statement for the first two months in Figure 7-3.

Sales		$32,000
Labor	8,000	
Materials	10,000	
Supplies	2,000	
Overhead	4,000	
Misc. & startup	2,000	
Total expenses	$26,000	
Net profit		$ 6,000

Figure 7-3 *Income statement for first two months*

The balance sheet in Figure 7-4 shows that the contractor did indeed make a net profit (before taxes) of $6,000.

Assets		
Current		
Cash	$	-0-
Accounts receivable		20,000
Inventory		5,000
Fixed		
Deposits		2,000
Equipment		31,000
Organization		1,000
Total assets		$59,000
Liabilities		
Current		
Bank overdraft		$ 8,000
Accounts payable		6,000
Loans -bank		10,000
Fixed		
Equipment		19,000
Total liabilities		$43,000
Net worth		
Capital		$10,000
Net profit		6,000
Total net worth		16,000
Total liabilities & net worth		$59,000

Figure 7-4 *Balance sheet for first two months*

This is a classic case. The business started off profitable, but short of money. The $40,000 this contractor started with (owner's capital plus the bank loans) just wasn't enough. The contractor should have had at least $48,000 to cover the business during the first two months.

You have to be optimistic when you start a business. You wouldn't even attempt it if you weren't. But optimism is a state of mind. Financing your business is not. You either have enough capital or you don't.

You're taking a long shot if you count on profits to provide working capital. But I must confess, I've done it and won. How? I made sure the jobs I did were small enough to start, finish and collect full payment within no more than four weeks.

Most remodeling jobs last much longer than that, though. And your final payment might not come in until a month or more after you finish the job. Without enough capital to cover your overhead, you're in a real bind.

It's strange but true that the higher your sales, the more capital you need. You'll invest more in accounts receivable, accounts payable, inventory, equipment, personnel, and overhead. If your business expands too fast, the cash problems can be as bad as if you were losing money.

It's not quite so bad to be short of cash and making a profit as it is to be short of cash and losing money besides. At least you're in a better position to borrow when you're making money. If you stay in the black, you'll catch up soon. But profitable or not, when you're short of cash you have to scramble to make ends meet.

Estimating cash flow is like estimating jobs. Neither is an exact science. There will always be surprises. Be ready for them. Keep a little cushion in reserve. Never plan to spend your last dollar. You may need one dollar more.

Borrowing Money

Why borrow money? You borrow because the yield on borrowed money will be more than the cost of borrowed money. You have ten dollars and an opportunity to make that ten dollars grow. But you need twenty to swing the deal. So you persuade a banker to lend you ten more. Now you have twenty — enough to do what you plan to do. That's called *leverage*.

Some contractors won't borrow even if they're in a good position to do so. They think borrowing is evil. They let their business suffer from underfinancing rather than stake some of their assets for a loan or pay interest.

Of course that's a matter of choice. If you never borrow, you'll never go bankrupt. But most contractors borrow at least occasionally. If for no other reason, they borrow to take advantage of trade discounts or to avoid late charges on accounts payable.

Lenders want three kinds of security. First, they want to see a source of funds available to repay the loan. Second, they want a lien against assets you own. If all else fails, the loan can be repaid by selling the assets. Finally, they want to rely on your character as a reliable debtor.

Unfortunately, contractors have a reputation for being high-risk borrowers. Too many contractors lack management skills. Many

contractors lack the business judgment needed to meet commitments when the unforeseen happens. However, if your operation is well managed and financially sound, you shouldn't have any trouble getting a loan when you need it.

The Banker's Attitude

Commercial banks are the best source for commercial loans. But expect banks to require a lot of security. Be prepared to deal with them professionally and openly.

Understand this about lenders. They're not in business to loan money. They're in business to *make* money. One big loan makes more money than a bunch of small ones. So you have to convince your banker that you're worth the bother.

Even if you don't plan to borrow money in the immediate future, it's good practice to have a contact at your bank. Get to know the manager or operations officer. It will help you cash checks now and maybe get a loan more easily in the future.

In any case, when you fill out a loan application, take it very seriously. Make your loan application a major production. Convince your banker that you're a knowledgeable professional. Provide an up-to-date business plan just the way I outlined it in the last chapter. That goes a long way toward reducing the credibility gap between you and a loan officer. Most bankers have never operated a business of their own, so they might not understand everything you present to them. But give them all the information they request — and supporting documentation if it seems appropriate. The sheer volume may be impressive enough by itself.

Your Attitude

Bankers will look at your character and credibility as a borrower. A bank's premise is that companies don't borrow and repay loans, *people* borrow and repay loans. When they extend credit to a company, they're betting on your ability as a manager.

Some banks will lend against assets with little regard to the credibility of the borrower. But it's still a good idea to put your best foot forward. Be enthusiastic about your operation. Show the background and knowledge that are expected of someone running a prosperous remodeling business. That helps guarantee serious consideration from your banker.

If you have a poor credit record or too few assets or little experience in the business, you're a less desirable borrower. But that probably won't disqualify you. Be honest about your problems. Don't try to cover up the weaknesses. Most lenders have heard all the stories and know all the tricks. It's better to be honest and take a little risk than it is to be deceptive. If you successfully use deception to get a loan, it'll show up soon enough, and the bank will make you *real* sorry.

Be Prepared

If you've prepared a complete business plan, you can show when and why you need a loan. If you're borrowing money just to establish credit, say so. But be sure you have a real purpose for the loan.

You almost always have to put up collateral to guarantee repayment of your loan. The collateral can be either your company's resources, your personal assets, or a guarantee from a third party. You'll need to prove that your relationship with the bank will be profitable for both you and them — especially them.

First and foremost, your lender will consider the financial condition of your business. It has to be financially sound. You need enough working capital, acceptable net worth ratios, consistent profit ratio, and the ability to service the loan. If your business plan, balance sheet, income statements, assets, credit references, work-in-progress, and contracts on hand reflect a successful operation, the lender will more likely approve your loan.

But those aren't all you need. The banker will look into your company's reputation, and your own, too. They'll check your credit standing, pricing methods, salary levels, insurance coverage, bonds, licenses, warranty policies, and business acumen. They may even study current trends and market conditions for remodeling in your area. The more money you want, the deeper they'll check.

You'll get one of four answers when you apply for a loan:

1) Your loan is flatly denied

2) They want more information

3) The bank is considering the loan and will contact you later

4) Your loan is approved

If your loan is approved, there's nothing more to say. If you're turned down, be objective and find out why. If you think you're getting the runaround from your lender, change banks. If the lender points out deficiencies or problem areas in your application, correct them if you can. Then present it for reconsideration, or apply to a different lender.

You usually can't borrow more than your working capital or net worth. But in some special cases, the banker may feel confident enough to advance more.

Don't Nitpick Over Loan Rates

Loan rates vary from bank to bank and depend on your negotiating position. If you're marginal, it wouldn't be prudent to try to squeeze the lender to reduce loan rates. I've never seen a case where a point or two on the loan made much difference to a remodeling contractor. Most borrowers are grateful for any kind of loan they can get. And I suspect some would be thankful even if they had to pay twice the current interest rate.

Maintaining Your Credit Position

Once you get a bank loan, you'll enter what should be an ongoing and profitable relationship for both parties. The better you do, the better the bank does. The key to maintaining your credit position with the bank is cooperation and communication. This just means that you should supply your lender with regular financial statements. Present them quarterly, or even monthly, if your financial condition is changing rapidly.

Keep the bank informed of any deviations from your original business plan. Let them know about progress or problems — pending or possibly impending. It's much easier to be candid with your banker than to try hiding things. Their purpose isn't to put you out of business, but to help you survive and thrive.

It's not mandatory that you keep all your accounts at the same bank. But you'll probably strengthen your position and reputation with them if you do. Don't exceed your line of credit or take out new loans from other sources without approval of your credit line banker. If you do, you do so at your own peril.

Types of Loans

Many types of loans are available. Some fall into the category of "creative financing," and are quite ingenious. Shop around and see for yourself. Here are a few of the more conventional types.

Bank loans

- Short term. These are generally for two to twelve months, usually for a specific purpose and self-liquidating. Temporary financing for work in progress falls into this category. The loan is repaid when the job is done.

- Term loans. These are one to five year installment loans for capital purchases such as vehicles or equipment. These loans often restrict your financial flexibility. They may have conditions restricting your salaries, further capital expenditures, and working capital. It's usually better to finance capital equipment through sources other than your bank, like GMAC for vehicles, for instance. Your operating line of credit isn't likely to be limited or reduced that way.

- Lines of credit, and loans against receivables.

Banks don't usually make it easy for a small contractor. You'll be expected to put up collateral and perhaps forced to accept liens against your home or equipment. You may be required to pledge stock or assign life insurance proceeds. You'll also be expected to personally guarantee all loans made to your company.

Banks are the best source for short term borrowing. Their interest rates are among the cheapest, but still costly. And rates are fairly uniform, so it doesn't do you much good to shop around. Sooner or later, almost all small contractors visit their "friendly" neighborhood banker. So make your peace right from the start.

Other sources

The world of business finance has changed a lot in the last ten years. What's available today may not be tomorrow. Your bank is the best source of information on what's available. I won't go into great detail, but here are some other sources for loans.

"Well, then how about a loan against my mechanic's lien?"

Small Business Administration

The SBA is an agency of the U.S. Government. It makes some direct loans. But it stands as guarantor for more loans made by commercial lenders than it makes direct loans. It also dispenses free management advice and technical information.

Some SBA programs are intended primarily for the disadvantaged, minorities, women, and the handicapped. If you fit one of these descriptions, consider applying at a local SBA office. Like all government agencies, SBA requires piles of extra paperwork and takes lots of time for processing.

SBA has a special requirement. You must have unusually strong collateral. You'll have to liquidate your personal investments and transfer the proceeds into your business. You'll be expected to limit your salary. You can't use the money to pay off existing creditors. And you can't use it for speculation or to buy an existing business.

However, the SBA favors loans that will result in increased employment for the local economy, particularly in economically depressed areas.

All conditions for applying for loans from banks or other conventional lending sources would also apply with the SBA. You still need a business plan, financial statements and asset lists, plus other requirements peculiar to the SBA.

The SBA is the last resort when you have nowhere else to go. If you're up against it, get the SBA number from your phone directory. They're a friendly bunch and truly want to help. If nothing else, you'll get sympathy and some free advice.

Friends and relatives: Many companies have been started and nurtured along by loans from friends and relatives. Of course, there's a risk. I'd rather default on a bank loan than I would on a loan from a relative. I don't have to sit across the dinner table from my banker every Christmas and Thanksgiving. My advice is to tap friends and relatives if you have to, but keep it businesslike. Draft loan papers, just like you would with a stranger. Maybe structure it as a limited partnership, with yourself as general partner and your relatives as limited partners.

Venture capitalists or private investors: You give up a share of ownership in return for the money invested. Your lawyer and accountant can help you with the paperwork.

Supplier credit: This is usually called *trade credit*. You can't get cash from suppliers, but you can buy materials on credit. Essentially, this is a loan. And when you don't pay for materials on time, you have, in effect, defaulted on that loan.

Some suppliers rely on credit reporting agencies for information about you before they'll open an account for you. Unlike a bank, suppliers don't generally ask you to sign promissory notes, or to put up collateral. They'll take a chance based on your credit history and reputation.

New suppliers will probably ask for a financial statement and credit references to confirm your ability to pay and payment history. Some will insist on your personal guarantee to back up your company's purchases as well.

On large material orders, suppliers may demand assignment of certain accounts receivable or the proceeds of your contract. An agreement may require your customer to pay the supplier directly, or make payments to you and the supplier jointly. California is one state that permits this.

In some places this isn't allowed. Since the owner's contract is with you, they're only responsible for paying you. You're responsible for paying subcontractors, suppliers, and the like. If you don't pay your bills, creditors can lay claim to the holdback portion (under the mechanic's lien act) of your contract. This protects the owner from having to pay twice for the same work. If the holdback funds aren't enough to pay the claims in full, the creditors can sue the contractor.

Most suppliers will assign a credit limit to your account. You'll have to make special arrangements to go over that limit. In any event, you have to pay your monthly purchases in full by the due date. Take advantage of supplier discounts for prompt payment. Your savings will be substantial over the course of a year. Saving 2 percent a month is like saving 24 percent per year — more than the interest you'd pay on a bank loan.

Your suppliers are like your bank in some ways. Treat them like financial partners. As your business grows and prospers, so will theirs. If you cooperate and let them know when you have problems, they'll try to help you. It's the old story: Look after them, and they'll look after you.

Placing Money

Work closely with lenders who specialize in home improvement loans. Your ability to arrange financing for customers is a big selling point with customers. Have financing ready for your customers and you'll close many more deals. Here's why I consider financing so important:

1)   You're vulnerable when you allow the customer to arrange his own financing. All the work you put into selling a job goes for nothing if the customer has trouble arranging the loan. So get involved here. Join forces with a banker to get the customer his loan. Make it a snap for the customer. Don't make them take time off from work to meet with the lender. Arrange things to fit *their* schedule. Make getting the loan easy and you've got an easy sale.

2)   Owners applying for money on their own are more likely to be rejected if their positions are marginal. They may not have the knowledge, experience, or persistence to qualify for the money needed.

3)   More often than not the owner's bank will suggest that they shop around for several bids and talk to several more contractors. This usually results in a price war. That can be dangerous if a lender recommends getting more bids. (If you follow my recommendations in Chapter 5, you'll seldom want to be the low bidder.)

4)   Once you have a working arrangement with a lender, there's less delay between signing the contract and starting construction. You don't have to wait for the loan to be disbursed from a lender to the owner, then to you.

Becoming a Loan Dealer

Your approach to the lending institution is the same, whether you're applying for funding for yourself or for your client. The requirements are about the same in both cases. The distinction is that you would be trying to qualify as the lender's dealer and not for a loan for yourself.

Once you're a qualified loan dealer, you can use the lender's credit materials along with your own sales literature in your sales kits. Just have your customer fill out the application, then send it on to the lender for processing.

The lender can reject the application, of course, so make sure your client has a good chance of qualifying before you go on to the next phase of the sale. Have your salesperson review the application carefully, and help the owner fill out the forms completely. The lender will teach you how to evaluate loan prospects. Here are three points all lenders will look for:

1) Credit standing: Your applicant's credit history carries heavy weight. It isn't enough just to pay the bills — they have to be paid *as agreed*. Delinquent payments are frowned upon. Join a credit reporting agency such as TRW. Get credit reports on your customers before you submit their applications to your lender. You'll know right away if there's trouble ahead.

If you receive a bad report on a prospect, ask for an explanation. Report the circumstances to your lender. Don't hold back anything. Lenders respect full disclosure.

2) Equity: The owners' equity in their home is the best guarantee the lender has of repayment. The equity is the current market value of the property less the amount the owner still owes on it. Many lenders require that the homeowner's equity must be 10 percent or more. Some lenders offer loans secured by equity alone with little regard for the owner's credit standing.

3) Income ratios: Lenders rarely make loans to those who have 40 percent or more of their net income committed to monthly payments. The percentage varies somewhat with various lenders.

You figure the income ratio by dividing the total monthly payments by the total net income. One spouse earns $2,000 net and the other $1,600 net, for a monthly total of $3,600. Suppose total monthly payments, including the new loan payment, are $1,200. This would mean that 33 percent of their income is committed to installment payments, well below the 40 percent maximum set by most lenders.

If monthly payments (including payments on the new loan) are 60 percent of net monthly income, chances are you're wasting your time trying to get the loan approved. Here's a hint: sometimes consolidating several short-term loans into one longer-term loan can get income ratios into the acceptable zone.

Once you're established as a loan dealer, your ability to arrange financing is an important part of every sale. "Financing available" and "easy payment plans" then become keystones of your promotional program.

Get involved with at least three financial institutions — one or more home improvement lenders, one or more secondary lenders specializing in reject or marginal accounts, and the bank where you keep your operating account.

Relationships with Lenders

It's not such a bad idea to cultivate a close business relationship with key lenders in your community. Applications from owners with high equity, good credit and low income ratios are seldom a problem. It's the borderline and marginal cases you have to fight for. Getting special consideration for those accounts can make the difference between a highly profitable year or just a so-so year.

If credit reports show a poor payment history, look for reasons. Perhaps the owner was on sick leave, or on strike, but now is back on the job with a steady income. All other things being equal, the lender should accept this application.

With a good credit report, satisfactory income ratio, but low equity, look for other supporting points you can emphasize. If your customer has twenty years at the same job and never had any payment problems, those are features to help qualify them.

Check all the owner's loans and payments closely whenever the income ratio appears excessive. If one or two loans will be paid off in a few months, would the ratio come into line then? Check again. Did he forget to mention any other sources of income?

Your salespeople should be able to evaluate a credit application. They should be able to tell almost immediately if the owner is deficient in any area. If so, be sure they know what steps to recommend to improve the owner's chances.

Watch for faulty judgment and overselling by your sales staff. A lender might turn down an application for a $25,000 remodeling job that would have sailed through if you scaled the project down to $20,000. That $5,000 might have put the owner's income ratio over the limit. Sales engineers know how to qualify customers and engineer successful sales — if you train them right.

Lending Money

If you're in a position to finance your customers yourself, go for it. But keep in mind when you extend credit that you're not a bank. Your primary business is contracting, not lending money. If you do give credit terms, make sure the project is worth the risk and very safe.

If your customer wants to begin remodeling work immediately and can't get a home improvement loan, you might be able to make yourself some extra money. You have to find out the same things any lender needs to know. How much equity does the owner have? Investigate his integrity, net worth and credit standing. If you're happy with the answers, offer to write a second mortgage (if a first is already in place). This would make you the contractor, creditor, and beneficiary.

This is a fine way to build an investment portfolio. Make it your goal to carry perhaps one job in ten this way if you can do so without jeopardizing company working capital.

There are benefits for the owner when he borrows directly from you. He doesn't have to shop for a lender and complete their forms. There are no broker or brokerage fees. There's no middleman or commission. There are no loan fees. There are no construction inspection fees. And work can usually begin almost immediately.

You benefit because you have a secure investment. You'll have a healthy monthly income from interest and principal payments. You earn interest on the profit from your job. You can still take advantage of your suppliers' credit and discount terms. You have saleable tangible assets in the mortgages. And you have borrowing power.

It seems that everyone involved can win in a carefully assembled scheme like this. As a remodeling contractor, you're positioned perfectly to make attractive second trust loans.

Scheduling and Collecting Contract Payments

Here's the remodeler's rule of thumb for collecting cash due:

- The deposit: Get as much as you can.

- Progress payments: Plan to collect for work done before you have to pay for it.

- The final payment: Try to collect the balance due on or before the completion day.

The final payment is the toughest. That's where we're most likely to get "stiffed." Some owners save all their phony complaints until the last day and then use them to hold back part of the final payment. We've all run into the "take this amount or leave it" attitude.

Most remodelers handling larger multi-trade jobs try to collect at least one third as the deposit when material arrives on site, one third midpoint through the job, and the last third on completion.

Specialists in kitchen and bath jobs insist on more up front. This is because such a large proportion of the job is the cost of the appliances. They require 50 percent when the contract is signed. They get another 40 percent when the cabinets, appliances or fixtures are delivered. And the balance of 10 percent is due on completion. It doesn't matter whether the job is $1,000 or $50,000, these ratios hold.

General remodeling work can command almost any payment schedule. Often, the larger the job, the less money up front. Sometimes there's no money up front — and still the contractor has to prove financial responsibility, put up performance bonds, payment bonds, material bonds, show coverage for liability insurance, etc. etc.

Conversely, the smallest remodeling jobs sometimes command the highest deposits — $1,500 deposit on a $3,000 job, for instance.

In some states (California is one), the maximum deposit any remodeler may accept is $1,000, or 10 percent of the job, whichever is less. But if you can post blanket performance bonds, you may take any amount as a deposit. Get $20,000 on a $30,000 job if you can. State laws regulating deposits vary, but I don't know of any state that regulates the amount that can be drawn during construction.

Get as much money up front as possible. Schedule as many draws into the contract as possible. Try to have more money in your hands than there is work completed. Make the final payment as small as you can — 5 percent would be ideal if there's no job holdback. If the job is subject to a 10 percent holdback through the mechanic's lien act, get heavier payments during construction.

Collecting

Have your credit or accounting department do the actual collecting of progress and final payments. I don't recommend that you leave this to your salespeople. They should concentrate on selling. But whoever does it, make sure they do it without delay. The money is, after all, yours.

A Final Word About Final Completion

The words *final completion* in your contract can be cause for argument. Does this sound familiar? Your customer has promised final payment when you finish work today. At the last moment he insists he doesn't have to pay you yet because the job isn't finished. Your painter still has to put another coat of paint on the inside of one closet. Zounds! The final payment is a whopping $5,000 and you were counting on it to cover your Friday payroll. And today's Friday!

You can avoid problems like that if your understanding with the customer uses the words *substantial completion*. That means you should get paid when the job is about 98 percent complete. Otherwise, owners can hold out large sums for small deficiencies. In the example above, there's no problem if the owner holds back $500 to be sure the closet gets painted. Even if that's ten times the value of the work, no problem. You'll get it Monday and collect the last $500. Fair enough.

Now that you know how to plan your business, and use money (yours and the bank's) to make more money, let's move on to another important topic: how to organize your growing business.

8

Building Your Company

Most remodelers start out as a one-man show. You'll do everything yourself until the business grows enough to support employees. There are advantages to having employees. But a disadvantage is that you have to delegate some of the responsibility and authority. And you have to organize the operation efficiently. In this chapter, I'll describe some of the key problems most remodeling companies have to overcome as they pass through successive growth levels.

Use the Resources Available

Before I get into the meat of this chapter, let me put in a plug for some of the fine associations that serve this industry. Trade associations are a good source of information for novice remodelers.

When you started out in this business, you probably had more questions than answers. That's normal. But you shouldn't have to dream up all the answers to every question. Your company probably isn't very different than a dozen others in your community. Some of them have already solved the problems you're facing today. Where can you share experience with other remodelers and find answers to your business questions? I recommend one of the many construction trade associations. They make it easy for contractors to share information and experience. There are many advantages to joining a group in your area:

1) You'll increase your industry connections. Other contractor members can be a source for information, contacts, trades, and employees. Some members might even be on state or local regulatory or planning boards. Those are always good contacts to have.

2) The association may have insurance, legal and accounting services available at group rates.

3) The association newsletter can keep you informed about industry trends and innovations.

4) Association trade shows and seminars offer opportunities for self-improvement and camaraderie.

Attend a few meetings as a guest before you join. Size up the officers and board of directors. Are these people the leaders of your business community? Check the reputation of association members. Then, if you like what you see, join.

There are disadvantages to joining any association. Membership can be expensive. It can also be time-consuming if you serve on committees or hold office. But even so, being in the swim of things is usually better than operating as a loner. Several of the larger national construction trade associations probably have local chapters in your community.

Getting the Ball Rolling

We'll assume you're a licensed contractor, if that's necessary where you work. You've planned your business and arranged for the necessary capital to begin operations. Now you're ready to build your company.

You can begin modestly if you want to. You can operate out of your house with family members helping with the books and answering the phone. You can place small ads in local newspapers and sell your own jobs. You can do all the work yourself and be a true one-man band — but you won't get rich that way. Essentially you're selling your time as a craftsman. There's nothing wrong with that, of course. But it's not building a career in the remodeling business. You'll be lucky to get five leads and make one sale during the first month. Worse, your customers will expect your prices to be low, *low*, LOW.

If you want to build a thriving construction company in the shortest time possible, make a serious commitment to the remodeling business. Begin with a strong marketing effort. Let's suppose you start out with

$50,000 in capital and a couple of employees. Here are some hypothetical numbers to illustrate what you might expect in sales and profits for the first two months.

First, let's calculate how many leads you could reasonably expect.

Advertising media	Leads
Newspaper ads	20
Yellow Page ads	6
Telemarketing	50
Showroom	4
Total leads (2 months)	**80**

This is probably a conservative estimate for a new company concentrating on sales. But it's better to be conservative at this stage than disappointed if your predictions are too optimistic. So what can you expect from 80 leads?

Let's assume the 80 leads result in 10 sales, a 1:8 ratio. Here's how this could turn out:

10 sales at $15,000 (average)		$ 150,000
Direct costs (labor & materials)	75,000	
Gross margin		75,000
Less: overhead at 25%	37,500	
Net profit (before taxes)		**$ 37,500**

This example is overly simplified, but it shows that even a new company can be profitable. Notice I haven't included selling costs, assuming you're doing the selling yourself. There would be a major expense if you paid a salesperson.

As time goes by, sales ratios should improve — from 1:8 to 1:7 or even 1:6. This would mean lower advertising cost per lead, and higher sales. If, after a couple months, you're not selling at least one in six or seven leads, start looking for a professional sales engineer to do it for you.

A reasonable sales volume for a new company might be two to three hundred thousand dollars a year — but only if your company is organized efficiently right from the start. That's what I intend to help you with in this chapter.

Delegating Responsibility

One thing you'll have to learn early in your business career is how to distribute part of the workload to others. It may seem easy if you haven't done it before. Believe me, it isn't. Sure, you can pass out work to others. But will they do it as well as you would have? With your attention to detail? With your sensitivity to customer needs and job requirements? As quickly and efficiently as you would have? And without wasting time and company resources? Answer those questions and you're beginning to understand the problem.

At some point the demands on you as owner-craftsman-salesman-bookkeeper and clerk will exceed your capability. Either you simply won't get the work done or you'll have to have assistance. Eventually you have to stop trying to do everything yourself and begin delegating authority and responsibility.

If you can't delegate, you'll never build a successful company. You have to be willing to recruit and train a staff, create lines of responsibility, monitor results, and then accept the consequences of what you've put in motion. Running a company is far more than assigning work.

Although you pass on the assignment to a subordinate, delegation doesn't relieve you from responsibility. Ultimately you're still responsible for everything your company does — for everything your subordinates do or fail to do.

When you delegate responsibility, you have to delegate enough authority so the person assigned the task gets the job done. Your superintendents are charged with buying materials, hiring and firing workers and making judgments about job procedures. They need authority to make decisions in the name of the company. That's the only way to get the results you expect.

When you're not driving every nail, selling every job and handling every detail, you have time to manage: solve problems, start new programs, find better ways of doing things, resolve disputes, supervise employees and anticipate crises. Sometimes that's more important than finishing up the Smith job or delivering materials to the Jones job. You need time for problem solving, marketing, sales, and financial matters. And you get it by giving some responsibilities to others.

What Is Management?

1) Planning, thinking about the future, looking ahead. You research, set goals, weigh contingencies, create methods for getting results, and more.

"Horace, I'm assigning you to ramrod our construction crews while I'm on vacation."

2) Organizing. You design, chart, and devise structure and policy most likely to maintain efficiency.

3) Directing. You guide your employees to carry out your policies without actually making decisions for them.

4) Promoting efficiency. Use your employees for what they're best at. Maybe your salesperson can type like a whiz, much better than your bookkeeper. But your bookkeeper can't sell. So let the salesperson stick to selling and leave the typing to the bookkeeper.

Have employees with less ability (and working at lower pay) do everything that doesn't require highly skilled (and higher pay) employees. That way more work gets done for each labor dollar spent. That's cost effective.

Delegate Everything, Except . . .

With a few exceptions, delegate every chance you get. Be willing to give up every task others can do as well as you can — even if you enjoy doing the task. These are often the tasks you may hold onto, even though they don't represent the best use of your energy and time.

In spite of the *delegate everything* edict, there are some things you shouldn't delegate. Remain in charge of these things, or you could be inviting trouble.

Policy making

You and your managers or key personnel may delegate tasks only within established policies. Don't delegate responsibility for making company policy.

Here's an example: Suppose your policy is to allow salespeople to extend credit for extra work up to a certain limit. Beyond that limit, the salesperson must get approval from a supervisor. Your marketing manager suggests revising the policy to give salespeople more flexibility. My answer would be "no." Only management has the broad perspective needed to set credit policy. Management should make that decision. Letting salespeople set credit limits would be like leaving the goats to mind the cabbage patch.

Crises

Good planning can avoid many crises. But every company has emergencies. Of course, every emergency can be unique. You can't have a company policy that covers every possible emergency. That's why you have to handle most emergency situations yourself. The only policy on emergencies might be that you be informed of the problem as early as possible.

Confidences

Some information is confidential — and should be — in every company: payroll data, employee records, bank records, financial statements, etc. You'll probably want to handle information like this yourself, rather than give employees access they could abuse. Don't delegate duties that involve secrets except to highly trusted, management-level subordinates.

Personnel matters

Most contractors spend a lot of time dealing directly with employees. I feel that's time well spent. Avoid delegating responsibility for supervision below the management level. Reprimanding or terminating an employee is never pleasant. But it should be you, not a subordinate that does it. Matters of discipline, especially those that result in termination, should be handled directly by a senior manager or the owner.

Praise is another sensitive issue. If someone is doing an especially good job, tell them yourself. Secondhand bouquets aren't appreciated as much as direct expressions of gratitude.

Disputes that can't be settled by the parties involved have to be settled by someone with more authority. If your two foremen are at loggerheads over priorities on the use of a vehicle, don't expect another foreman to resolve the problem.

Delegate Levels

Don't delegate delegation. Don't depend on a third person to decide an issue that involves division of authority. When you delegate, make it clear that the decision is yours and the instructions are coming from you.

Superintendents and foremen are low-level delegators. They have their hands on the job. They may have someone watch part of the job for them. But they have to keep control of (and responsibility for) the work themselves. At this level, delegation is usually limited and temporary.

Higher-level managers may delegate entire functions. Your office manager is responsible for payroll, but may delegate the details to a payroll clerk, then review the weekly summary reports. Mid-level managers set priorities and monitor results. They don't have to watch continually because most routine tasks don't need constant attention.

Above the superintendent level, you delegate much more authority. Higher-level managers need wider latitude. They expect the freedom to choose their own way of getting the job done. This removes you further from the actual tasks and lets you rely almost entirely on managers and their subordinates.

Work Crew Efficiency

The most efficient work crew is usually the smallest number of tradesmen that can do the work assigned. Larger crews almost always work less efficiently. A six-man carpentry crew, for example, is nearly always a mistake, even when you're raising walls. For most tasks in the remodeling business, a crew of one is most efficient. The ideal work schedule, in my opinion, is ten jobs with a one-man crew assigned to each.

A two-person crew made up of a journeyman carpenter jack-of-everything and an assistant, or apprentice, has the efficiency of three ordinary tradesmen. It's hard to prove this, but it's easy to see when it happens.

A three-person crew (a crackerjack lead person and two good helpers) returns you only the equivalent of four ordinary workers. Use this size crew for jobs where deadlines are important.

A four-person crew is sometimes no more efficient than three ordinary workers. If you must use four on a job, try to split them into two two-person crews and assign them to different parts of the job.

Your choice of work crew sizes has a major effect on profits. Labor is the biggest cost on most remodeling jobs. Some contractors don't understand this. Improve productivity 20 percent (it's not hard to do) and you've probably doubled profits.

A two-person crew headed by a lead carpenter is highly effective. This crew can handle most small- and medium-sized jobs very easily. Here are some persuasive reasons for using a lead carpenter system.

1) You always have on site a knowledgeable person with authority to use materials, labor and equipment as needed.

2) The labor cost of work done will be lower when both highly skilled (high pay) and less skilled (lower pay) tradesmen are on a job.

3) Many experienced carpenters are willing to work under an incentive program that rewards their higher productivity. Estimate the cost of a portion of the work. Then let your lead carpenter give you a bid on that work. If the lead carpenter does the work for less than your estimate, split the savings with him according to some formula.

4) Disharmony is very rare on a crew of two headed by an experienced lead carpenter.

5) Labor costs, material waste, customer relations, and deadlines are much easier to control when someone with authority and knowledge is always available on the job.

You can assign lead carpenter crews to large projects that can be divided into several parts. Have a subcontractor do the demolition. Then have your crew do the carpentry work. The lead carpenter on your mini-crew can coordinate both your work and the work of subcontractors.

Company Crews versus Subcontractors

Every contractor has wrestled the issue of whether to use employees or subcontractors. As a practical matter, the smallest remodeling companies don't have a choice. While dollar volume in a remodeling company is below several hundred thousand dollars a year, you won't have skilled workers on staff to handle more than a few basic trades.

But even some larger companies that have dozens of tradesmen on staff subcontract much of their work. Subcontractors usually offer specialized workers at competitive prices — and they eliminate your labor burden. You don't have to meet a weekly payroll for the people employed by your subcontractors. This is a form of delegation — although delegation not to individuals, but to companies who will take on the work as directed.

Of course, you lose some control when using subcontractors rather than your own crews. For example, it's difficult to get them to work on a precise timetable. Subs have their own schedules and work on your job when they can. When they're busy, your job may have to wait. Also, it's harder to control quality on work done by subcontractors. You can't supervise a sub's workers directly. Fortunately, the quality of work by most subcontractors is usually good. But you'll always have to do some monitoring of their work.

I usually have my crews handle rough and finish carpentry, concrete, decorating, and painting. There's usually enough work in my shop to keep several good employees busy all the time. But I use subs for electrical, plumbing, heating, air conditioning, roofing, ceramics, floor covering, masonry, excavation, insulation, windows, cabinetry, pools and drywall.

Even if you have enough volume to keep someone trained in a specialty trade busy, consider the extra costs very carefully. You'll probably need warehouse space to store materials needed by specialty trades. Most specialty trades require at least some specialized (and usually expensive) equipment. That's an extra burden. And the equipment has to be maintained and stored when not in use. Those are good reasons to leave specialty work to the specialists.

To be successful in the remodeling business, you'll need to work with several good subs in each trade. It's been said that a remodeler is no better than his subs. I believe it. Find a few good subs in your community and treat them right. It pays.

I recommend using at least two subcontractors for each of the major trades. When you're inundated with work, you need more than one source for each trade. That's the only way to be reasonably certain your jobs will be started without undue delay. If your favorite plumbing sub is too busy to even give a quote, you'd better have an alternate ready.

When you use subs, they guarantee their work and the equipment they install. If there's a defect, the sub's responsible. Of course, you guarantee the whole job to the owner. But if a subcontractor's work is faulty, that sub should make good on your guarantee to the owner.

Problems with Subs

Working with subcontractors isn't always a picnic. Some are hard to deal with. Others are notorious for not showing up as promised. I've had jobs sit dead in the water for days because a plumber didn't show up. Try explaining that to an owner who's cooking on a hot plate in the bathroom because the kitchen sink isn't hooked up yet. Keep your subs posted on their expected start date. But don't exaggerate or do too much wishful thinking. Remodelers who insist on a sub starting work before the job is ready for them are losing credibility, and may get hit with extra charges.

Some subcontractors are hard to reach on the phone during working hours. If you don't know where they're working, you can only reach them in the evening. Some carry pagers, but that's still no guarantee that they'll return your call right away. Favor subs who are easy to reach on the phone.

Subcontractor's Prices

Subcontractor prices vary just like remodeler prices. No two will be the same for the same job. Price differences don't depend on the size of the sub, either. My experiences is that some small subs quote too low because they don't know their costs and are afraid to include a reasonable profit. Some big subs can quote low because they keep their overhead lower than smaller companies. I know several relatively large subcontractors that handle an extraordinary volume of work in relation to their overhead.

Big subs are often more reliable. But you may prefer the more personal touch you're likely to get from a small sub on the job.

Big subs have one advantage. They usually can afford to wait a little longer for their money. While a small sub can work more closely with you, they usually can't afford this wait. This can put crushing cash demands on your company. Make it a practice to pay subcontractors only when the owner pays you. Make this part of your agreement with the subcontractor.

If you have a reputation with subs for being cheap (a "grinder") or for not paying on time, you'll get very little personal attention. They'll put less skilled workers on your job or even treat your job as a filler. And they'll probably quote your jobs at a higher price. Treat subs with respect and you'll have less aggravation and better results.

A Last Word About Subs

Make certain all your subcontractors are indeed contractors. Once we had to fire a subcontractor because he was overbilling us — charging for work not part of the contract. We let it pass a few times, until finally we had enough. He was cheating us and finally we refused to pay. In retaliation, he complained to the labor board claiming he was an employee and not a contractor. Employees have special rights under the law and are entitled to prompt payment for their labor. Subcontractors have rights too, but not the same as employees. Fortunately, we could show that he was working as an (unlicensed) contractor and not an employee. We've been more careful about who works for us since that incident.

How Your Company Will Grow

Once you begin to hire subcontractors and delegate some tasks, you'll need to define your employees' jobs and show how they relate to yours and others in your company. An organization chart shows lines of authority at a glance. I'll use organization charts here to show how your company might be set up.

To be a good organizer in any company, you have to hire staff to meet your needs and no more. For instance, you hire enough salespeople to service as many leads as you can supply consistently. The same should be true of your design or clerical people. If they're overloaded temporarily, offer them overtime until the backlog is erased. Another solution would be to hire temporaries or send some of the work to free-lancers.

Of course, it's a mistake to be understaffed. You might think you can save money that way. The truth is, this false economy can lead to slipshod workmanship and missed deadlines. On the other hand, you'll lose money paying people who aren't producing. The balance is critical, but it's better to err slightly on the side of being overstaffed in the long run.

Figures 8-1 through 8-7 show successive levels of growth. In practice, there are no clear divisions between these levels. You'll hire people gradually, one at a time. Your organization chart will change slowly. Positions will overlap as your company passes from one level to the next.

Figure 8-1 is the basic "org" chart for a startup remodeling business. The president is usually the owner and probably also superintendent, estimator and salesman.

Now compare Figure 8-2. Despite appearances, overhead has only increased 15 percent while sales have increased 100 percent. Suppose monthly salaries in Figure 8-1 were:

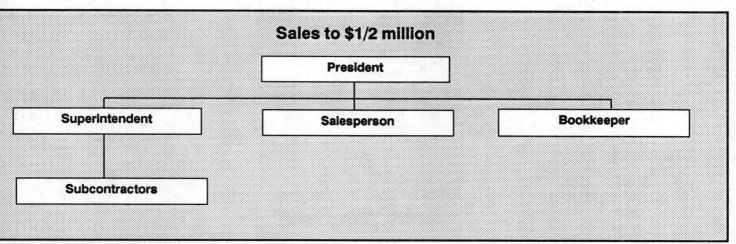

Figure 8-1   *Level 1 - Startup*

President	$3,500
Superintendent	3,000
Bookkeeper	1,500
Total	**$8,000**

Salaries will increase at Figure 8-1 (Level 2), but not as much as sales. Here are Level 2 salaries:

President	$3,500
Superintendent	3,000
Bookkeeper	1,500
Receptionist	1,200
Drafter	N.A.
Lead carpenter	N.A.
3 salespeople	N.A.
Total	**$9,200**

Why are the costs for drafting and carpentry "not applicable?" Because they're not overhead. You had those expenses in Figure 8-1 when subs were doing the work. They were part of your direct expense. Here we assume you have enough work to employ a drafter full time. Your new carpenter is now doing the work that you subcontracted out before, so there's no cost increase here. You'll have more control over work schedules and quality with the lead carpenter on your payroll.

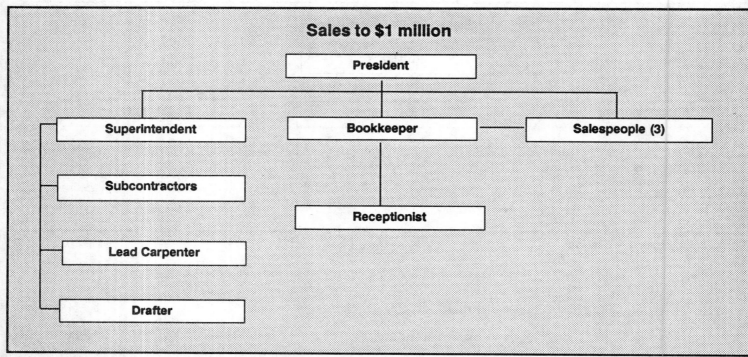

Figure 8-2 *Level 2 - First expansion after startup*

If your salespeople are on straight commission contracts, they'll add little to your overhead no matter how much business they produce.

Utilities, maintenance, supplies, insurance, telephone and employee contributions may be slightly higher at Level 2 than they were at Level 1. But rent probably isn't up at all. Yet sales are double.

Level 3 in Figure 8-3 is another plateau. You've outgrown Level 2, but Level 3 is a little top-heavy to be profitable. You've doubled your supervisory staff and added a sales manager, a finance manager, a secretary, and support people. Now, as president-manager, you directly supervise two superintendents, the bookkeeper, sales manager, finance manager, a designer and your secretary. You want to get through this period as quickly as possible and hurdle into a profitable Level 4.

You'll encounter these plateaus at various stages of company growth. Expect them but treat them as temporary defects rather than permanent disabilities.

In Figure 8-4 you see the next growth level. You still supervise the same number of positions directly, but some of those staff members are delegating responsibility to more people.

I call this level the *daylight stage*. You're beginning to come out of the darkness and starting to see the daylight — what your company can become in the future. You promote your best superintendent to

"Instead of returning the deposit to the homeowner, I used the money to buy a car. That's why I'm not the finance manager anymore."

production manager, and hire another superintendent. The bookkeeper from Level 3 becomes the new office manager. The drafter is now a qualified designer and a junior drafter is hired.

Choose the finance manager very carefully. You'll have to depend on this person to guide the company as it grows. You may even want to groom that person to be your first vice president. Someone with a degree in business or economics and some construction experience will make a good choice.

Notice that Figure 8-4 shows a secretary. An executive secretary can carry most of the office routine while you're doing other things. That's important. At the $2 million a year level you're going to be out of the office more than you're in the office.

Figure 8-5 shows another layer of management and more staff. If you haven't already done so, you'll probably incorporate at this stage. Now you're both president and chairman of the board of directors. The board you choose will help direct the course, growth, and expansion of the business.

Board of Directors

Once you reach a million dollars or more in annual sales, your company can probably benefit from having a board of directors. These should be

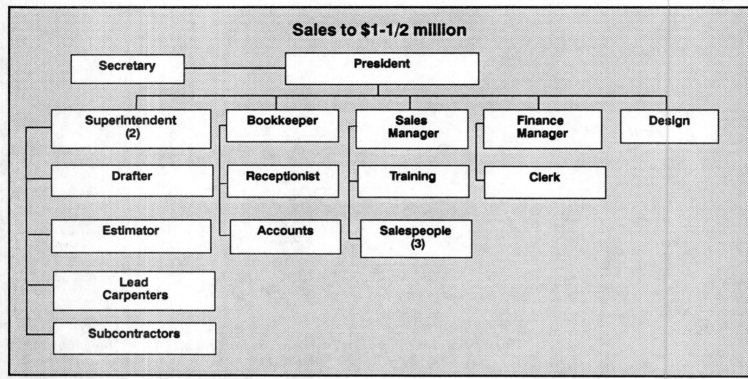

Figure 8-3   *Level 3 - Plateau stage*

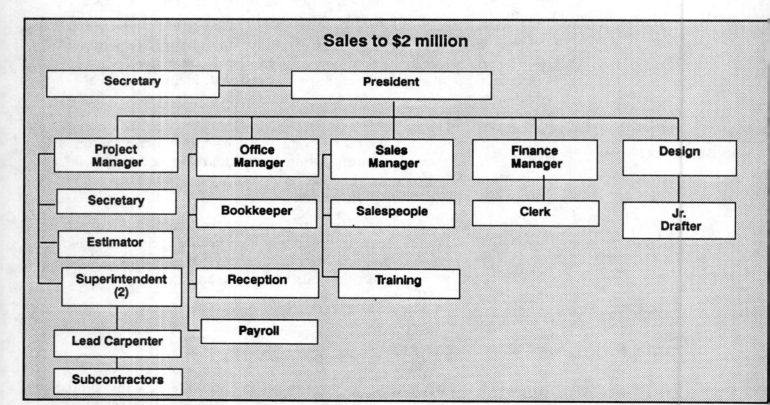

Figure 8-4   *Level 4 - Daylight*

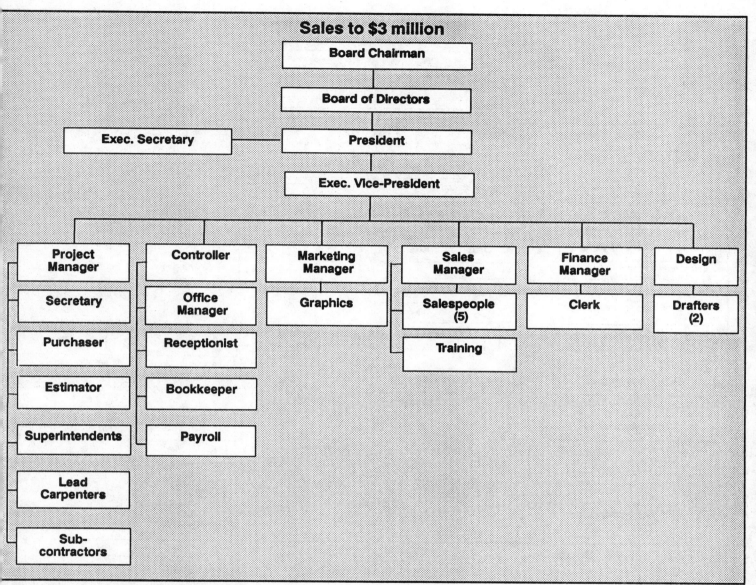

Figure 8-5 *Level 5 - Upwardly mobile*

experienced professional people in your community who meet with you occasionally to monitor progress and review operations. Most of the board should be "outside" directors that don't work for you and don't have a financial interest in the business.

My ideal board would include the following:

1) *Lawyer*: A lawyer specializing in business and construction law can contribute much to your plans.

2) *Accountant*: An alert C.P.A. but someone other than the C.P.A. who prepares your tax returns.

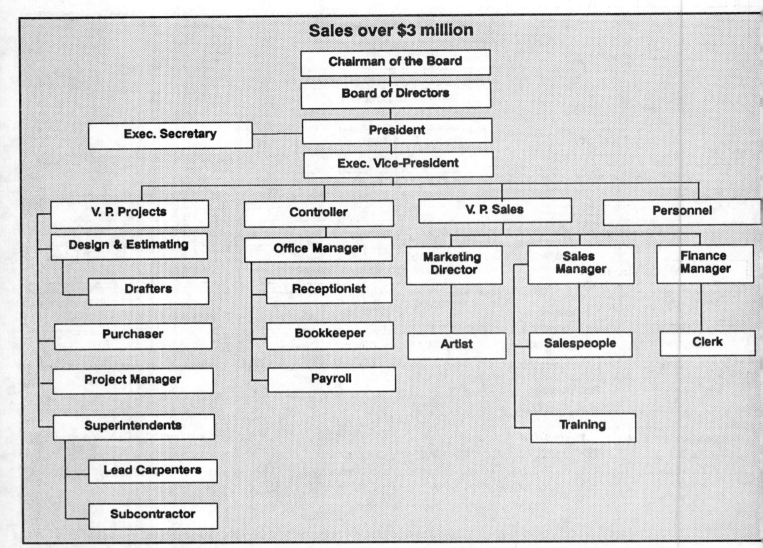

Figure 8-6 *Level 6 - Becoming*

3) *Money Manager:* Someone in real estate, banking or insurance who is experienced in financial matters.

4) *Contractors:* A recently-retired high volume contractor can lend a different perspective as you plan for growth.

The ideal board member is well respected in his or her field and has good connections in the community. If you had to hire people like that, the price would be very high. But many public-spirited people sit on boards for a modest annual fee. For $100 a day per member and the price of lunch, you can probably attract very qualified board members, especially if you keep them informed on company business. Listen carefully to the advice they offer, and follow that advice regularly.

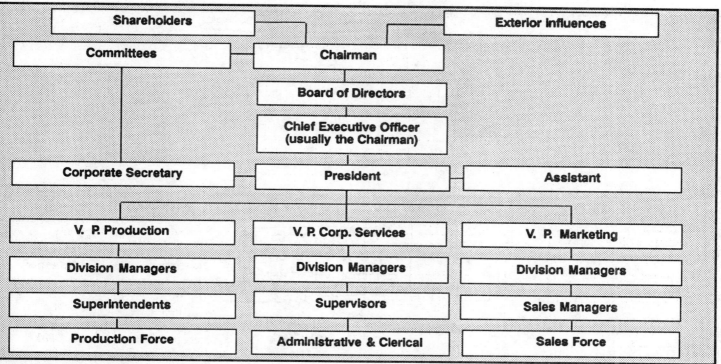

Figure 8-7   Level 7 - Big

Notice also that Level 5 (Figure 8-5) shows a full-time marketing director to manage public relations, advertising and promotion. You could create an advertising agency under this person's direction. The agency takes a 15 percent commission on company ads, creating another profit center in the company. Most larger remodelers use the commission to help pay the marketing director's salary.

At Level 5 your immediate problem is focusing on long-term goals. Many of your former duties at Level 4 can now be delegated to an executive vice president. You'll add a controller who's qualified to make financial forecasts, set budgets and keep the company on a firm financial footing.

The graphic artist working for the marketing director produces brochures and ads, and could work for the design department as well.

At Level 5 your company will be buying materials and supplies in high volume. You'll need a purchasing agent working with the production department to supervise the buying. This person will more than earn his or her salary by getting the best prices and keeping material deliveries on schedule.

At Level 6 (Figure 8-6) your company has vice presidents in charge of sales and production. I've found that people promoted from within the company are usually best at handling this responsibility. But for specialized work like personnel management or estimating, you'll usually do better to hire experts from outside the company.

From this point, the organization chart won't change very much as the company grows. Of course, you may add regional and district sales managers as you expand your marketing territory. But except for middle management positions which you'll fill as needed, all the key executive offices are filled.

Naturally the office staff will grow as sales volume increases. In the beginning, only a few people are involved, each with a broad range of duties. As your business expands, each person specializes more and more. So job descriptions change with the size of your company. I'll talk more about this in the next chapter.

Around the Corner

Eventually you'll step up to chairman of the board of directors and select someone else to run the company as president. The title Chief Executive Officer (CEO) is usually given to the person who's actually running the company, making day-to-day decisions. In some companies, the CEO is the chairman of the board of directors. Usually the CEO is the president. Chairman of the board may also be chairman of the executive committee, but usually isn't involved in daily operations. For our discussion, I'll assume that you're the CEO.

Figure 8-7 shows the organization chart for a big company. Many construction and engineering contractors get this big. But very few remodelers make it. Even so, you're lucky to be in the construction business. It may be the only industry left where you can start out with little capital, no special skills, no special education and still build a multi-million dollar company in your own lifetime.

Notice in Figure 8-7, Level 7 shows stockholders. At this point (over $10 million a year) most companies have sold stock to investors to raise capital for operations. The stockholders elect the board of directors and the board selects the president. The president, in the center, is responsible to those above him and directs those below him in Figure 8-7. Even if the president is both chairman and chief executive officer, he or she is responsible to both the board of directors and shareholders.

Why would you want to turn the presidency of your company over to someone else? Some contractors simply don't have the management skills to run a very large company efficiently. The business has gotten away from them. There's a danger when owner-managers who start their own companies try to hold onto the reins too long. They may not recognize that problems related to growth are directly related to their own management style or failure to delegate authority.

Finding Your Style

Design your organization so that you have to supervise only as many subordinates as you can manage effectively. For some, that might be only one person — an executive vice president. For others, it could be a number of vice presidents or managers.

Delegate authority to the lowest possible organizational level. Develop employees with expert knowledge of operations and situations who are competent in predicting the results and implications of their decisions. Match your people to their jobs.

You can't supervise everyone all the time. Let employees decide how the work will be done. Focus on results, not methods. True, this can lead to confusion and duplication of effort, especially if you don't define goals clearly. But it also works more efficiently and encourages initiative in employees. Let your employees use their imagination and creativity to get the job done.

Consider Franchising

At some point in the growth and development of your company, you may consider franchising, either as a seller, or as a buyer. I'm going to use the rest of this chapter to describe some things every remodeling contractor should consider about home improvement franchising. I'm convinced that home improvement franchises are changing this business. Whether or not you would consider operating a home improvement franchise, you should know something about this important topic.

The U.S. Department of Commerce says, "Franchising has achieved a phenomenal growth rate over the past several years and continues to offer tremendous opportunities to individuals and companies seeking wider distribution for their products and services." These words are significant because until recently, fly-by-night and rip-off artists gave franchising a black eye. It now enjoys wide public acceptance.

J. Naisbitt, in his book, *The Future of Franchising*, says "Construction, home improvements, and remodeling, is the second-fastest-growing franchise category of all, with annual sales growth (1985 - 1990) estimated at 20 percent."

Franchising today is no longer the exclusive province of the big boys. Small companies often become successful franchisors and franchisees. Any well organized, profitable business manager should investigate franchising when it's time to make major expansion decisions.

What Is Franchising?

Franchising lets a remodeling contractor operate under a marketing plan prescribed by the franchisor. The franchisor permits use of the name, trademark or logo, and advertising in return for fees and royalties.

One type of franchise requires the franchisee to begin a whole new business, like McDonald's. Another type, like Century 21, converts existing businesses. Remodelers usually fit this category. The franchisor provides management training for the new recruits. Each addition broadens the referral network, and builds advertising power for the entire organization.

Franchising works for remodeling contracting because there's no widely recognized name in the industry. People feel uncomfortable buying from a company they don't know. Franchising overcomes this problem.

Consider these statistics:

1) Franchise sales will account for 50 percent of all retail sales in 1990.

2) The power of franchising provides a 10 to 1 success ratio over a non-franchised business.

3) About 60 percent of non-franchised new businesses fail in their first two years, with a 90 percent failure rate within 10 years.

4) The remodeling and home services market represents a $100 billion industry with an annual growth rate of 20 percent. This market is one of the fastest growing areas for franchising.

Should You Join a Franchise?

What business can a novice enter with an investment of less than $30,000, a training period of a week or two, and have better than a 90 percent chance of success? How about starting out with less than $5,000 and watching profits return during your first week of operation? I've seen that done over and over.

Satisfied franchisees say it's an easy way to enter the business, stay in the business longer, and to become more successful. Here's why:

1) The primary investment is about the same for a franchise as for an independent remodeling contractor. However, total investment may be more when you consider continuing fees and royalties.

2) You'll get extensive training and assistance, consultation service, quality control, and supervision. You may have access to accounting, estimating, interior design, drafting and design services.

3) You'll have the advantage of advertising saturation you couldn't afford on your own.

4) Good marketing and promotional assistance by an aggressive franchisor will give the franchisee an edge on the competition.

5) Territorial protection will increase your odds for establishing a firm toehold in the business. But it won't stop competition from coming in under other names.

6) An established franchise offering reduces your risk of failure.

7) You may have a buy-back clause if you decide to leave the business for any reason.

8) A franchisor may offer financing to help you start your business.

9) Construction, including home improvement, is one of the nation's fastest-growing industries. As small independents fold, they'll be replaced by more stable franchises with the strength to withstand economic slowdowns.

10)   Affiliation with a major franchisor may help you attract better employees, just like top real estate salespeople are attracted to Century 21.

11)   You can take advantage of bulk purchasing power.

12)   Customers are often willing to pay premium prices for brand name recognition and confidence.

13)   You'll have access to other marketing tools such as competitive consumer finance programs, professional presentation materials and effective sales aids.

If becoming a franchisee appeals to you, there are many franchise organizations for you to choose from. *Mr. Build* is no doubt the pioneer, and by far the largest, most organized, and probably the best property service (formerly called home improvement) franchisor in America. They're considered the industry standard for comparison. Of course, there are others. The Yellow Pages of most metropolitan telephone books will probably list several franchise operations.

The Franchisor's Point of View: Advantages

But buying a franchise isn't the only choice. If you're already running a successful remodeling business, consider opening offices in another area as a franchise of your business. Here are some advantages to becoming a franchisor.

Put more capital into your business

You can expand your business with minimum risk and a potential for big profit by becoming a franchisor. You don't have to invest your own money or borrow from others. You retain full control of the parent company, and you don't have to pledge your assets as collateral.

Franchisees own their own businesses while they become investors in yours. You base fees on gross sales rather than profit because it's easier to monitor. As a franchisor, you can expect revenue to come from the following:

1)   Franchise fee, a one-time fee to join the franchise program.

2)   Royalties paid weekly or monthly, based on gross sales.

3)   Advertising fees — you don't do anything for nothing.

4)   Charges for sales leads.

5)   Sale of materials such as windows or siding and sale of supplies such as uniforms, printed forms, etc.

6) Provide management, accounting, or payroll service. This not only helps the franchisees, but also gives you information to monitor their operations.

Expansion without increased supervisory responsibility

You still have to train your franchisee. But your function is that of overseer, to counsel and direct when needed.

Increase your buying power

As your franchise operation grows, you can buy supplies and materials much cheaper. Increased purchasing volume brings discounts to you and your franchisees. Volume discounts also apply to advertising.

Drawbacks for the Franchisor

- Remember, you don't own the franchisee's business, and he's not your employee. You can't fire him.

- If you turn your branch offices into franchises, you'll have to give up the hands-on control of those businesses.

- You have an obligation to franchisees, of course. If they don't make money, they may blame you and claim misrepresentation, fraud, or inadequate training. Legal costs can be high. Choose your franchisees carefully, train them well and maintain a good relationship with them.

Franchisees with the Right Stuff

Of course, you want the best contractors and tradespeople as franchisees. Find them by getting your franchise brochure into the hands of prospects. Have a full color brochure designed and printed by professionals. Aim for a successful market. Remember, franchisees have to begin with enough money to cover startup costs.

Beware Unmanageable Growth

Believe it or not, selling franchises too successfully can be a drawback. If you sell franchises beyond your ability to manage them, the results will be very unpredictable. Take a step at a time. Sell a limited number of franchises in a limited, easily accessible area until your organization can cope with more expansion.

In any event, the rule is to walk before you run. A very real danger a remodeler contractor-franchisor faces is the temptation of selling more franchises than you can properly control. It's surprisingly easy to sell these franchises because the initial fee can be quite low. Many are in the $5,000 to $15,000 range.

The Steps to Become a Franchisor

Suppose you've had your remodeling business for several years. You've always done a fair volume, and enjoy a good reputation in the area. You have a good sales staff and a good training system. You're interested in franchising and want more information. Now what?

First of all, you have to treat franchising as a separate business from your contracting operation. It's a challenge apart from the one you met creating the remodeling business.

Franchise requirements

Many states have adopted special laws that apply to franchises. Some states require franchisors to register and agree to provide each franchisee with a formal agreement and a statement of disclosure before offering franchises for sale.

■ State laws: A dozen or more states require franchisors to furnish extensive information about their offering and the background of the principals. Others that don't have franchise laws as such still require franchisors to comply with certain regulations under their business opportunity laws.

■ Federal laws: Fairly tough federal laws apply to all states. Contact the Federal Trade Commission for details of franchising requirements. The Uniform Franchise Offering Circular they offer dictates the contents of a franchise offering and a timetable for filing.

You'll be required to file a disclosure statement that reveals the financial history of your franchising company and its directors and officers. You'll have to describe the duties, responsibilities and cost of your franchise offering, following a comprehensive and detailed format.

Federal and state governments are vigorous in their enforcement of franchise laws, and will impose stiff fines and even prison terms for violations.

The Franchise Agreement

It's mandatory under both federal and state laws to provide a formal contract that clearly specifies all the terms between the franchisor and the franchisee. Work closely with a lawyer who specializes in franchise agreements on this. Don't try to do it yourself or use standard boilerplate forms. There's too much at stake for everyone concerned.

Some questions to consider

1) Can I insist that the franchisee buy building materials such as windows or cabinets from me?

Generally, no. But there are exceptions that depend on your product line. If this is an important issue for you, check it out thoroughly. The laws vary between states.

2) Can I dictate prices for the franchisees to charge?

Absolutely not. This is price fixing. However, you may provide suggested prices as guidelines and leave it to the franchisee to decide.

3) Can I sell in the same territory as my franchisee?

Not if you granted an exclusive territory to the franchisee. Even if you didn't, it wouldn't benefit either of you to compete directly with your own franchisee.

4) If a franchisee refuses to conduct business according to my operations manual, would I be within my rights to terminate the contract?

You would have strong grounds to do so. However, you'll have to show overwhelming evidence. Try to avoid litigation. Anticipate this problem and cover the possibility in your contract and your operations manual.

Franchise fees

You can only collect one franchise fee, so consider carefully how much that should be. Here are some ways to decide:

■ How much did you spend developing the program?

■ What were your marketing and selling costs?

■ How much will you spend on training (including materials)?

■ What will be the franchisee return on investment?

■ How much do your competitors charge?

■ Will you have to keep the fee low to gain momentum, or is your operation so impressive and appealing that you can name your own price?

You want your initial fee to cover all your sales and startup service costs. One major franchisor charges an initial fee of $10,750. Here's a breakdown:

One time advertising charge:	$350
Insurance/warranty fund:	500
Startup costs:	3,000
Includes painting/logos on vehicle, decals, employee training, uniforms	
Franchisor retains:	**$6,900**

When you figure sales costs, include commission, employee benefits and overhead. Consider time and materials to establish accounting, estimating, and other office systems, along with personnel to monitor operations during the early weeks.

Royalties

■ Your royalty fee structure is critical. You live or die as a franchisor by this. One franchisor charges a $500 monthly service fee plus another $350 for advertising. They also charge an annual royalty fee of $300. You can collect these fees monthly or even weekly. The more often, the better. The more service you provide, the higher your royalty fee should be.

Territory

■ Set a franchisee's territory by area, by population count or by income bracket. Protect your franchisees by making their territories exclusive.

Contract duration

■ Limit your franchise contracts to not more than four years before they're subject to renewal. Two years is better. You know that remodeling contractors live and die with changes in the economic cycle. And home improvement contracting is a very stressful business. Be ready to deal with franchisees who can't maintain a high level of intensity.

Trademarks and logos

■ Register your trademark and logo with the federal government. That way, no one else can adopt your trademark and operate under the banner of your success. Your mark tells the public that anyone displaying it operates under a certain standard. It presents your image, so design it carefully. Your attorney can help you register a trademark and logo.

The Operations and Procedures Manual

■ Your manual is nearly as important as your contract. You've probably made lots of expensive mistakes on your road to success. You don't want your franchisees to repeat them. Make your operations manual as clear and detailed as you can so they can succeed right from the start.

■ Your operations manual will contain confidential material and trade secrets. Make it clear that the manual remains your property and is to be returned to you upon termination of the franchise agreement.

Don't leave anything out. Cover every form the franchisee is to use, how to fill it out, where to send it, and when. Include instructions on hiring, training and evaluating personnel. Describe in detail everything you will supply and everything the franchisee is expected to provide. Write down everything you do to run a successful business, and how you do it.

Training

Here's where the franchisee gets to learn your system, and you find out how good he is, and how enthusiastic. Include an escape clause in your contract in case either of you finds the arrangement unsatisfactory during the training process.

Make your classroom training and supporting literature professional. Explain your entire system. Everything pertaining to your system and forms should be thoroughly covered, both in the classroom and on the job. Don't leave anything to chance. Your franchisees need hands-on training in actual daily operations. You must provide that opportunity. The training period may be from a few days to two weeks.

Let the Pros Do It

If you decide to franchise your success, get expert professional help. You can get help two ways:

1) Contract with a lawyer, an accountant and a consultant who specialize in franchise arrangements. Choose these advisors carefully. You need a "zero defect" task force for a job this important.

2) Hire a franchise development specialist. This one-stop approach puts you in the hands of a team that's thoroughly grounded in franchise business practices and laws.

■ Check their track record. Ask for a list of clients.

■ Look for a company with a strong mix of marketing and operational experience, with access to legal experts in franchising.

■ The franchise specialists should be fully equipped to serve you as a resource center.

You can expect a franchise development specialist to:

1) Analyze your business with an eye to your chance for success.

2) Develop a plan to qualify you as a legal franchisor. The specialist should make sure development of your franchise operation doesn't outrun the cash you have available for that purpose.

3) Help you with management decisions regarding training, supervision, financial controls, and equipment, material and supply purchases for your franchisees.

4) Assist you in defining services, fees, and royalties and establishing a cooperative advertising program.

5) Advise you on the content of your Franchise Agreement and Operations Manual.

6) Prepare and file all necessary legal documents.

7) Help you develop and carry out an effective sales program.

Remember, franchising is just one way to expand your business. Another is to increase sales from your current location.

In the next chapter I'll outline the specifics of the job descriptions to fill the boxes on your organizational chart.

9

Make Jobs Fit Descriptions

In most businesses, management level jobs come with a written job description. It's a convenient way to be sure the person holding the job understands his or her responsibilities. A job description should also include standards by which the person holding the job is judged. I've found that written job descriptions save me a lot of time, prevent misunderstandings and make a convenient standard when evaluating employees for raises and promotion. They're also very handy when interviewing applicants for a vacant position.

No matter what size your remodeling company, I recommend that you write up the essential responsibilities and duties for every position in your company. Probably one side of one sheet would be enough for even the most important jobs. Define each position clearly and specifically.

Use the job descriptions to compare your positions with those of other companies when you make salary surveys. You can also use them to set salary ranges within your own organization. Review the descriptions at least once a year to keep them consistent with what your workers are actually doing. Include the job descriptions in your company manual, which we'll discuss in the next chapter.

Figure 9-1 is a job description format you can adapt for your use. Take the time to prepare the sections in as much detail as you can.

(C O M P A N Y   N A M E)

POSITION DESCRIPTION

Job Title _____ Job Code _____

Date _____ Department _____

Written by _____ Exempt or Nonexempt _____

Approved by _____ Pay Scale _____

Qualifications: _____

_____

_____

_____

Summary statement: _____

_____

_____

_____

Assigned responsibilities or duties: _____

_____

_____

_____

Supervisor or rater: _____

Figure 9-1 *Job description format*

Discuss the job description with applicants for that job. Ask what qualifications they have to do what's required. Then, after someone is hired, take the time to review the job description and discuss problems that have come up. With any luck, most employees will do at least a little more than is in their job description. When that happens, congratulate that employee and then include those responsibilities in their job description. Sometime the reverse is true and you'll have to strike something out of a job description. That's O.K. too. Just be sure the job description fits the job that needs to be done.

"See here, Horsely— you've been here three months;
when do the brains get into gear?"

After a little revising and supplementing, you'll have an accurate description for each job. But let your employees know that the description reflects *minimum* standards. Everyone is invited to do more. And, in any case, keep your job descriptions up-to-date when positions and duties change.

As the company grows, the job descriptions become more specialized. A person who did a variety of tasks when the company was small may have time for only one or two as the volume increases. A job that once took an hour a day may now take five.

To help you draft job descriptions for your company, I'll suggest what the summary statement of each job description might say in a medium-size remodeling company. Note in Figure 9-1 where the summary statement appears.

Board Chairman

If you're the principal stockholder in your corporation, you can name yourself as board chairman and president. If you also have subsidiary companies, you'd name someone else president of each of them.

As chairman, your primary concern should be smooth and efficient operation, increased profitability and opportunities for expansion. For example, you might want to try commercial remodeling or custom home building.

Board of Directors

Your board members set policy for the company. They ratify, approve or amend suggestions brought to them about company operations and procedures. All major policy decisions by the president are subject to review by the board. Because most boards meet only a few times a year, they don't get involved in most routine decisions.

President

The company president guides the company's day-to-day action. What he or she does is always subject to review or approval by the board of directors.

■ The President in Level 1: Startup (sales to $500,000)

Look back to Figure 8-1 in the previous chapter. Remember what I described as a Level 1 company? When you're the president of a very small company, you'll likely be the salesperson, superintendent, estimator, finance manager, advertising manager, designer, bookkeeper, typist, and janitor too. A startup remodeler wears many hats. But don't try to wear too many. Being president, salesperson and superintendent is more than enough for anyone.

■ The President in Level 2: First Expansion (sales to $1 million)

Now you've added a receptionist, draftsman, lead carpenter and a salesperson or two. You'll spend more time on training and supervision while you're still wearing most of the hats from Level 1.

■ The President in Level 3: Plateau Stage (sales to $1-1/2 million)

This is a crossroad stage where you stop most of your hands-on work and devote more time to running the company. You'll probably still give final approval on new jobs and watch over the accounts payable. Beyond that you'll probably spend more time supervising each department and less time handling the details.

■ The President in Level 4: Daylight Level (sales to $2 million)

You'll probably focus on a particular part of the business (such as marketing or supervising work on the site) and spend most time there. With a bigger staff you'll concentrate more on improving company efficiency.

■ The President in Level 5: Upwardly Mobile (sales to $3 million)

You'll need to groom someone, probably your finance manager, as an executive vice president. You'll expect this person to follow your procedures and run the business with little guidance from you.

Executive Vice President - Level 5 plus

The executive vice president takes over from you as commander-in-chief. Now that person is the troubleshooter, the motivator, the guiding light for the rest of the company. He answers only to you and the board of directors and has authority over the rest of the organization.

Vice President of Projects

If you open a second office or when volume requires more than two or three job superintendents, a vice president in charge of construction may be needed. That person will supervise production personnel: superintendents, the buyer, estimator, designer, lead carpenters, and so forth. Together they schedule and complete the jobs from start to finish.

Marketing Director

The marketing director looks after all the advertising, promotions, artwork, literature, and public relations. This person executes all your marketing programs. He or she should set sales quotas, design and place advertising, and train and supervise the salespeople.

Controller

The controller does the cost analysis, cash flows, budgeting, projections, and financial statements. In a company over $4 or $5 million, the controller should be a certified public accountant. The finance department, under the controller's direction, handles accounts payable, receivables and payroll, grants credit, and handles financing and banking.

Finance Manager - Level 4

The finance manager's job is to shop and place mortgages for your customers. You may or may not need a finance manager at this level. It depends on the kind of work you do, and the size of your jobs. If you only go after larger contracts, you could be selling two million dollars with only two or three jobs.

You probably will need a good finance manager if most of your work is in the $5,000 to $50,000 range. It can take a full-time person to shop for the money your customers need to get their jobs done.

Estimator

Your estimator works closely with the sales staff and the designer or drafter to fine tune the field estimates against the latest pricing information. The estimator also checks for omissions from contracts. It wouldn't do to miss a 30 foot glulam beam because the salesperson didn't realize you'd need one to support the upper floor.

The estimator also maintains your price book, updates material cost records, and uses job cost records to monitor labor charges.

Project Manager - Level 4 and Over

The project manager schedules the subcontractors, coordinates deliveries and checks on the work crews. Your project manager or superintendent has one other major role. He or she is responsible for seeing that the customer is satisfied with the work being done. Here are some of the project manager's assigned duties:

1) Check out new job sites, note special conditions, verify prices.

2) Set up jobs for construction start. Review specifications and drawings. Check receipt of all permits. Negotiate subcontracts. Coordinate schedules and brief superintendents on job. Write work orders. Produce progress reports.

3) Meet with salesperson and customer before work begins for final review of details.

4) Record jobs costs for preparation of draws or payments.

5) Resolve any job problems.

6) Price and complete change orders and extra work orders.

7) Distribute all paperwork to appropriate departments for further processing.

8) Assist job supervisors with personnel management, training and discipline. Create incentive programs to increase production.

9) Meet regularly with department members to exchange information and solve problems.

10) Monitor each job to keep costs within budget limits.

11) Maintain all production equipment and vehicles.

12) Prepare quality control reports, substantial completion forms, waivers of liens, etc. for each completed job.

13) Approve subcontractor bills for payment. Check supplier invoices against materials received and verify that credit has been issued for returned merchandise.

14) Approve payroll hours and rates before sending to payroll department for payment.

These are just some of the things a project manager does. Your list may be even longer. This list shows the kind of detail you should include in your job descriptions.

Purchasing Agent

Your purchasing agent should understand the type of work your company handles and must know how to read plans and specifications. Your purchasing agent (buyer) should save more than his or her salary by limiting abuses by workers, subcontractors, and vendors.

Personnel Manager

Appoint one person to manage the screening, selecting, and hiring of new employees. This person should keep records of performance, promotions, changes in pay rate and any reprimands given to employees. This is essential information when making performance reviews.

Superintendents

Smaller remodeling companies have superintendents, not project managers. As a company grows, a project manager will be needed to relieve superintendents of the administrative chores they had been handling. Then the superintendent's job description can concentrate more on construction and less on paperwork.

The superintendent works with building inspectors, receives materials, supervises crews on the job, solves job problems as they come up and coordinates with subcontractors.

Supervisors manage people. They're field generals. It's important your office staff give each superintendent enough authority to direct all the field work without interference. No one should tell the superintendents how to run a job. It's enough to hold them accountable for their performance.

Lead Carpenter

Lead carpenters are selected because of their skill and willingness to take responsibility for satisfactory job completion. The lead carpenter on a remodeling job is a working supervisor, leading tradesmen by setting an example for them. Your lead carpenter should also oversee the work of subcontractors, keep track of materials, and review the work of crew members. But there's more. The position includes responsibility for customer relations, change orders and extra work orders, cleanups, and maintaining schedules.

The lead carpenter does practically the same things as a superintendent does. But unlike a superintendent, the lead carpenter doesn't leave the job until it's done. That makes the lead carpenter's job an ideal training ground for superintendents. A successful lead carpenter is often promoted to superintendent where he or she can supervise several jobs at once.

Trade Workers

Hire both specialists and people who are proficient at more than one trade. There's a wide variety of work in the remodeling business. Your ideal workers are all-around tradespeople who can do more than one job.

Designer/Drafter - Level 2 and Above

This person prepares preliminary drawings from the salesperson's sketches. Those preliminary drawings are the ones the sales manager uses to get final approval from the owner. The finance manager also uses them to shop for funds, if you'll be helping the client get financing.

Once the contract is signed, the drafter inspects the site and prepares the scaled working drawings. This person might also apply for the building permits, and do simple architectural and interior design.

Office Manager

The office manager needs to be familiar with all office functions and routines. Duties include supervising and training office personnel, assigning tasks, and monitoring the workload. The office manager might be promoted from the previous position of bookkeeper.

Your office manager does the following, among other things:

1) Prepares sales commission reports and draws.

2) Reports on sales performance and projections — leads, sales, ratios.

3) Monitors advertising — keeps track of lead sources, cost per lead.

4) Analyzes costs and relates them to job types. Reports on ratios for overhead and profit margin.

5) Supervises all administrative jobs, including payroll, collections, billing, banking, collection and distribution of sales leads, contract preparation, and tax returns.

Bookkeeper

The bookkeeper posts all the ledgers and journals, enters the daily bills and usually writes the checks and maintains the checkbook balance. This person might process accounts payable, receivable, and payroll, unless your volume is large enough to employ clerks for these operations.

In today's computerized office, the bookkeeper must also know your accounting software programs thoroughly.

Sales Manager

When you reach a volume of two million dollars or more, you'll probably need a sales manager. That person will lead, direct, train and motivate your sales staff, and will also sell.

The sales manager conducts sales meetings to review pending jobs, sales lead productivity, and sales strategies. Some remodeling companies have these meetings twice a week. This is the time for pep talks, constructive criticism, congratulations and awards. Describe new products and changes in financial trends and regulations. Distribute price changes. Make the meetings interesting and stimulating.

The sales manager should:

1) Review all new contracts, estimates and job plans.

2) Check customer credit applications, verify employment and financial history.

3) Recruit, hire and supervise training of new salespeople.

4) Assign sales leads.

5) Design contests and incentive programs.

I don't advise promoting your sales manager from the ranks of your star salespeople. You'll probably lose a good producer and gain a bad sales manager. Salespeople don't necessarily make good teachers and managers, I've learned. Keep them doing what they do best.

Remodeling Salespeople

Here are some typical duties:

1) Maintain a tidy and orderly sales kit, including the price book, samples, contract documents and sales forms.

2) Work full-time prospecting, selling and checking on work in progress.

3) Follow up on all leads.

Your salespeople should have signed the company Sales Agreement or Training Agreement described earlier. They, like all your employees, will also be expected to conform to company policies and standards. More about that in the next chapter.

10

Setting Your Style

Every company has its own way of doing business. I call that your *business style*. It's reflected in how you deal with customers, how you treat employees, how you deal with problems, how you handle office routine, and in just about everything you do.

Let's look at an example. I know a remodeler who's very customer-oriented. I'll call his company Remodeler A. With Remodeler A, the customer is always right. Everyone on the payroll will do whatever's necessary to satisfy customers. When something goes wrong, making it right again is top priority work. Remodeler A has a written policy on how to handle complaints and who should do what. Everyone on the payroll knows the policy and their responsibility when there's a complaint.

Remodeler B is a little different. Customer complaints are an annoyance to most employees. A customer with a complaint usually has to talk to several people before someone accepts responsibility for fixing the problem. Even then, getting satisfaction is a hit-or-miss proposition. Sometimes the problem gets fixed only when a worker on the job decides to do what the customer wants. And there's no supervision. Sometimes problems aren't fixed at all. The customer just gets tired of complaining about it.

Obviously, Remodeler B is headed for trouble. Customer complaints are going unresolved. Any company that lives off sales and referrals gets nowhere by ignoring customer needs. And whose fault is it when the company stagnates? Obviously, the boss gets the blame. The boss is in charge. Why doesn't he do something? There could be a thousand reasons. Maybe he hates getting into disputes with customers. More likely he's just too busy. Complaints about little details are the last thing he wants to handle — so he usually doesn't. No problem. Nothing says he has to deal with trivia. But someone has to! Ignoring any problem is a mistake.

Here's what the boss at Remodeler B should do. He needs a company policy — some accepted way to deal with customer complaints. How are disputes processed? Who does what? Which job description includes resolving customer disputes? If a dispute can't be settled by that person, what happens next? Those are the questions a good policy statement should resolve. And if your company doesn't have written policies that cover issues like that, your future probably isn't much more attractive than Remodeler B's future.

That's just one example of what I call company style. It's your way of doing business. And what sets the company style? All company employees do. But one person has far more influence than any other. Of course, that's the boss — the owner. And the most effective way to use that influence is through written policy statements that establish company procedures. No employee has to wonder what he or she should do if the answer is in a policy statement.

Every company has policies. In most small companies, few or none of these policies are written down and approved by anyone. People just develop routine ways of doing things. These routines are passed from employee to employee as accepted procedure — even if there's no written policy that covers the subject. But the usual procedure can become a bad habit that does more harm than good. The remedy is a written policy, approved by the boss and circulated to all employees.

Here's another advantage to having written policies rather than relying on informal procedures. Writing up a policy and getting it approved forces the boss to think about what should be done, who should do it, and who should supervise to be sure it's done right. Adopting a written policy forces people in authority to face problems and develop ways of dealing with them. Written policies also give managers ammunition when someone makes a mistake. If following a written policy would have avoided an error, the employee involved should be willing to acknowledge the oversight. That may be the biggest advantage of all.

Of course, when you've got more than three or four written policy statements, it's time to collect them in a policy manual, available to all of your employees. And that's the primary subject of this chapter — your company policy manual.

Use your company manual to explain your rules and regulations. Give each new employee a copy and briefly explain the contents. The manual, along with the employee's job description, lets them know what's expected of them, and what they can expect in return. Enforce company policies and expect everyone to abide by them. Let everyone know that violating a written policy is a serious matter.

The Outline of Your Manual

There's a lot to cover in a comprehensive policy manual. Don't try to develop a manual in a few days or weeks. Instead, add to it as needed so it keeps pace with the growth of your company. Include a table of contents and an index to make using the manual easier.

To make your task easier, I've included on the following pages major portions of the policy manual I use. Policies are in italics. My comments are in plain text.

1) Goals and attitudes. Begin the first section with a statement something like this:

The goal of Goodguys Construction Company is to become the leader in the residential remodeling field. To reach this goal we find ways to serve our customer needs better than any other remodeling company in this community.

Next, make a pitch to your employees:

Every member of our company plays an important role in our growth. No job is considered to be more important than another. It takes many different skills and levels of experience to do our job. Everyone from carpenter's helpers to the company president is paid in proportion to their contribution to our goal.

2) Products and services. Describe the materials you install and the kinds of jobs you handle.

3) Organization chart. Show the lines of authority in your company.

4) Job opportunities. How do employees get pay raises or advance to better positions within the company?

5) Practices, procedures and directives. This is the meat of your manual. It includes the actual rules and regulations and instructions on company procedures.

Personnel Policies

Jobs in different departments or sections have varying pay levels. Decide on those levels and ranges when you write the job descriptions. You'll hire every employee for a specific purpose. Give each of them a job title and a written job description. The job description should tell the new employee exactly who they report to and take orders from.

Interviewing and Evaluating

Most employers interview job applicants. Conduct your interview in private and keep the atmosphere friendly and relaxed. Don't be overbearing. Avoid offensive questions. Listen intently to the answers you're given.

Be sure everyone in your company who interviews employment candidates understands the provisions of the Civil Rights Act and the Equal Employment Opportunities Commission regulations. You can't say or do anything that could be interpreted as discriminatory or that restricts employment because of race, color, religion, sex, national origin, ancestry, age, medical condition (cancer related), physical handicap or marital status.

At this writing, you're permitted to ask for the following:

- applicant's name and address

- a person to notify in case of emergency (you can't specify that the person be a relative)

- level of education, hobbies

- work history and positions held

- affiliation with job-related organizations not related to race, religion, color, or national origin

Here are some things you may *not* ask:

- a married woman's maiden name

- whether the applicant owns or rents their home

- age, or dates for graduation, military service, etc. which would reveal age

- nationality or place of birth

■ questions which indicate applicant's sex, marital status, or number of dependents

■ presence of physical disabilities or handicaps, condition of general health

■ religious affiliation

■ whether applicant has ever been arrested

■ a list of organizations applicant belongs to

■ name and address of relatives, except parents or guardians of minor applicants

Once you've hired someone, you must verify the new employee's eligibility for employment in compliance with regulations of the Immigration and Naturalization Service. You can ask to see information that you're not permitted to request *before* you hire them, including a driver's license, Social Security card, birth certificate, passport or Alien Registration Card, among others.

Consult your state's department of employment and the I.N.S. for current information on hiring practices and regulations.

When your applicant is filling a sensitive position that requires them to handle money or confidential documents, check references carefully.

Hiring Policies

■ Will you fill vacancies from within your own company? If so, describe where job openings will be posted and how an employee requests a transfer.

Employees with adequate qualifications may request transfer to other departments if positions become available. Use Form XXX which you can get from the personnel manager.

Tell the employees where to send their request for transfer, whether to the respective supervisor or the personnel manager.

■ Who is responsible for placing help wanted ads?

■ Describe your policy for rehiring former employees. Will you rehire people who quit? Will you call back people who were laid off?

■ Define your categories of employment:

Full-time employees are those who work at least 35 hours each week all year. Part-time employees work at least 20 hours a week. Casual workers are employed only when needed and on an "on call" basis.

Specify what company benefits each category of employee is entitled to.

■ Will you hire more than one person from the same family?

Probationary Period

■ How long is probation?

■ What benefits or privileges are restricted during probation?

■ What conditions lead to terminating the probation?

I suggest that you have the new employee's supervisor review the worker's progress about half way through the probationary period and again at the end of the period.

Training

You want to train all new employees, not just your sales staff, to do things *your* way. You can also offer training programs as employee incentives — they can prepare for promotions and further their careers. Mention in your personnel manual whether you'll reimburse employees for work-related seminars or courses.

Company-sponsored educational programs approved by management are limited to $500 per person per year.

Performance Evaluation

■ How often will you review your employees' performance?

■ Will you make "field promotions" when appropriate, at times other than scheduled review dates?

Figure 10-1 is a format for a performance review. Here's an example of the procedure you might adopt for using the review form:

(Your company name) will review the performance of every employee twice each year during the months of December and June.

PERFORMANCE APPRAISAL

Employee's Name _____ Job Title _____

Reviewer's Name _____ Performance Review Date _____

Use the following scale to evaluate the employee's performance as compared to the norm of his or her position.

1. **Very Good** - Employee consistently meets or exceeds established standards and desired results.

2. **Good** - Employee consistently meets established standards; sometimes exceeds, and never falls short of desired results.

3. **Satisfactory** - Employee meets established standards; usually meets, and seldom falls short of desired results.

4. **Improvement Needed** - Employee meets established standards but lacks consistency; seldom exceeds and often falls short of desired results.

	Very Good	Good	Satisfactory	Improv. Needed	Comments
Job skills					
Work knowledge					
Ability to organize					
Work quality					
Communication					
Teamwork					
Deadlines					
Dependability					
Judgment					

Figure 10-1 *Performance appraisal*

Review employee's performance against established objectives for this evaluation period.

_____

Areas needing improvement

_____

Objectives set for next evaluation period

_____

Summary of evaluation

_____

Recommended pay adjustment

_____

Employee comments (attach separate sheet if needed)

_____

Employee's signature _____ Date _____

Reviewer's signature _____ Date _____

Officer's signature _____ Date _____

Figure 10-1 (cont'd) *Performance appraisal*

The employee and his or her supervisor will discuss the review in an interview. The supervisor will record the employee's comments during the interview on the evaluation form.

Employees are encouraged to:

1) Inquire about their performance regularly.

2) Accept higher responsibilities and show initiative.

3) Be aware of opportunities for advancement within the company.

4) Request help to a goal-oriented path for advancement.

5) Be aware of training programs available to improve skills leading to promotion.

The reviewer will determine if a raise is warranted and will recommend the amount based upon funds available to the department. Merit raises are based on dedication, extra effort and above-average performance. The company does not approve merit increases automatically or at a preset interval. Final review and approval of merit increase recommendations will be made at the executive level.

Motivation and Discipline

Give some thought to your management style and the "perks" you offer. Sometimes picnics and parties are worth far more in building employee satisfaction and cooperation than they cost. Of course, tangible rewards such as profit sharing, stock options or bonuses are important too.

All successful companies have ways of maintaining company discipline. You need it yourself if you hope to carry out your plans. And you need to impose it on your staff to get the job done the way you direct. Let your employees know that supervisors will record all disciplinary action in the employee's confidential personnel file.

- Tardiness: Decide if you'll use a time clock. Whether you do or not, define the consequences for being late:

    An employee who is late to work more than three times in a month will receive a reprimand and payroll deduction.

- The "Bootstrap Notice": Give written notices to employees who perform below company standards. The idea behind a bootstrap notice is to give the employee a specified amount of time to improve performance. If the manager is satisfied with the performance, nothing more comes of it. If performance doesn't improve, there is cause for further action.

- Demotions: Rarely, an employee who had been doing substandard work may agree to accept a lower pay level (if the company thinks the person is worth keeping). For instance, an employee can persuade a manager to give them another chance to bring performance up to standard.

- Disciplinary regulations: Specify what action supervisors can take in case of flagrant or repeated violations of company policies. A verbal admonition is often enough to prevent minor violations from being repeated. More serious offenses may invite demotions, pay reductions, fines, or dismissal.

Grievances

Any employee may ask for a hearing and file a written complaint or grievance with the department manager.

Decide how you'll handle employee grievances. What will the next step be, once an employee files a complaint? Will you appoint a committee, or attempt to resolve the problem yourself by meeting with the employee and his or her supervisor?

Decide on a policy concerning appeals to decisions resulting from grievances. Will you permit appeals, or will the grievance committee's decision be final. Will you require employees to represent themselves, or can they have a third party represent them in a grievance hearing?

If your employees are union members, there may be some restrictions and requirements in your union contract that have a bearing on the way you handle employee grievances. Your state labor board has information on the subject, too.

Dismissal

- State your company's policy regarding written notice or severance pay in the case of layoff or firing.

  Employees who are dismissed while on probation, who quit work voluntarily, or who have been fired, are not eligible for any form of severance pay.

Termination

- How much notice will you require in case of voluntary termination?

■ Will the notice be the same for all levels of employees?

Be careful with disciplining or terminating employees. If an employee, or former employee, takes you to court, chances are you'll lose. Courts seem to sympathize with the little guy victimized by the tyrant boss.

Employee Compensation

Salary ranges for each job classification will be reviewed annually and adjusted to reflect the industry standard. The company's policy is to pay wages that are equitable with those of similar operations within the same territory. Pay levels are proportionate to the experience, skill, and performance of each individual.

■ Specify which employees will be salaried and which ones are paid hourly.

■ Will you allow salary advances? Under what circumstances?

Officers

Officers receive a salary which may be enhanced with a bonus program. Senior management is responsible for establishing pay rates and for creating incentives for officers.

Directors and Vice Presidents

Compensation is flexible at this level of management. When a person successfully accomplishes various objectives which significantly improve the financial position of the company, they expect a raise. You can create income schemes to fit their particular needs. You may mutually agree to compensation other than cash.

Management

Here are some policies you might adopt for your superintendents and office managers:

Department managers are eligible for incentive bonuses when increased profits are related to their respective departments.

Middle managers within a department are at the forefront of their projects. Their initiative — and their ability to conduct, maintain, and improve work schedules, quality, and costs — have a direct relationship to merit bonuses.

Overtime

Forty hours per week is the standard for hourly employees. Work over 40 hours is treated as overtime. Salaried employees receive no overtime pay. Hours between 40 and 48 will be paid at the rate of time and a half. Hours in excess of 48 will be paid at double time. Hourly employees may not work overtime unless requested to do so by their supervisor or manager.

■ Will you allow "comp" time? Check local regulations for time limits for taking compensatory time off.

Paydays

■ When is payday? What period is covered?

Pay periods end on Wednesday with paychecks distributed the following Friday.

Benefits

■ Will you offer a profit-sharing plan? Who is eligible? When? How will the employees become vested?

■ Will you pay bonuses for extraordinary performance?

■ Are employees and subcontractors who work exclusively for the company entitled to discounts on company services? Can they buy materials through the company to take advantage of wholesale prices?

Employees (and subcontractors) may purchase materials through the company at invoice plus 10 percent. Purchases must be made through the purchasing office, and approved by the controller. The company does not guarantee anything for anyone under these circumstances, and all purchases must be made on a cash basis. Purchasing privileges are for the employee's use only, and may not be extended to relatives and friends.

You should probably specify that your employees are prohibited from reselling any merchandise they buy through the company.

■ Describe in detail what kind of health and medical insurance you'll provide, when an employee becomes eligible, who to contact for information, how to file claims, and whether your employees will have to share the cost of coverage for themselves or their families.

Holidays

Specify all statutory and any optional holidays your company observes. Are employees required to work the day before and after to receive holiday pay? Will you offer additional personal holidays? How much will you pay employees who agree to work on holidays?

Salaried employees are credited with one paid personal holiday for each year's employment, to a maximum of ten days per year. These are in addition to regularly scheduled holidays.

Sick Leave

■ Define the circumstances under which employees will be paid for time off because of illness. Will you include time off for doctor or dentist appointments?

■ How much sick leave will you allow per year? Check your local laws for minimum requirements.

■ Notification: Who should employees call when they're sick? When should they call?

■ Will you require a doctor's statement after a certain time?

■ Define your policy on maternity leave.

■ How will you deal with unused sick leave?

■ How will sick leave time be earned? Will sick leave be available during probation? Will it vary with length of service?

Personal Leave

■ Will you allow a certain number of days each year, or consider each request as it occurs?

■ With or without pay?

■ Consider what events qualify for allowed leave time:

Court appearance or jury duty

Childbirth by mother, wife or daughter

Tax audit

Death in the immediate family

Marriage, honeymoon

Training/education

Decide how employees will accumulate vacation time. Will you pay for vacation time not used at the end of each year? How much time can a worker "save up" and use at one time?

Reimbursed Employee Expenses

■ Will you allow reimbursement of auto expenses? Under what circumstances? Will you pay by the mile or reimburse cost of gasoline?

Most remodelers own light-duty trucks — pickups, vans, or flatbeds. Trucks are expensive, both to own and operate, and they can be a drain on your working capital. Some contractors are now using employee-owned vehicles instead. The company pays for gas or mileage, and provides a monthly or job allowance. Employees seem to like this arrangement because the extra income helps them pay for their vehicles.

A word of caution though: Be sure the employee has adequate auto insurance in force (in the $1 or $2 million range), and that your company is specifically covered by an endorsement on their policy.

Company Regulations

You might think of this as your *don't* list. It can be as detailed as you choose. You can separate the regulations into two classes, maxi and mini. Gross violation of a maxi rule can be grounds for dismissal. Some of the things you might cover are the following:

■ Stealing company equipment, materials

■ Divulging confidential information, secrets, techniques, to competitors or outside sources

■ Making destructive criticism of any sort that works to the detriment of the company

MADAM CLAIRE VOYANT
SPECIAL SUBSCRIPTION
RATES TO CONTRACTORS

"...and your secretary is dating your superintendent. That's briefly wha
I see. For further details, see my contractor's newsletter."

■ Griping or malicious behavior that's destructive to fellow employees

■ Using or being under the influence of alcohol or drugs on the job

■ Fighting, either on the job site or on company property

■ Using abusive or profane language, or insubordinate behavior toward a supervisor.

■ Spouse or immediate relative working for a competitor

■ False information on employment application

■ Falsifying time cards

■ Damaging equipment or injuring people through negligence or carelessness.

■ Socializing excessively during working hours

■ Taking excessive time off

■ Frequent tardiness

- Solicitations by employees

- Parties on company premises

- Excessive visiting by friends or relatives of employees

Conduct on the Job Site

We all hope our employees will use good common sense, be considerate of people's property and feelings, presentable in appearance, and polite. Unfortunately, that's just not true of everyone. Here are some things you may want to mention specifically in your company manual.

Appearance

All employees are expected to make a clean and neat appearance appropriate for the type of work they're performing. Workers should start each day with clean clothes. Bare feet or torn clothing are inappropriate. If you don't want employees wearing shorts on the job, say so.

Guidelines for Site Workers

The efficient worker does not attract undue attention on the job site. Work swiftly and quietly. Don't sing, argue, talk incessantly, use coarse language or bring unnecessary attention to yourself. Radios are prohibited.

Include paragraphs to address use of alcohol, drugs, and smoking materials, and specify the consequences for doing so.

Make it the superintendent's responsibility to see that sanitary facilities are available for work crews at all times.

Maintain a clean work area. Use plenty of tarps and poly sheets to contain paint splatter, sawdust, etc. Remove debris from the site when needed, at least once a week. Leave the job site broom clean at the end of every shift. Building materials should be neatly stacked at all times. Don't leave nails sticking out of loose lumber, and shield any sharp or dangerous objects. Secure all tools every time you leave the work area. Lock all doors and windows at the end of your shift.

Avoid advances with sexual overtones. If it happens, leave and return when conditions allow you to work without interruption or annoyance. Don't make advances or comments that could be misinterpreted.

Common courtesy dictates that the job manager or superintendent introduce each crew worker to the owner. Announce your work schedule and notify the owner of schedule changes.

Practice politeness and respect. Use "please" and "thank you." Don't use the owner's first names unless they invite you to do so.

Don't accept food or drink from the owner, nor offer it yourself. There have been cases where owners have asked tradesmen to supply materials and labor not called for in the contract. It's harder to say no to someone who's just given you lunch.

Use the telephone only for expediting the work on hand. Keep calls brief. Don't take personal calls on the job site.

Don't use the owner's equipment or tools. We don't want to be responsible if the vacuum cleaner stops working or the ladder breaks just after you used them.

Dress code and uniforms

Uniforms are not unusual for remodeling companies, especially franchise companies. Matching cap, shirt, trousers, and jacket with logo and company name in company colors enhance your image. Uniforms promote employee pride and give them a feeling of belonging.

A simple shirt with your logo (and the employee's name on the pocket) and matching cap is all you really need. Specify whether your company will pay for all or part of the uniform, and the cleaning costs.

If you don't use uniforms, consider a dress code for your personnel.

"You've got the job, Miss Grundsby, but no blue jeans please."

Accidents

Describe the procedure to use in the event of an accident on the job. Who should call for emergency treatment, and how? Which doctor to consult in a non-emergency situation? What forms need to be filled out?

Suggestions

Will you invite suggestions from your employees? Where will the suggestion box be located? Will you consider anonymous suggestions? Will there be incentives for productive suggestions?

> *Suggestions which directly result in savings or increased profits to the company will be rewarded by . . . .*

Specify what the award will be. A bonus? A raise? A weekend for two to a nearby resort?

Use of Petty Cash Fund

Define how your petty cash fund will be managed. Who will have access to it? For what purpose is it to be used? Will you allow employees to cash checks or borrow from the fund?

Use of Company Property

■ May employees borrow company equipment, vehicles or tools for their personal use?

■ What is your policy regarding damage to company property? Will employees be charged for waste or damage due to negligence?

■ Define your policy for employee use of company telephones or telephone credit cards.

Housekeeping

Your employees should take pride in maintaining pleasant working conditions and an efficient environment. Here are some rules you might use:

1) Clear desk tops at the close of each business day.

2) Refile all papers — files, plans, literature — when you're finished with them.

3) Keep eating areas and coffee areas clean. Wash and put away all utensils.

4) Replace all furniture, equipment, tools, and vehicles to their proper location after use.

■ Designate responsibility for routine office maintenance and trash collection.

■ Who cleans restrooms, washes floors and windows, etc.

Smoking

Will you permit smoking on company premises? In designated areas? What restrictions should construction crews observe?

Rest Periods

Define the frequency and duration for lunch and coffee breaks.

Moonlighting

Employees may not moonlight in the same line of work as that of the company — regardless of the size of the job — without express permission. Accepting work from the company's customers is also forbidden.

Customer Relations

The most visible display of your company's style is in the way you treat your customers and prospects. Be very detailed in your manual about how your employees present your company to outsiders.

How do you answer the telephone? A curt "Goodguys," growled through a wad of gum makes a much different impression from, "Good morning, Goodguys Construction, may I help you?" in a cheerful, upbeat voice. Put the script for your standard telephone greeting in your policy manual. Then, make sure your employees read it.

How accessible do you want to be? Will you permit certain people in your company to have their calls screened, or do you prefer that all callers be put through immediately?

Product Information

Make sure people in your front office know about the materials and products you use — how to maintain them, and who to call for emergency repairs. Keep a file of warranty information readily available, and assign someone to keep the file up-to-date.

Designate in your policy manual and job descriptions a person who's responsible for customer support. Require that people who answer your phone know who that person is so customers aren't transferred from one person to another several times before they get the information they called for.

Complaints and Disputes

Devise a very specific procedure for handling customer complaints so their resolution isn't left to chance. Who takes the initial call? What kind of form do they fill out? Who do they give the form to? What happens then?

If the complaint is about a job in process, the customer will most likely complain to the superintendent or a worker on the job. Instruct those people to record all complaints, and describe what was done to settle them. Use the same form as your front office staff does, or instruct your workers to write complaint information into the job log. You may want them to do both. If they can't resolve the situation on the spot, be sure they know who to notify in your company to take care of it.

You can avoid most disputes over price or materials by writing clean contracts, but sometimes you'll have problems anyway. Your company policy should state clearly who has the authority to make decisions in these cases — what your superintendent or salesperson can do on their own, and what they must refer to management.

Purchasing Policies

Procedures for your buyers tie in closely with those of your sales and estimating departments, so be sure everyone knows what your policies are. Some questions you need to answer are these:

1) What materials will you buy in quantity, and how much will you buy, to take advantage of price breaks? (That will depend largely on your capacity to store inventory.)

2) Will you have a dollar limit over which you won't buy without getting competitive bids? Will purchases over a designated amount require approval from management?

3) How often does your buyer have to research prices on "staple" items like stud lumber, plywood, nails, etc.

4) Are there sources you won't deal with, or materials or product brands you won't use?

Keep a tight rein on your buying procedures, and you'll improve your profit margin.

Subcontracting

■ How do subs get on your bid list?

■ Will you issue blanket contracts to subs, and then use purchase orders for individual jobs?

■ Are there some operations you'll always sub out? Never sub out?

■ The tax collectors can be difficult over the fine line of distinction between an independent contractor and an employee. Be sure you know the difference, and that your company policy is very clear about who you'll consider as a subcontractor.

Supervisor's Responsibility and Authority

Their job descriptions should say exactly how much authority your foremen and superintendents have, and what they're accountable for. Your company policy forms the basis for those descriptions. Here are some of the policy decisions you have to make.

1) Will supervisors do their own interviewing and hiring?

2) How much control will they have over the pay rates of those working under them?

3) How many projects will each supervisor be expected to oversee at one time? How frequently do you expect them to visit each job site? Daily? Twice a day? At their own discretion?

4) What will their relationship be to your customers? How much authority do they have to negotiate change orders?

5) Will your job superintendent be responsible for scheduling and calling in subs, or does someone else do that? Do you have clerical staff whose job it is to help supervisors with their paperwork?

In each of these cases, and throughout your company, things will run more smoothly if your company policy is clear. Everyone will know who does what, who they answer to, and who they can expect to help them get their own jobs done. If you don't already have a company manual, get busy and write one. It may seem like a nuisance job — one that doesn't return immediate rewards you can put in the bank. But it will pay off in the long run, in a company that works more efficiently, and thus more profitably.

Include instructions in your company manual for updating and distributing the manual itself. A good company policy manual is never "finished." Make it as complete as you can, but design it so it's easy to change when that's necessary.

In the next chapter, we'll discuss specific procedures for handling the paperwork every office generates.

11

Streamline Your Office

I hope you find this chapter to be the most useful in this book. It's about the nuts and bolts of running a remodeling business. I'm going to describe step by step how a job goes from initial contact to final completion. My focus will be on office procedures and how the paperwork flows. But you'll also get a glimpse of what's happening in the field.

First, a note about licenses. Although contractors don't have to be licensed in all states, many of the larger states now require it. If you do any work in those states, you'll have to be licensed. At this writing, 22 states require licenses. Twelve more are considering it, and the movement is gaining momentum. California has licensed contractors since 1931. Several other states require a showing of competency in academic and technical skills and several years of construction experience.

Most contractors support mandatory licensing. Competent, experienced contractors don't want competition from the incompetent and inexperienced to give everyone in the industry a bad reputation. License examinations probably keep some of the unfit out of the business. Examination requirements certainly raise the competence of applicants. And the threat of revocation persuades license holders to act responsibly. Everything considered, licensing is probably good for the remodeling industry.

The Sales Lead

Let's start this chapter by reviewing our discussion of leads in Chapter 2. You use a lead sheet to record facts about a prospective customer. Those prospects may come as a result of advertising or telemarketing, or they may just walk into your showroom. Remember to have your receptionist follow up to qualify and confirm the lead.

The Lead Log

Keep a log for your sales leads. Enter in your lead book the time, date, prospect's name, phone number, address, and type of work being considered. If possible, get the source of the lead (newspaper, direct mail promotion, etc.). You'll save advertising dollars if you keep good records of where your sales leads come from. When your sales reach the million dollar mark, you'll be committing $50,000 to $100,000 a year to advertising. You could be wasting a large part of that if your newspaper display advertising, for instance, isn't producing leads. You won't know that without an accurate tally.

Once you've logged and tallied the sales lead, pass it along to the sales manager. The sales manager in turn assigns the lead to a salesperson who calls on the potential customer.

Prepare the Estimate

Figure 11-1 is the first page of a form you use to update your prices before estimating a job. You'll notice that it contains the same index numbers as the Book Price List discussed in Chapter 5 (reproduced in Appendix C). You can use that as a guide to create your own estimating and price updating forms.

Notice there are *three* different forms you'll use in the estimating process. The Remodeler's Estimate List (Figure 11-1) is the one your estimator uses to update your Book Price List. The Unit Cost Price List contains the latest information from your Book Price List. It's the form the salespeople use in the field to sell a job. Appendix C also contains a copy of the entire Unit Cost Price List. Keep all three lists confidential — never show them to prospects, clients, or other outsiders. You may even consider limiting their distribution within your company.

Index No.	Category	Current Selling Price	Actual Cost	Change	Revised Selling Price
1.00	**GENERAL**				
1.01	Plans & specifications				
1.03	Models, renderings	ea			
1.05	Engineering				
	(2nd flr, + $)				
1.10	Soil testing				
1.15	Building permits	(%)			
1.16	Special permits				
1.26	Rentals — pumps, scaffolding	/hr			
1.32	Insurance — liability				
2.00	**DEMOLITION**				
2.01	Roof tearoff to ceiling line & cleanup	psf			
2.04	Stripping (shingles only)	psf			
2.06	Remove - 4" concrete slab	psf			
2.08	Remove - masonry wall	plf			
2.10	Remove - frame/stucco	plf			
	(Remove beam @ $8.00 plf)	plf			
2.12	Remove - bearing wall	plf			
2.14	Remove - nonbearing wall	plf			
2.16	Remove - stucco	psf			
2.20	Site cleanup	3% of project			
2.24	Equipment rentals	/hr			
3.00	**EXCAVATION**				
3.01	Footings - no concrete	plf			
3.05	Soil removal	cu yd			
3.24	Tree removal	/tree			
4.00	**CONCRETE**				
4.05	Concrete footings - including excavating, formwork, & pouring	plf			
4.06	Concrete footings - expansive soil re: 2nd floor	plf			
4.10	4" concrete slab no R.B.	psf			
4.12	6" concrete slab no R.B.	psf			
4.14	4" concrete aggregate slab no R.B.	psf			
4.20	Concrete 36" porch stairs	/trd			
4.22	Concrete 72" porch stairs	/trd			
4.30	Concrete porch deck 36" x 36"	ea			
4.40	Fireplace foundation	ea			
4.50	Wire mesh, internal 6 x 6 gauge	psf			
4.52	external 10 x 10 gauge	psf			

Figure 11-1 *Remodeler's estimate list*

Here's how to use the Remodeler's Estimate List:

1)   Under Current Selling Price, insert the latest price from your Book Price List.

2)   In the next column, Actual Cost, calculate your present labor and materials cost, plus overhead and profit.

3)   Put the difference between the first two columns in the Change column, and indicate whether the change is plus (+) or minus (-).

4)   Show only the prices that have changed in the Revised Selling Price column.

5)   Transfer the prices from the Revised Selling Price column into the Book Price List, and update the Unit Cost Price List.

Figure 11-2 is a filled out sample of the Remodeler's Estimate List, and part of the corresponding page from the Book Price List. "N/C" in the Revised Selling Price column means "no change."

Figure 11-3 is an example of a job I estimated using the Unit Cost Price List. You update that list every time you revise your Book Price List. That way your sales staff has the latest prices and can use this form in the field when they survey a job and prepare the initial estimate.

The Sales Contract

Refer back to Chapter 3 for details about writing contracts. Make sure all the blanks are completely filled out. Be sure the contract is signed and initialed where required by both parties. The sales manager should check the selling price against your book price. Have your estimator check them also. At this point, you'll know if the job was sold at par book price, over book price, or short book price.

If you discover an error or decide that the work can't be done for the contract price, there are several options. First, try for a "kicker." Get the prospect to agree on a higher price. Explain that the contract wasn't approved by the office manager and chief estimator because it omitted some important item. Either the contract price has to be increased or certain work has to be specifically excluded. Most owners will agree to compromise if there was a legitimate error in the estimate and contract. Not all, though.

Index No.	Category	Current Selling Price	Actual Cost	Change	Revised Selling Price
1.00	GENERAL				
1.01	Plans & specifications	400	400	⊗	N.C.
1.03	Models, renderings				
1.05	Engineering				
	(2nd flr, + $)				
1.10	Soil testing	(%)			
1.15	Building permits	(2 %)			N.C.
1.16	Special permits				
1.26	Rentals - pumps, scaffolding, etc.				
1.32	Insurance - liability				
2.00	DEMOLITION				
2.01	Roof tearoff to ceiling line & cleanup	2.00 psf	2.20	+ .20	2.20
2.04	Stripping (shingles only)	.50 psf	.45	− .05	.45
2.06	Remove - 4" concrete slab	1.80 psf	2.25		2.25
2.08	Remove - masonry wall	45.00 plf	54.00		54.00
2.10	Remove - frame/stucco	plf			N.C.
2.		plf			

Book Price List		
Index no.	**Category**	**Unit Price**
1.00	GENERAL	
1.01	Plans & specifications	400.00 each
1.03	Models, renderings	400.00 each
1.05	Engineering (for 2nd, add $500 -750)	/bid
1.10	Soil testing	/bid
1.15	Building permits	2% of project
1.16	Special permits	2% of project
1.26	Rentals - pumps, scaffolding, etc.	300.00 min
1.32	Insurance - liability	2.5%
2.00	DEMOLITION	
2.01	Roof tearoff - to ceiling line & cleanup	2.00 psf
2.04	Roof stripping (shingles only)	.50 psf
2.06	Removal - concrete slab - 4" thick	1.80 psf
2.08	Removal - exterior wall - masonry	45.00 plf
2.10	Removal - exterior wall - frame/stucco	35.00 plf

Figure 11-2 *Book price list*

UNIT COST PRICE LIST

Name _____ Contract no. _____

Address _____ Job no. _____

City _____ Date _____

Phone _____ Prepared by _____

No.	Items	Qty	Unit	Cost	Amount
1.00	**GENERAL**				
1.01	Plans & specifications		each	400.00	$
1.03	Models, renderings		each	400.00	$
1.05	Engineering		/bid		$
	(2nd flr, + $)		/bid		$
1.10	Soil testing		/bid		$
1.15	Building permits		project	2%	$
1.16	Special permits		project	2%	$
1.26	Rentals — pumps, scaffolding, etc		min	300.00	$
1.32	Insurance —liability		project	2.5%	$
2.00	**DEMOLITION**				
2.01	Roof tearoff to ceiling line & cleanup	570	psf	2.00	$ 1,140 —
2.04	Stripping (shingles only)		psf	.50	$
2.06	Remove - 4" conc. slab		psf	1.80	$
2.08	Remove - masonry wall		plf	45.00	$
2.10	Remove - frame/stucco		plf	35.00	$
	(Remove beam @ $8 plf)		plf		$
2.12	Remove - bearing wall		plf	35.00	$
2.14	Remove - nonbear wall		plf	33.00	$
2.16	Remove - stucco, plaster		psf	.80	$
2.20	Site cleanup		project	3%	$
2.24	Equipment rental		hr	55.00	$
3.00	**EXCAVATION**				
3.01	Footings - no concrete		plf		$
3.05	Soil removal		cu yd		$
3.24	Tree removal		tree	100.00	$
4.00	**CONCRETE**				
4.05	Conc. ftgs. - incl. excavating, formwork, & pouring		plf	22.00	$
4.06	Conc. ftgs - expansive soil re: 2nd floor		plf	35.00	$
4.10	4" conc. slab no R.B.		psf	5.00	$
4.12	6" conc. slab no R.B.		psf	7.00	$
4.14	4" conc. aggr. slab no R.B.		psf	7.00	$
4.20	Conc. 36" porch stairs		/trd	50.00	$
4.22	Conc. 72" porch stairs		/trd	65.00	$
4.30	Conc. porch-deck 3" x 36"		ea	200.00	$
4.40	Fireplace foundation		ea	400.00	$
4.50	Wire mesh, int. 6x6 ga		psf	1.00	$
4.52	ext. 10x10 ga		psf	1.50	$
4.60	Reinforcing bars		plf	2.00	$
4.70	Conc. underpin/corner		ea	220.00	$
4.72	Drain tile		psf	4.00	$
COLUMN 1 SUBTOTAL					$ 1,140 —

No.	Items	Qty	Unit	Cost	Amount
4.80	Vapor barrier		ea	75.00	$
4.86	Concrete pumping		min	250.00	$
4.92	Concrete cutting/coring		ea	250.00	$
5.00	**MASONRY**				
5.01	Fireplace - shingle story: masonry/raised hearth/6' mantle/8' brick veneer		ea	3500.00	$
5.10	Brick veneer		psf	21.00	$
5.20	Stone veneer		psf	24.00	$
5.30	Stone veneer - precast		psf	21.00	$
5.40	Pre-engineered fireplace - single story: raised hearth/6' mantle/8' brk vnr.		ea	2850.00	$
	2nd floor as above add			1000.00	
5.50	Fireplace hearth		plf	77.00	$
5.54	Mex-tile		psf	22.00	$
5.70	Ceramic tile - std gr.		psf	20.00	$
5.72	Ceramic tile - designer gr.		psf	24.00	$
5.80	Raise existing chimney		plf	325.00	$
6.00	**CARPENTRY**				
6.01	Subflr., - joists, 5/8 T&G ply, R-9 insul.	570	psf	5.50	$ 3,135 —
6.04	Underlayment, 1/2" plywood		psf	1.25	$
6.10	Insulation, R-11		psf	.80	$
6.12	R-19		psf	1.30	$
6.14	R-30		psf	1.80	$
6.20	Decking-treated jst/dckg		psf	8.80	$
6.30	Handrails		plf	20.00	$
6.32	Railing - std. wrt iron		plf	22.00	$
6.40	Wall system - Studs/R-11/paperwrap		plf	27.50	$
6.42	Studs/R-11/alum/drywall		plf	88.00	$
6.44	Studs/R-11/brk/drywall		plf	165.00	$
6.46	Studs/R-11/3/8 ply sheer/plyw		plf	38.50	$
6.48	Studs/R-11/stucco, drywall	106	plf	88.00	$ 9,328 —
6.50	Studs/R-11/stone, drywall		plf	190.00	$
6.52	Partitions-studs/plates only	85	plf	20.00	$ 1,700 —
6.54	Cut opening - window/door, lintel incl		ea	220.00	$
6.56	Stairs-open tread: plywood		/cs	400.00	$
6.58	Closed raisers: plywood	1	/cs	550.00	$ 550 —
6.60	Stairs-open tread: plywood		/trd	35.00	$
6.62	Closed risers: plywood		/trd	40.00	$
6.66	Roof tie-in: flashing	1	ea	350.00	$ 350 —
COLUMN 2 SUBTOTAL					$15,063 —

Figure 11-3 *Unit cost price list*

No.	Items	Qty	Unit	Cost	Amount
6.68	Roof system - gable, hip-shed, rafters, joists/ply shtg/R-30/composition/shingles or built-up *27x40*	*840*	psf	8.80	$ *7,392 -*
6.70	Roofing - shingles		psf	2.00	$
6.72	Roofing - wood shakes		psf	4.00	$
6.73	Roofing - wood shakes - fire retardant		psf	6.60	$
6.74	Roofing - tile		psf	7.70	$
6.75	Roofing - hot, blt-up, or cold		psf	1.65	$
6.76	Siding - redwood		psf	6.50	$
6.77	Siding - T-111 (ply sht)		psf	2.75	$
7.00	**INTERIOR FINISH**				
7.01	Drywall - standard wall	*1360*	psf	2.00	$ *2,720 -*
7.03	Drywall - ceiling	*570*	psf	3.00	$ *1,710 -*
7.05	Drywall - textured ceiling		psf	1.95	$
7.07	Drywall - fireguard		psf	3.00	$
7.08	Drywall - boarding only/no tape/no finish		/panel	30.00	$
7.09	Drywall patching - 1 side, 1 opng		/opng	200.00	$
7.11	Plaster- standard wall		psf	4.00	$
7.13	Plaster - ceiling		psf	5.00	$
7.15	Plaster patching - 1 side, 1 opng		/opng	200.00	$
7.17	Insulation - blown		min	300.00	$
7.19	Suspended ceiling - Tec bar		psf	4.00	$
7.21	Floor covering - vinyl asbestos		psf	5.00	$
7.23	Floor covering - resilient sheet		/yd	12-30	$
7.25	Floor covering - indr/outdr carpets		/yd	16.00	$
7.25	Wood panels ($20 panel cost)		panel	80.00	$
7.29	Interior doors - H.C. with passage sets	*2*	ea	220.00	$ *440 -*
7.31	- S.C. with passage sets		ea	400.00	$
7.33	- Pocket slide		ea	100.00	$
7.35	- Bi-fold louvered	*4*	ea	120.00	$ *480 -*
7.37	Millwork - baseboard/casing/trim		plf	3.00	$
7.39	3.5" crown moulding		plf	4.00	$
7.41	Kitchen cabinet soffits		plf	20.00	$
7.43	– Illuminated soffits		plf	40.00	$
7.45	– Sunshine ceiling		psf	22.00	$
7.47	Open beams - structural	*30*	plf	55.50	$ *1,665 -*
COLUMN 3 SUBTOTAL					$ *14,407*

No.	Items	Qty	Unit	Cost	Amount
7.49	Open beams - false		plf	15.00	$
7.51	Kitchen cabinets - standard, - wall cabinets		plf	100.00	$
7.53	- Counter cabinets		plf	150.00	$
7.55	- Kitchen cabinets - custom		by quote		$
7.61	Counter tops - plastic lam. - self edge, splash	*4*	plf	90.00	$ *360 -*
7.63	- Ceramic tile		plf	80.00	$
8.00	**ELECTRICAL**				$
8.01	Duplex outlets	*7*	ea	60.00	$ *420 -*
8.03	Switches - standard	*3*	ea	60.00	$ *180 -*
8.05	Switches - 3 way	*1*	ea	120.00	$ *120 -*
8.07	Switches dimmer		ea	80.00	$
8.09	Light outlet	*4*	ea	60.00	$ *240 -*
8.11	Doorbell button		ea	60.00	$
8.13	TV jack		ea	60.00	$
8.15	Dishwasher hookup		ea	200.00	$
8.17	Garbage disposal hookup		ea	200.00	$
8.21	Range hookup		ea	300.00	$
8.23	Bathroom exhaust fan & switch		ea	250.00	$
8.25	Kitchen exhaust fan & switch		ea	450.00	$
8.41	Circuits - 110 V	*2*	ea	200.00	$ *400 -*
8.43	Circuits - 220 V		ea	300.00	$
8.44	100 amp panel - relocate or install		ea	1000.00	$
8.45	200 amp panel - relocate or install		ea	1400.00	$
8.46	Sidepanel		ea	250.00	$
8.47	Service head - extension		ea	380.00	$
8.48	Underground circuit - $200.00 min. ea		plf	12.00	$
8.55	Ground fault circuit interuptor		ea	250.00	$
8.57	Thermostat		ea	250.00	$
8.61	Floodlighting		ea	100.00	
8.63	Flourescent lighting 4'x2 tube		ea	200.00	$
8.65	Incandescent lighting		ea	90.00	$
8.67	Smoke detector	*2*	ea	110.00	$ *220 -*
8.71	Garage door electric opener		ea	400.00	$
8.81	Garage door remote opener		ea	100.00	$
9.00	**PLUMBING**				
9.01	Bathtub - standard grade	*1*	ea	800.00	$ *800*
COLUMN 4 SUBTOTAL					$ *2,740*

Figure 11-3 (cont'd) *Unit cost price list*

No.	Items	Qty	Unit	Cost	Amount
9.03	Toilet - standard grade	1	ea	800.00	$ 800 —
9.05	Washbasin - standard grade	1	ea	800.00	$ 800 —
9.11	Color fixtures		ea	100.00	$
9.21	Bidet - standard grade		ea	800.00	$
9.23	Shower - fiberglass, curtain rod		ea	800.00	$
9.25	Shower - sliding doors		ea	200.00	$
9.27	Shower - corner swing door		ea	600.00	$
9.29	Kitchen S/S sink - single bowl		ea	800.00	$
9.31	Kitchen S/S sink - double bowl		ea	900.00	$
9.33	Shower head over bathtub		ea	250.00	$
9.35	Faucets		ea	125.00	$
9.37	Bar sink		ea	800.00	$
9.43	Laundry tray		ea	350.00	$
9.45	Washer standpipe		ea	250.00	$
9.51	Garbage disposal hookup		ea	200.00	$
9.53	Hot water heater		ea	800.00	$
9.55	- enclosure for heater		ea	300.00	$
9.57	Sewer line - $250.00 min.		plf	35.00	$
9.59	Water line - $500 base plus		plf	30.00	$
9.71	Gas line		plf	30.00	$
9.81	Vent stack - 14' H for single story	24	plf	30.00	$ 720 —
9.91	Medicine cabinet - standard	1	ea	100.00	$ 100 —
9.92	Tissue holder/bath curtain rod	1	set	50.00	$ 50 —
10.00	**EXTERIOR FINISH**				
10.01	Stucco		psf	4.50	$
10.05	Siding - vinyl or aluminum		/sq	480.00	$
10.09	- Cedar		/sq	560.00	$
COLUMN 5 SUBTOTAL					**$ 2,470**

No.	Items	Qty	Unit	Cost	Amount
10.21	Stone veneer		psf	30.00	$
10.25	Brick veneer		psf	16.00	$
10.31	Roofing - asphalt shingles - 235#		/sq	180.00	$
10.33	Spanish tile		/sq	600.00	$
10.35	Cedar shake		/sq	400.00	$
10.41	Windows - aluminum frame - anodized		UI	2.25	$
10.43	- Aluminum picture 60 united inches	372	UI	3.50	$ 1,302 —
10.47	- Wood frame		UI	7.30	$
10.49	- Glass - replace fixed		UI	3.50	$
10.51	Doors - S.C. with locksets	1	ea	600.00	$ 600 —
10.53	- Patio - aluminum sliding to 6' wide		ea	600.00	$
10.55	- Patio - wood sliding to 6' wide		ea	1,000.00	$
10.61	Gutters with downpipes - aluminum		plf	10.00	$
10.65	Fascia boards - aluminum		plf	5.00	$
10.67	Garage doors - std. 8'		ea	600.00	$
10.69	Garage doors - std. 16'		ea	900.00	$
10.71	Weatherstripping		/door	40.00	$
10.73	Window screens		ea	55.00	$
11.00	**HVAC**				
11.09	Air conditioner			inquire	$
11.21	Gas furnace - wall type		ea	1500.00	$
11.31	Thermostat		ea	200.00	$
11.41	Sheet metal work - ducts: $20/run mi	30	plf	40.00	$ 1,200
COLUMN 6 SUBTOTAL					**$ 3,102 —**

Notes

    * VERY GOOD PROSPECT

    DO NOT USE HIGH PRESSURE

    PROJECT PROFESSIONAL IMAGE!

Figure 11-3 (cont'd) *Unit cost price list*

Size

Width _____ lf

Length _____ lf

Area _____ sf

Subtotals

Column 1 $ *1,140 -*
Column 2 $ *15,063 -*
Column 3 $ *14,407 -*
Column 4 $ *2,740 -*
Column 5 $ *2,470 -*
Column 6 $ *3,102 -*

TOTAL $ *38,922*
Contingencies $ *3,892*
Sales tax $ *0*

TOTAL $ *42,814 -*
Escrow fee $ *0*

TOTAL $ *42,814 -*

_____ % interest

Approximate monthly

Payment $_____ Years _____

Notes

Quoted $ 46,800 -

Figure 11-3 (cont'd) *Unit cost price list*

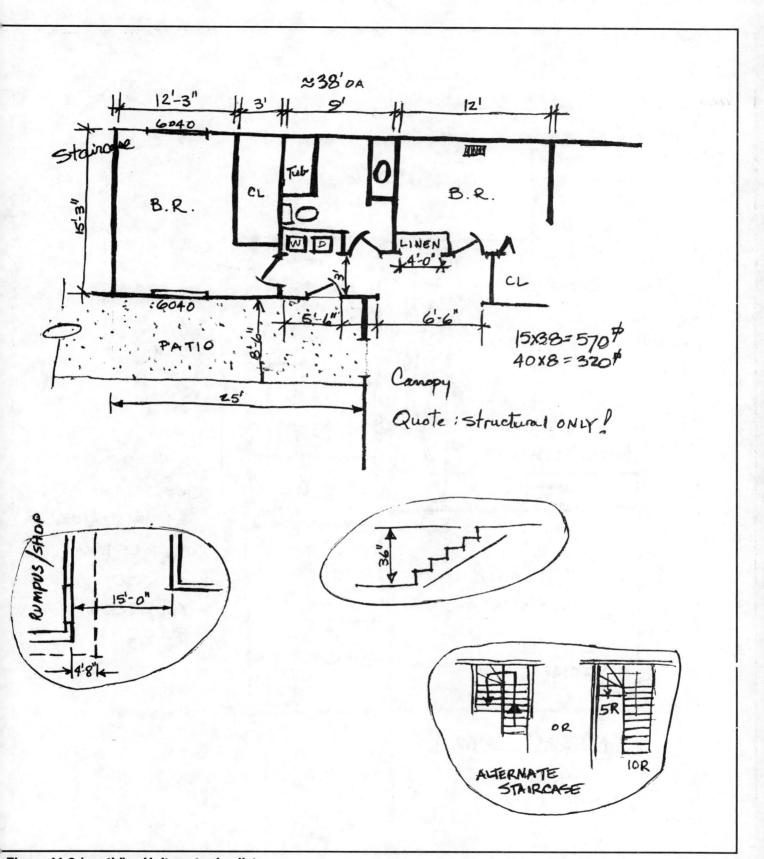

≈38' OA

12'-3"   3'   9'   12'

6040

Staircase

15'-3"

B.R.

CL

Tub

W D

B.R.

LINEN
4'-0"

CL

6040

PATIO

8'-6"

5'-6"   6'-6"

25'

15×38=570
40×8=320

Canopy

Quote: structural ONLY!

RUMPUS/SHOP

15'-0"

4'-8"

36"

ALTERNATE
STAIRCASE

5R

OR

10R

Figure 11-3 (cont'd)   *Unit cost price list*

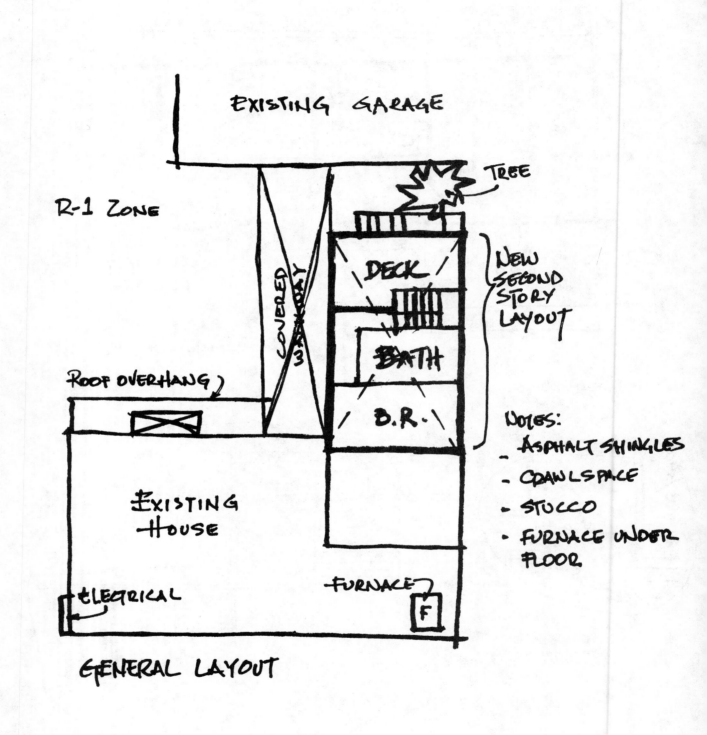

Figure 11-3 (cont'd) *Unit cost price list*

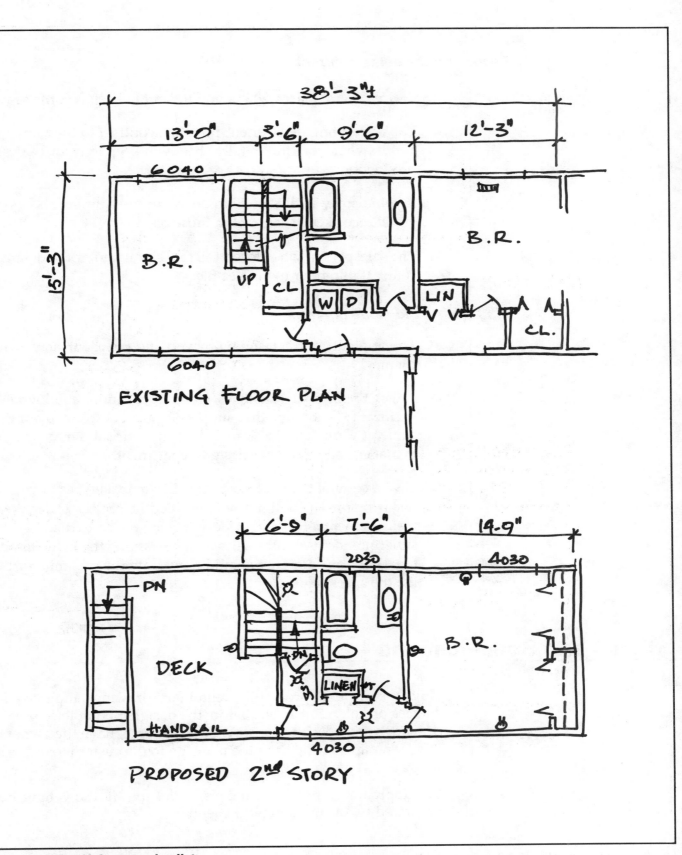

EXISTING FLOOR PLAN

PROPOSED 2ND STORY

Figure 11-3 (cont'd) *Unit cost price list*

Recording the sales contract

There are several places where you'll want to keep records of your sales.

■ The accounting department posts the contract to the sales journal and to whatever kind of tally sheet you keep to record sales production.

■ If you display a sales bulletin board, or are running a sales contest, you'll record each contract in those places.

■ The salesperson who closed the sale should enter the details of the contract into their own sales file.

Distributing the sales contract

■ The original contract, signed by you and the client, stays with the client.

■ Attach the estimate, sketches, credit application, employment verification and any other supporting papers to a copy of the contract. Circulate that information to your sales manager, finance manager, estimator, and design department.

■ Give a copy of the Unit Cost Price List and sketches to your design department. The designer will inspect the project and make detailed measurements. Have your design chief, the construction superintendent and the salesperson examine the field survey together. Your designer should now draw the preliminary plans and list the specifications.

Plans and Specifications

Have the owner approve the preliminary drawings and make final choices on color, finish, etc. before the designer completes the working drawings and specifications. At the same time, have the owner also sign any loan papers. Copies of the plans go to the customer and to a lender, if one is involved.

You apply for permits after the plans and specifications have been approved by the owner and the lender.

Figure Actual Job Costs

Order materials, make labor cost estimates and get quotes from your subcontractors.

Here's a hint: If your superintendent's files contain prices, show your exact costs for labor and materials, and the prices "as quoted" by the subtrades. If your superintendent knows you've allowed extra for a sub's part of the job, he might pass that information along. The sub might then find a way to increase his billing, knowing you won't lose anything on the deal.

Figure the Sales Commission

Prepare the most accurate estimate possible from the construction plans and specs. I call this the *selling price breakdown*. If the salesperson omitted anything in the original bid, you'll find it when detailed construction plans are drawn. Sales commissions should be based on this selling price breakdown.

Daily Job Inspections

The superintendent's job file should have the plans, specifications, permits, costs, contract copies, work schedules, and roster of workers and list of subs on the job. The superintendent will need this information when making daily job inspections.

Each time a superintendent inspects a job, they make notes on the Job Progress Report (Figure 11-4). The project manager and owner can see at a glance how the job is coming by checking this report. You can also use this form to check on the superintendent's work.

If work is behind schedule, have your superintendent make a note of it, and explain why. He should also show what steps he's taking to get the job back on track. Use the form to record everything — meetings with owners, architects, engineers, and inspectors, complete with their names. List any visitors to the site as well. That would include salespeople soliciting business or delivering quotes, subs looking for work, and even casual visitors touring the site.

Design the form in duplicate so the superintendent can turn one in to the office each day, with another for his files.

JOB PROGRESS REPORT

Job no._____   Report no._____
Name_____   Date:_____
Project: _____   Weather:_____
Location: _____
Job tel. no.: _____

Work performed by General Contractor: _____

Work performed by subcontractors: _____

Other activities: _____

Comments: _____

Superintendent

Category	No. of workers	
	General	Subcontractor
Foreman - carpenter		
Carpenters		
Carpenter - helpers		
Laborer		
Concrete		
Masons		
Tilesetters		
Steel workers		
Plasterer		
Electricians		
Plumbers		
Drywallers		
HVAC workers		
Painters		
Glaziers		
Total		
Equipment:		

Figure 11-4 *Job progress report*

Extra Work Orders and Change Orders

Construction is too complex to anticipate every problem before work begins. And it's too expensive to do it over if you don't like the first try. That's why changes are inevitable. You can expect plan changes or extra work on every job. That's the remodeling business. So instead of resisting changes, welcome them. They're part of your job, so relax and enjoy it.

But here's the important point. Changes and extra work aren't at your expense. They're at the owner's expense. And you're going to make an appropriate charge for every change the owner requests. You're happy to make the change, if the owner agrees on your price and your schedule, and if the owner is willing to sign the change order.

Making changes under any other circumstances is foolish. You're almost sure to have a dispute over the cost and may have to sue to collect. Assume that you'll get paid for extra work if, and only if, you can present a signed work order showing the amount due.

Here's another potential problem. I had an owner tell my superintendent to install a left-hand-opening door instead of the right-hand-opening door shown in the drawings. No problem. There wouldn't be any extra charge because the door hadn't been ordered yet. I gave the O.K. to make the change without a signed change order. When the job was completed a month later, the final payment came in a thousand dollars short. The owner now claimed the wrong door was installed. As long as that part of the job didn't agree with the plans and specs, he felt justified in holding back $1,000. I begged the owner to remember that he specifically requested the change to a left-hand-opening door. The owner didn't remember any such thing.

Consider extra work and changes as additional contracts and treat them that way. Write down all details, specifications, prices, and payment terms no matter how minor the change. Insist that your customer sign all change orders. If the order's not in writing, you don't do the work.

Extra Work — Owner Optional

Price extra work without any discount. Don't cut prices just because it's extra work on an existing contract. Collect in advance if you can, or get a deposit and an agreement for payment in full when the extra work is completed.

Extra Work — Mandatory

Sometimes you'll have the building inspector or fire inspector demand extra work on a job. The owner has to comply. These mandatory changes aren't the contractor's financial responsibility since the building department approved the original plans and issued permits based on them.

I'm not recommending it, but some remodeling contractors quote prices considerably higher than they expect to collect for extra work. That gives them room to compromise when an owner offers less than you request. You can split the difference, make your 50 percent on the change and still maintain the owner's good will.

Bill for mandatory extra work the same as for extra work the owner has requested. If the owner won't pay before extra work begins, insist on payment when the extra work is completed. You always want the proportion of cash received to date to exceed the proportion of work completed to date.

For a large job, you'll probably have weekly payment draws. If the owner can't pay before you complete the extra work, have the owner secure the amount with a note and deed of trust or mortgage. This way, if the owner defaults on the note, you can threaten foreclosure. With a mortgage or trust deed you're guaranteed payment eventually. On sale of the property your lien will appear on the title report. The new owner will insist that the lien be cleared before title passes.

There's another way to deal with mandatory extras when the owner can't afford them. Try a trade-off in the contract. The owner may be willing to accept a less expensive floor covering or give up the concrete patio in exchange for installing what the inspector requires. Trade-offs like this are seldom equal, though. There's usually a balance due either you or the owner. Figure 11-5 shows an example of an unequal trade-off.

Insist on written change orders for your subcontractors too, whether extra costs are involved or not. Figure 11-6 is an example of an Extra Work and Change Order.

Issuing Subcontracts

If your company is like mine, you hire subcontractors to do a lot of the work. Be sure your contracts with them are in writing. Insist that they submit written bids that describe the work and the cost to you.

When you're trying to sell a job, you'll often use a sub's standard price or get a price quote over the phone. But get written confirmation from the sub without delay when you close the sale. Of course, it's always

Extra Work Order

	Charge	Credit
) Delete entry tile work		$300.00
) Reduce two 8' sliding glass doors to 6'		300.00
TOTAL		$600.00
) Supply and install 80 SF fireproof cedar shingles	$720.00	
) Supply and install 1 GFI	100.00	
TOTAL	$820.00	
Amount due	$220.00	

Figure 11-5   Extra work order

better to get a written quote from a sub before submitting your price on any job. But it simply isn't practical to solicit dozens of small bids for a project you may never get. There are going to be some misunderstandings and occasionally some expensive surprises. But you should be able to anticipate most problems and still come out ahead.

A word of caution here: There's a fine line between subcontractors and employees. Both your state government and the federal government are very diligent about collecting taxes on wages paid to employees. But no withholding is required on payments made to subcontractors. Usually there's no problem if your subcontractors withhold taxes on wages paid to their employees. Even if your subcontractors are self-employed tradesmen, you won't have a problem if those tradesmen are reporting their income as wages, carry insurance and supervise their own work.

But if you're paying for materials, directing how the "sub" does the work and paying a lump sum for labor, that "sub" is probably an employee for state and federal purposes. You may be liable for taxes that should have been withheld. Both state and the federal governments may be a little slow in discovering what you owe. But they have very effective ways of collecting once your name shows up on their computer.

Some remodelers have "master" contracts with their regular subs. These agreements cover all present and future work. Contract clauses should require that they file a certificate of insurance with you and that they make no changes in the job except in writing. Each new job becomes an addition to the master contract. This saves having to prepare a whole new contract for each job.

Extra Work & Change Order

For:
To:

Project:	Date:
	Job no.

You are hereby authorized to make the following change(s) on the project named above:

Work under this work order shall be performed under the same terms and conditions as stipulated in the original contract.

Changes approved:	Original contract amount: $_____
	Change no.:_____ $_____
By:_____ OWNER	By:_____ CONTRACTOR

Figure 11-6 *Extra work & change order*

Don't assume that any subcontractor has adequate insurance. Get a certificate of insurance. Your subs should all have workers' compensation insurance and liability insurance. If a contractor's license is required, get the license number. Call the license board to be sure the sub is in good standing with your state. In some states it's a misdemeanor, or even a felony, to use unlicensed contractors. The burden is on the general contractor to determine the legitimacy of their subs.

Subcontract Forms

In Chapter 4, we discussed contracts between you and your customer. Many of the same contract terms apply to contracts you have with subs.

Beware the so-called "standard" contract, particularly if you're working as a subcontractor yourself. A "standard" contract you sign today may be quite different from one you signed a few months ago, even though they look about the same. You won't know unless you read it carefully. There's no such thing as a standard contract that's suitable for everyone in every situation.

Long form subcontract blanks are available from the American Institute of Architects and the Associated General Contractors of America. They're several pages long and are generally considered fair to both the owner and the contractor. To order these forms, look in the Yellow Pages for your local contractor's association, or call or write the following:

American Subcontractors Association
1004 Duke Street
Alexandria, VA 22314
(304) 684-3450

Remodelers Council
National Association of Home Builders
15th & M Streets, NW
Washington, DC 20005
(800) 368-5242, ext. 463, or (202) 822-0463

Some associations require that you be a member before they'll sell you their forms. Others will be only too happy to sell to you, but they may charge more for non-members.

You can get short form construction subcontracts from many better stationery stores. Some favor the contractor and some favor the subcontractor. Don't use one of these forms unless you understand what the terms mean and are satisfied that it protects you. Using a form you don't understand isn't much better that relying on a verbal contract.

Be sure any subcontract you use includes "hold-harmless" or indemnity clauses that require the sub to reimburse the owner or prime contractor for losses due to the sub's negligence. Figure 11-7 is an example of a subcontract agreement that favors the prime (general) contractor.

Bills from Subcontractors

Set up a system to pay subcontractor's bills promptly. As soon as they're received, date stamp them and forward them to the job superintendent for approval. The superintendent approves the bills only if the work has in fact been done satisfactorily and according to the specifications.

Have your subcontractors bill each job individually and supply properly completed lien releases. Let them know how many copies you require of their bills.

The Job Cost Record

Have your accounting department keep a running tally of each job. When you pay bills related to a job, record the amount on the job cost sheet. Figure 11-8 shows a filled out Job Cost Sheet. Figure 11-9 is a blank copy for your use.

The "Marketer" space is for the name or initials of the telemarketer who made the original contact with the client. The "Rep" is the person who sold the job. These spaces identify who gets the commissions.

List your actual costs in the top section headed, "Book Price - Cost - Actual." Show who you paid, how much, the check number and the date. The last three lines in that section are employees. I show the check number for reference only, because the amounts shown are gross wages. The actual paychecks are for less after deductions, but the gross salary is what comes out of my pocket.

Don't overlook the workers' comp section. The amount you pay can be significant. In my case, it's 20.34 percent of gross wages.

The total of the "Amt. Extd" column is $2,330.92, but for the rest of the figuring, I rounded that to $2,331.

Just below the Total is a box to calculate your ideal selling price. I use a markup factor of 2.2. That's the amount it takes to cover profit and overhead. Multiply cost by 2.2 to get $5,128.20. The difference between the contract price and the ideal selling price is the amount over book,

AGREEMENT BETWEEN PRIME CONTRACTOR & SUBCONTRACTOR

Goodguys Remodeling Company

Date: _____

Name _____ Phone _____

Job Name _____ Address _____

Job Address _____ _____

City, State, Zip _____ _____

The Subcontractor shall furnish all labor and materials necessary to complete the work described below according to the specifications and/or plans, and the prime contract between the Prime Contractor and the Subcontractor, namely

Plans/Contract Description

Description of Work: _____

_____

_____

_____

_____

_____

_____

Subcontract Price:

The Subcontract price is ($ _____) Dollars

which includes, but is not limited to, the cost of all required permits, inspections, insurance, workers' compensation, and taxes.

The Subcontractor shall apply to the Prime Contractor for progress payments on or before the _____ day of each month covering the work performed and the cost of the materials installed at the site in proportion to the subcontract price.

The Prime Contractor shall hold back _____ percent pursuant to the Mechanic's Lien Act, with the balance due and payable within _____ days after the completion date. Holdback money shall become due and payable only in accordance with the Mechanic's Lien Act

Commencement of Work Schedule:

The Subcontractor shall perform the work in accordance with the schedule provided by the Prime Contractor. The Prime Contractor may make reasonable adjustments on the work during the course of construction. The Subcontractor's work shall be deemed to be substantially complete when approved in writing by the Prime Contractor.

_____ _____
Prime Contractor   Lic.No.   Subcontractor   Lic. No.

_____ _____
Signature   Signature

Figure 11-7 *Agreement between prime contractor and subcontractor*

TERMS & CONDITIONS

1) **Prime Contractor's Right To Do Work**. If the Subcontractor fails to perform any provisions of the subcontract, the Prime Contractor shall notify the Subcontractor in writing of the default with instructions to make corrections within three working days. If the Subcontractor fails to correct the default, the Prime Contractor may, without prejudice to any other right or remedy it may have, correct the default and deduct the cost thereof from the payment then or thereafter due to the Subcontractor. If the cost of the default exceeds the amount due, the difference shall be paid to the Prime Contractor by the Subcontractor within 20 days after correction of the default.

2) **Delays**. If there are delays in the performance of the Subcontractor's work by any cause that the Prime Contractor determines justifiable, the subcontract schedule shall be extended for such reasonable time as determined by the Prime Contractor.

3) **Right of Termination**. The Prime Contractor may, by giving three days written notice, terminate this subcontract if the Subcontractor: (i) is adjudged bankrupt or makes a general assignment for the benefit of creditors; or (ii) if a trustee in bankruptcy is appointed; or (iii) refuses or fails to supply sufficient and properly skilled workmen or workmanship, materials or construction machinery and equipment, for the scheduled performance of the work; or (iv) fails to make payments to its trades, suppliers, or workmen; or (v) persistently disregards laws or regulations, or the Prime Contractor's reasonable instructions; or (vi) otherwise violates the provisions of this subcontract.

Upon termination of this subcontract, the Prime Contractor shall: (i) withhold further payments; and (ii) take possession of any materials, use the construction machinery and equipment, subject to the rights of third parties, and complete the work to be performed hereunder by whatever means the Prime Contractor considers expedient without undue delay or expense.

4) **Warranty**. At the Subcontractor's own expense, the Subcontractor shall correct any defects or deficiencies in the work due to faulty materials and/or workmanship appearing within a one year period after the completion of the project. The Subcontractor shall correct and/or pay for any damage to other work resulting from corrections required. The Prime Contractor shall serve written notice to the Subcontractor within a reasonable time after discovery of any defects or deficiencies. The Subcontractor shall indemnify and hold harmless the Prime Contractor from claims, losses, costs, damages, suits or proceedings by third parties arising from or attributable to the Subcontractor's performance.

5) **Insurance**. The Subcontractor shall provide and maintain in full force and effect workers' compensation insurance and comprehensive liability insurance in amounts as required under either the Prime Contractor's contract with the owner of the project, or as determined as adequate by the Prime Contractor.

6) **Changes or Extra Work**. The Prime Contractor may make changes such as altering, adding to, or deleting from the work, and adjusting the subcontract and price accordingly. The Subcontractor shall make no change without a written change order or extra work order from the Prime Contractor.

7) **Cleanup**. The Subcontractor shall remove all of their own waste materials from the site each day. A charge or chargeback for cleanup costs from monies due the Subcontractor shall be made for failure to satisfactorily perform these functions.

After this subcontract is complete, the Subcontractor shall remove all surplus materials, tools, machinery, equipment, waste materials and debris, and leave the site in a clean and tidy condition to the satisfaction of the Prime Contractor.

8) **Rejected Work**. Defective work from poor workmanship, defective materials, or damage through neglect or other acts or omissions whether incorporated into the work or not, which has been rejected by the Prime Contractor shall be promptly removed and replaced by the Subcontractor. Work damaged or destroyed by such removal or replacement shall be repaired promptly.

If determined by the Prime Contractor that it is not expedient to correct defective work or work not performed in accordance with the plans and specifications, the Prime Contractor may deduct from the subcontract price the difference in cost between the work done and that required in the plans and specifications.

9) **Entire Agreement**. This constitutes the entire agreement between the parties and supersedes all previous agreements, verbal or written, expressed or implied, statutory or otherwise.

10) **Arbitration**. If arbitration relating to the Subcontractor's work is begun, whether initiated by the owner or the Prime Contractor, such shall be held in accordance with the arbitration terms of the prime contract. Otherwise, any dispute shall upon delivery of a written demand by one party to the other(s), be referred to arbitration pursuant to the provisions of the Rules of the American Arbitration Association.

Special Provisions: _____
_____
_____
_____
_____
_____

Figure 11-7 (cont'd)   *Agreement between prime contractor and subcontractor*

JOB SHEET

CONFIDENTIAL

ame:	Contract no.:
dress:	Date:
	Contract amount: $

		Deposit: $_____ Draws:	Date:
lephone:			
arketer:	Rep:	Final: $	Date:

ork description:

Book Price — Cost — Actual

Labor & Materials	Price	Chk. no.	Date pd.	Amt. extd.	Workspace
	$			$	
	$			$	
	$			$	
	$			$	
	$			$	
	$			$	
	$			$	
	$			$	
	$			$	
	$			$	
	$			$	
rkers' comp	_____% x $_____		——>	$	

| | | | | Total | *$ |

Sales cost	Base	O/B x .5	Chk. no.	2.2 x *_____ = $_____
es rep.	$	$		$
nager				$
rketers				$
			Total	$
ras:				Cost total $
				$
		Volume this week $_____		_____% OH $
ort by:		Date:		Grand total $

Figure 11-8 *Job cost sheet*

JOB SHEET

CONFIDENTIAL

Name:	Contract no.:
Address:	Date:
	Contract amount: $
Telephone:	Deposit: $_____ Date: Draws:
Marketer: Rep:	Final: $ Date:
Work description:	

Book Price — Cost — Actual

Labor & Materials	Price	Chk. no.	Date pd.	Amt. extd.	Workspace
	$			$	
	$			$	
	$			$	
	$			$	
	$			$	
	$			$	
	$			$	
	$			$	
	$			$	
	$			$	
	$			$	
Workers' comp	_____% x $_____		——>	$	

Total *$

2.2 x *_____ = $_____

Sales cost	Base	O/B x .5	Chk. no.		
Sales rep.	$	$		$	
Manager				$	
Marketers				$	
			Total	$	

Extras:		Cost total $
		$
	Volume this week $_____	_____% OH $
Report by:	Date:	Grand total $

Figure 11-9 *Blank job cost sheet*

$521.80. That's the amount my sales people aim for — they get half of it as a bonus.

My sales rep gets 8 percent of the contract price, plus half the amount over book. The manager gets a flat 2 percent of the gross sale, and the telephone solicitor gets 1.5 percent.

In the small workspace, you can see my gross profit of $2,408.35. My net profit is that amount, less *overhead*, the amount it costs me for rent, utilities, insurance, taxes, and other expenses I have to pay to stay in business.

The Job Log Book

Have your superintendents keep a separate log book or journal for each job. Pages of the log book should be stitched or glued and numbered, not loose leaf or spiral bound. Make it a policy that pages never be torn out. This way you won't lose information, and people can't alter or cover up facts.

Your superintendent should record in the job log anything that might be important later: delivery of materials, work completed each day, conversations with the owner, even trivia like a helper's cut finger. Check the log book regularly to keep track of what's going on. When the job is finished, keep the log in the permanent job file. You might need it later as evidence if there's a problem or a threatened lawsuit.

The Monthly Job Summary

Make a summary report every month of the work completed the previous month. Show the gross margin on each job and compare estimated to actual costs. If costs are exceeding estimates, you know it's time to make changes in your price book, adjust your markup, revise subcontractor costs, or change sales techniques.

Billing Your Customer

Keep current with your progress billings to customers. This is especially important for cost plus contracts. Keep the owner informed about work in progress and costs to date. Submit invoices regularly. Don't surprise the owners and they won't surprise you.

When you do cost plus work, be completely open about job costs. Furnish invoices, time sheets, receipts and charges with your itemized statement. Show your margin, the "plus" in cost plus contracts, as a separate item. Make copies of all documents for your file. The originals go to the owner to prove you haven't tampered with the invoices or records. And remember, pass along any discounts to the owner.

Your Facilities and Equipment

Here are a couple of tips to make your in-house procedures run more efficiently and profitably. First of all, a word about inventory. Unless your operation is highly specialized, don't carry any. It usually doesn't pay off to keep salvaged and surplus materials. Rental space, utilities, insurance and labor for handling material will cost more than what you save by storing materials.

Instead, return excess materials for credit. Sell off salvage materials, or just plain give them away. Don't fall in love with them and keep them around. I make an exception to this rule for some nails, 2 x 4s, or plywood at the back of my shop. A few odds and ends are handy if you have to make some quick repairs or handle insurance work. Just don't get carried away.

Keeping in Touch

Remodeling construction is a complex business. It requires good communications, both from your office to the site and from the site to your superintendent, wherever that superintendent may be. The faster information moves and the more reliable the means of communication, the better for you. I've found that pagers and cellular phones can more than pay their way. But you have to prevent unauthorized use of the equipment.

In the next chapter, I'll suggest ways an inexpensive personal computer can streamline your office procedures.

12

The High Tech Remodeler

Not long ago, the only office equipment most remodeling contractors needed was a typewriter and a filing cabinet. How times have changed. Now, even small offices have a telephone answering machine, copier, personal computer, and fax machine. Every piece of equipment adds power to your operation, but none so much as the computer.

Today, personal computers and sophisticated software packages are widely available and affordable. Many vendors offer programs designed especially for contractors: accounting, estimating, and scheduling. A computer can make both your office and on-site operation more efficient, saving you time and money.

Don't be intimidated by computers. You can learn to run a computer the same way you learned to drive a car. And if you get stuck, there are plenty of computer specialists out there, all eager (for a fee) to help. Public schools and community colleges offer quickie courses that can help you get started off right.

Contractors have been slow to jump on the computer bandwagon. But for those who learn to use it effectively, a computer can become as essential to your business as your skill saw or pickup truck. Your question shouldn't be whether to use a computer. Rather it should be how soon and what software to try. This chapter will help you answer those and other important questions.

Hardware

Until recently, you could make a mistake by buying a computer first and then trying to find the software that would do what you wanted to do. That's no longer a problem. There's so much software available today that no matter what application you have in mind, there's a program to fill your needs.

If you're starting from scratch, visit a few computer stores to see what's available.

Software

Software is the name for programs that run the computers. Software costs can run from under $100 for simple programs to thousands of dollars for sophisticated, advanced systems. Some programs are vital to a remodeling operation; others are just nice to have.

Choose your software carefully. Compare programs and look for unique and outstanding features. I'll usually spend a little more for a program with extra features. I won't use all the power right away. It takes weeks to get proficient in some of the more powerful programs. But when I need the features, I don't want to discover that they aren't available. Look for programs that will grow with your business, even if they're a little more complex.

You don't have to know how the engine in your car works to drive it. Neither do you have to be an electronics engineer to get the most from your computer. You just need some appropriate software and some time to learn to use it. Let's see what computer programs can do for you.

The Applications Software Library

Application programs are sets of instructions that tell the computer how to do a certain job. The first thing you have to do before you buy software is decide how you want to apply it. Make a list of the things you want to do. Decide what kinds of reports you want to produce. Assign priorities — which jobs are "musts" and which are less essential. The more detail you put into your wish list, the better your chances of finding the programs to do just what you need.

Your local computer store offers a wide variety of computer programs designed for business use. Ask for demonstrations of the programs that interest you most. Competition between software companies is as intense as competition in the remodeling business. Don't buy the first program you see. Consider carefully. Take some time to decide. You'll find elegant features in many programs, at no additional cost. All these features mean more power. And more power means more efficiency. And more efficiency means more profits. This is what attracted me. I've always been in favor of more profits, and if a computer is the way to do that, I'm all for it.

"Quick! Get our super on the phone!"

Don't start out with a full library of programs. Select one or two key programs at the beginning. When you've mastered those, consider others. As a rule of thumb, assume that you'll have to spend an hour learning each program for each $5 of purchase price. A program that costs you $100 is going to take you about 20 hours to learn. The more expensive the program, the more learning time you should allow.

Here's a brief rundown of some of the kinds of software you might consider. In each category, I've described a program and named one that I can recommend. Of course, new programs will have made this list obsolete before you read these words. But the descriptions that follow should give you a place to start.

Sales

One excellent sales support program is *Maximizer*. It helps salespeople organize their sales effort, reach more prospects and follow up their leads. Maximizer lets you store everything you need to know about your customers. It prompts you with reminders of appointments, and records your expenses. It will calculate payments, schedules, outstanding balances, and more from its payment analysis feature. You can keep a correspondence file and as many standard letters as you please. Get additional information from:

Richmond Software, Inc.
#420 - 6400 Roberts St.
Burnaby, B.C. V5G 4C9
Canada

Word Processing

Word processing programs have replaced the typewriter for nearly everything, even typing checks and envelopes. Nearly every business can use a word processing program. You use it for letters, manuals, reports and advertising materials.

Many word processing programs include outlining features that let you organize and restructure your ideas before you put them on paper. Most have a built-in dictionary (to check your spelling) and thesaurus (to help you find the word you're searching for). Most programs let you change type styles and type sizes to improve the way documents look. You can open several documents at once and copy text from one to another. That's handy when you're drawing up contracts. Some let you insert drawings and charts in your letters.

Microsoft Word is a good, powerful program backed up by a leading company in the personal computer field. But Microsoft Word is only one of literally hundreds of good word processing programs on the market today.

Microsoft Word
Microsoft Corporation
16011 NE 36th Way
Redmond, WA 98073-9717

Estimating

Word processing programs and the personal computer have replaced the typewriter in most business offices. But estimating programs haven't replaced the pencil and scratch pad on the desk of most estimators yet. Here's why.

First, keeping current material prices in the computer is a nuisance, even if you usually estimate only 300 or 400 different items. It's easier to call for prices when you need them rather than update the computer every time prices change. But if the program doesn't have current prices on file, what good is it? Of course, you can buy "current" cost data on disk from several publishers. But the price is usually high (more than $100 a month) and the costs are usually national average costs, not what your lumberyard or your plumbing subcontractor is charging.

Second, most computer screens are only 80 characters wide. That's a problem if you want to display each line of an estimate on an 80-character screen. You have only about 20 characters available to describe what you're estimating. The rest of the screen is needed to show the number of units, labor cost, material cost, equipment cost and total cost. How can you describe "1/2-inch water-resistant gypsum wallboard taped and textured on two sides" in 20 characters? In most estimating programs it comes out something like:

1/2" WR GYPBRD T&T2S

That may make perfect sense to you if you see those abbreviations every day. But it's probably Greek to both your prospect and the loan officer. For your estimates to be understood by anyone, you need the flexibility of a word processing program. You need room to describe exactly what's included in and excluded from the estimate. And I've never seen an estimating program that does that.

Still, many construction estimators are using computers to compile estimates — usually because they're both fast and because they don't make math mistakes (if you work carefully).

I see more applications for a computer in doing quantity take-off from plans than I do for price estimating. A digitizer that attaches to your computer can compute area or volume very quickly from where you lay a pointer on the plans. That's a big help if you do a lot of quantity take-offs. But most remodelers don't. And digitizers (with the software needed to run them) are usually more expensive than the computer itself.

Accounting

Even if you use an outside accounting service, a computer can improve the speed and accuracy of recording income and expenses. Basic accounting packages include general ledger, accounts payable, accounts receivable and payroll. Many also have inventory control, as well as sales and profit analysis. The functions are integrated so that one posting puts information into several files at once. You can have instant bottom line — immediate updates — fast reports and breakdowns. These programs are easier to set up and learn.

Computer Assisted Drawing

Sometimes called CAD or CADD, short for computer assisted drawing, or drafting, or design, or drafting and design, these all do the same thing — drawings. CAD can't design for you, but it can help you draw. Even if you can't draw, with a little practice you can make exquisite drawings with CAD packages. CAD packages are accurate in drawing to scale, and they're fast.

You can even get CAD software to do three dimensional drawings. Imagine, after you've done the floor plan and elevations of a room addition, or a new kitchen proposal, you can produce perspective drawings from different vantage points to show your customer what the proposed addition or remodeling will look like. Impressive? You bet. It's got me more than a few sales.

If drafting and design are a major part of your remodeling business, consider buying a CAD program. Prices begin at about $100. But note that the best CAD programs require faster, more expensive computers with a special math chip.

CAD programs are offered by many dealers. Most would be glad to give you a demonstration. You can get information and demo disks from:

American Small Business Computers, Inc.
118 South Mill Street
Pryor, OK 74361

or:

Sonnet Systems Ltd.
12151 Vulcan Way
Richmond, B.C. V6V 1J7
Canada

Project Management

Project management programs can help you schedule complex jobs to shorten the construction period. They do this by using the Critical Path Method to create a PERT chart. I'll explain more about scheduling in Chapter 13. If you handle larger jobs and are having trouble with scheduling, a management program may help. Most programs automatically update projects and schedules when you key in changes to any element.

Many programs analyze and level resource use, analyze risks and allow "what-if" studies. One vendor for project management programs is:

Time Line
Breakthrough Software
505B San Marin Drive
Novato, CA 94945

Decision Making

You don't *need* a computer to make decisions or solve problems. But decision-making programs can help pinpoint alternatives and organize your thinking. They use evaluation techniques like Monte Carlo analysis to get answers from inexact numbers. Linear programming finds optimum approaches to complex decisions. Decision trees evaluate and make tactical decisions. Risk simulation predicts results.

Computer programs don't guarantee you'll always come up with the right answer. They can't set goals, determine alternatives, assign weights or evaluate facts. You still have to do that. If you make poor judgments, no computer program can help you. However, if you're reasonable when you enter variables and predictions, you'll increase the odds in your favor.

Get more information from:

Confidence Factor
Simple Software, Inc.
2 Pinewood
Irvine, CA 92714

Computer programs are only tools. None are any better than the operator using them. And the more powerful the tool, the more experience the operator needs and the greater the risk if there's a mistake. Your local computer store isn't selling magic, just ways of helping you do a better job. You still have to do the work — and probably always will.

Fax Machines

Fax stands for "facsimile transmission." It's a way to send pictures over telephone lines. You feed sheets of paper with an image into the fax in your office and sheets of paper with the same image come out the fax at the destination. It's both fast and cheap. Many remodelers use fax to send drawings, lists, estimates, plans, and contracts quickly and cheaply. Fax machines have nearly eliminated the need for courier services. Of course, you still can't send checks by fax. But nearly everything else you can put on paper will go.

Basic fax machines are available for as little as $500. I recommend buying a fax machine with the latest functions. You can now get them with a built-in answering machine, telephone, copier and a switcher. The switcher lets you use only one telephone line for both fax operations and ordinary telephone calls. Without it, you'll probably need a separate phone line just for the fax.

How essential is a computer or a fax machine to remodelers? I suppose you can survive without them. Of course, you could also walk to the office from home every day and you could cut studs with a handsaw. But I don't know anybody that does. The computer is rapidly becoming just as necessary as the car and the power saw.

13

Scheduling Your Jobs

Scheduling is an important part of your remodeling business. You can schedule small jobs by instinct, but you'll need something more accurate and powerful for large projects. PERT (Program Evaluation Review Technique) and CPM (Critical Path Method) are tools you can use to design schedules that work.

The two techniques are practically the same, so I won't distinguish between them in the discussion that follows. Both systems help you make the best use of time when you plan a job.

PERT is especially suitable for major projects like the renovation of a large office building. But you can also benefit by using PERT for smaller projects, especially if your jobs keep slipping behind schedule and you're not sure why.

PERT Basics

Construction follows a certain order. You can't apply wallboard until the wall is framed. You know about how long each part of a job will take. A PERT schedule uses what you know about the order of construction,

ACCURATE REMODELERS

D.W.

"Ouch, he's right! It's right here on the chart. Whatchamacalit activity."

and how long each task takes, to organize the job so it's finished on time.

A PERT chart lets you see at a glance if work is on schedule while there's still time to make corrections. You can see which tasks are critical to meeting your deadline. And you can see where shortcuts are possible if the job falls behind schedule.

Each task is called an *activity* in PERT language. Installing cabinets is an activity, for example. Starting and completing an activity is called an *event*. The total of the longest sequence of events is the least time any job will take.

Plotting the Job

Begin plotting a job by listing all activities that make up the project. That might range from preparing the drawings to installing the appliances. I like to work backward from the end of the job, listing all the activities that have to be done to complete each event. Sometimes that's easier than starting from the beginning and trying to think of each activity that can start as each event is finished.

When you've listed every activity, plot them on paper. You'll create a graph (called a *network* in PERT) that shows each activity in its logical order. Every activity is represented by an arrow that points to the next activity, which can't begin until the first is completed. Look at Figure 13-1. There are seven activities leading to six events. Events 2, 3 and 5 can't begin until Event 1 is complete, and Event 4 can't begin until both 2 and 3 are done. Event 6 is dependent on Event 5, but independent of Events 2, 3 and 4.

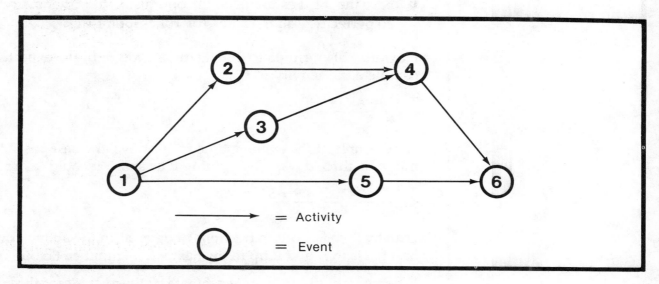

Figure 13-1 *A PERT network*

You can develop a mini network for each activity and then combine those into a master network for the entire job. You're not likely to have many remodeling jobs *that* complicated, however. You can schedule most remodeling jobs with just one network.

The network isn't drawn to scale. In other words, the length of the arrow doesn't indicate the length of time the activity will take. You'll label each arrow with the name of the activity and the number of days that activity will take. When that's done, you can calculate the total number of days needed to complete the project.

Estimating the Activity Time

There are two ways to find the time needed for each activity:

1) Make a single estimate for each activity, based on your past experience.

2) Use an average based on three estimates for each activity. This is what I do. Make your three estimates this way:

■ Estimate the average time it takes to complete the activity under normal conditions. Call that "Ta" for Time-average.

■ Make a pessimistic estimate, where everything that can go wrong will go wrong, barring a major disaster. That's "Tp" for Time-pessimistic.

■ Base the third estimate on the optimistic view that everything will go perfectly. Call that "To" for Time-optimistic.

Now use this formula to find Te (time-expected), the expected time to complete the activity:

$$Te = \frac{To + 4Ta + Tp}{6}$$

For example, if the average time is five days, the best possible time might be three days. If everything falls apart, it could take nine days:

$$Te = \frac{3 + (4 \times 5) + 9}{6} = 5.3 \text{ days}$$

Usually it comes out to fractions of days, as in the above example. Your best bet is to round it up to the next whole number. So our answer is 6.

Whether you use the single estimate or the average-of-three method depends on your experience and the size of your project. The single

".... And we'll get in some fishing during this slack time."

estimate is O.K. for simple jobs and new construction. On complicated remodeling jobs, averaging the three estimates is probably safer and more reliable.

Finding the Critical Path

Once you've estimated the time for each activity and drawn the network, find the *critical path*. Whenever two or more activities are scheduled simultaneously, one path will take longer than the others. That's the critical path.

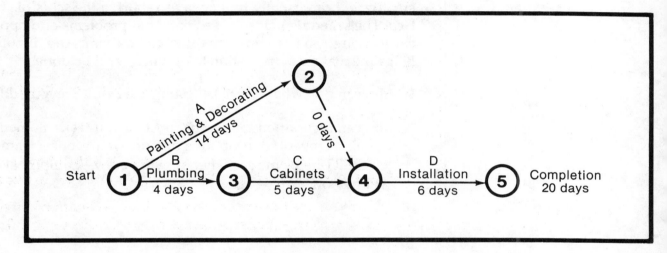

Figure 13-2 *PERT network showing a critical path*

Look at the completed network in Figure 13-2. The last activity is installing the appliances. That can't be done until the painting and decorating (Activity A), plumbing (Activity B) and cabinets (Activity C) are complete. Activity A is estimated to take 14 days. Activities B and C should take a total of nine days. Activity A then, is the critical path.

If A takes more than 14 days, and activity D can't be shortened to make up the difference, the builder misses the 20 day deadline. That's why it's critical. However, there's some *slack* in the path through Events 3 and 4. The slack is the difference between 14 days on the critical path and nine days on the other. There are five days slack (or "float" in PERT language). If the plumbing or cabinets are delayed a day or two, it won't affect the completion date at all.

Notice the dotted arrow between Events 2 and 4. It's there only to show the relationship between two activities. That's called a *dummy variable*.

It's an imaginary activity that doesn't require any time to complete, but prevents the beginning of an activity that follows it. Appliance installation can't begin until completion of painting and decorating, even if the plumbing and cabinets are finished.

PERT and Job Planning

I usually make a PERT diagram on larger jobs, especially when the owners will be in the home during construction. Every extra day of building is another day of agony for them. PERT forces me to think creatively. I can usually find a way to shorten the schedule by a day or two. The schedule helps me see potential problems and opportunities early enough so I can do something about them. And, if nothing else, it helps me make a better estimate of when we'll be done.

■ You can do "what-if" trials, testing the results several different ways.

■ You can focus attention on the most critical tasks. Sometimes it pays to pull a crew off one job for a day or two to concentrate on another job. PERT helps me see when moving crews, equipment or materials will pay off.

PERT and Production

I suggest recording the actual times needed to complete each activity as it's finished. If your network is up-to-date, predicting the final completion date should be easy. And you'll see delays (and probably cost overruns) quickly so you can make corrections while there's still time.

PERT Limitations

PERT isn't a substitute for good management. It's only a planning tool. For PERT to work effectively, the superintendent and project manager should have a chance to review the network and approve it before it's final. That means your superintendents and project managers need to know something about creating PERT charts. But I've found that a few minutes of explanation are all that's needed. The payoff can be worth many times the cost.

A Final Word

This book represents an ambitious undertaking on my part. I've tried to give you the benefit of my experience — in developing sales and promotional materials, in estimating, and in running a successful company.

Over the past twenty years I've helped many contractors get started in this business. They began by following my lead, then gradually they developed their own combination of business techniques that worked for their situations. Most are now successful remodeling contractors.

The information and advice I gave them was the same as I'm giving you in this book. The rest is up to you. Planning and managing a contracting company is a complex job. I know that not everything you'll ever need to know is covered here, but this book *can* be a valuable resource and guide to help you along the way. It's a tool to help you build and conduct a business in a professional manner. Contracting for excellence is an art, and you are the artist.

I wish I could share in your excitement as you move up in the business world and join the ranks of "successful" remodeling contractors. You can write me in care of the publisher, Craftsman Book Company, and perhaps we can exchange ideas or tell a few horror or success stories. The address is in the front of the book. I hope to hear from you.

Good Luck!

Appendix A

Homeowner's Survival Manual

Having the home you're living in remodeled is a dust-filled, inconvenient, stressful experience. Many homeowners balk at getting remodeling done just *because* of the mess and inconvenience. It's to your interest, as the person selling the remodeling, to reassure the customer that it won't be quite as bad as he may fear. And keeping the customer informed is probably one of the best ways. If he knows what is going to happen, he can be ready for it. One way to do this is with a pamphlet you can give your customer.

Here are some suggestions for a pamphlet you could use as a sales tool that a homeowner facing a remodeling project would welcome.

Begin with a covering letter something like the one on the next page.

Goodguys Remodeling Company

777 Main Street
Anytown, USA 90007

Dear Homeowner:

We are pleased you selected us to do the work on your property and appreciate your confidence in us. We will do our best to carry out the terms of the agreement to your satisfaction.

We've written this booklet to outline for you the various stages of remodeling construction, so you'll have a clearer understanding of what is going to happen, and be prepared for any inconvenience that is an unavoidable part of having your home remodeled. We know from experience that once it's all over, you'll be pleased with the result. But when the work is in progress, it can be trying, especially if you do not know what is involved beforehand.

This booklet is to help you understand the remodeling process. But booklets can't cover everything, and we're sure you'll have questions we've missed. So, if you need further information, just ask us. We'll be pleased to accommodate.

Sincerely,

Goodguys Remodeling Company

You can add more to the letter, but you need to keep it simple and short for it to be most effective.

In the booklet itself, include these subjects and elaborate as you see fit:

■ A brief description of the remodeling industry

■ How to prepare for the work

■ What happens after the contract is signed.

■ Anticipate customer complaints and answer them before they come up.

■ A look at the contractor's side. Explain it from the contractor's point of view.

If you produce a well-done publication of this sort, be assured you'll be one of the very rare ones, and will stand apart from "those other remodelers." This is another way to fine-tune your sales and public relations effort.

It isn't necessary for you to put everything that follows in your own publication. Add to it or change the wording to suit your own conditions. Consider some of the benefits that your company can gain from this piece.

1) You'll save the time your office staff might otherwise spend answering common, repetitive questions.

2) It's a way to help your own crews understand your operating philosophy.

3) It's a framework for consistency and fairness.

The following is a sample booklet. Use as much of it as you like.

The Remodeling Business

The remodeling business is still relatively new. It only became a recognized industry after the second world war. It wasn't so long ago when homeowners called a handyman or "jack of all trades" for improvements or repairs. His work wasn't cheap, and it usually took a long time.

Now, even the smallest remodeling contractor has to conduct his business just like any large corporation. He has to concern himself with cost control, scheduling, purchasing, payroll, workers' comp, contract and construction law, insurance, bonds, overhead, and more.

Our biggest challenge to giving you the best possible service is in finding and keeping competent and experienced personnel. Our business of remodeling and renovation work is harder than building from scratch. We usually have to demolish, blend in and build — all while you're living on the premises. Our goal is to do that with the least possible disruption of your comfort and lifestyle.

Each remodeling job is unique. All remodeling jobs are custom jobs. There is no other situation with the same conditions. Your project, be it large or small, is like no other.

Preparing for the Work

If you'll be living on the premises during your remodeling job, prepare in advance for inconveniences that may occur. By doing so, you'll be able to avoid frustrations, conflicts, and misunderstandings. The job will go much more smoothly.

1) Protect and cover your furniture and carpets that will be exposed in the work area. We'll make every effort to avoid damage to your property, but an easily-damaged item left where men are carrying in lumber and tools is at risk. It's necessary that you take the responsibility for protecting or removing such items.

2) Remove all pictures, artwork, mirrors, and drapes from the work area before work begins. Dust is an inevitable product of remodeling. It's far easier to take them out of the area than it is to try to clean the dust out of them later.

3) Remove, and put in safekeeping away from the work area, any valuables such as jewelry, cash, coin collections, etc. Our workmen are, to the best of our knowledge, completely honest. But it's possible that in the disruption of remodeling, a valuable item could be mislaid. If you remove everything valuable from the area, there's no risk, and no suspicion.

4) Arrange with our superintendent so crews have access to the work area between 8:00 a.m. and 5:00 p.m. Monday through Friday (and weekends by mutual

consent). Please note: If our workers can't gain access to the work area on a day it was arranged they should work, as much as a half-day of work may be lost as we move the crew to another job. The crew must still be paid, so you may be subject to a minimum charge of $100 each time this happens.

5) Our workers and subcontractors are instructed not to use the homeowner's tools, that is, hand tools, electric tools, ladders, hoses, wheelbarrows, and the like.

6) Remove from the work areas and access routes all plants and objects of value you wish to preserve.

7) Please secure your pets. Cats are by nature curious, and there have been cases of the animals being trapped inside wall and floor cavities they were exploring. Dogs will normally protect your house from strangers, and construction crews are strangers to them. We don't want any confrontations.

8) Check your homeowner's insurance policy for adequate coverage against all risks during construction.

Procedures

Once you've agreed to the details of your project, you'll receive a copy of your signed contract. Then the following will take place:

Funding

If you are financing the project yourself, you may be required to deposit the total contract price with an escrow company. If you need financing, we may be able to assist you. It can take several weeks to process a loan application, although credit approval may only take a few days.

Measuring the Job

After the contract is signed, expect our designer to visit your home to verify all measurements, inspect conditions, and reaffirm the intended work to be done and materials to be used.

Timing

Allow about ten days for a simple single-story addition, new kitchen, or bath remodeling. Allow about three weeks for a two-story addition. Times will vary for different jobs, of course, since it depends on the complexity, size, and other factors. We take pride in efficient scheduling though, and we're usually faster than our competition.

Review of Plans

After the drawings are complete, you'll be required to review them for final changes or any corrections. Design or drawing changes after your acceptance, regardless of extent, will be charged as "extra work," at the rate of _____, or a minimum charge of _____, whichever is greater.

Permits

(Include here a note about how long it takes to get building permits in your area, and any additional information unique to your situation.)

+ Some areas have local "homeowner's associations" which insist on approving any form of construction work. If you're located in such an area, allow extra time for this procedure.

+ Two-story projects can be complex and may require additional time to process. After reviewing the drawings with you, we may have to send the plans out for engineering. This can take an additional two or three weeks. Then the sealed drawings are sent to the city's building department and checked extensively. Expect an elapsed time of one to two months before receipt of the building permit.

+ Rest assured that we will honor the contract price despite any cost increases that occur during any permit delays.

Difficulties Homeowners Have Experienced

Our main reason for preparing this booklet was to forewarn you of some problems that might come up during your project and to help you prepare for them. Most homeowners haven't been through a remodeling project and don't really know what to expect. It's a messy, disruptive process, and it sometimes doesn't seem worth it until it's complete and you see how good it looks. Then you forget the mess.

Sometimes homeowners feel they're not receiving the service or quality of materials and workmanship they expected. Therefore, good communications is the key to clearer understanding and reasonable expectations. In no special order, here are answers to some of the more common misunderstandings:

Homeowner: Lumber and supplies were delivered and piled on our driveway. Now we can't get in or out of our garage.

Answer: It's illegal to leave materials on the sidewalk, boulevard, or street curb. So we usually have supplies unloaded on the driveway, unless you instruct us to put them on your lawn. We'll do this if you prefer, but piles of heavy lumber on your lawn may kill the grass underneath.

Homeowner: We haven't seen anyone on our job for three days. What's going on?

Answer: Our crews usually start a job and attack the project with zeal until completion. We lose money when a job drags on. But sometimes we have to wait for materials to arrive. For example, if the new stove you requested doesn't come from the factory when it should, we not only can't install it, but we may not be able to complete another part of the job, such as the countertops, because countertops are sometimes built *around* the stove. So if you miss the workmen on the job for a day, or two or three, it's because they are waiting for materials to arrive, or for something else to occur before they can proceed. When this happens, we'll try to have someone call you. We try to keep the homeowner informed.

Homeowner: We stayed home all day expecting your workers to come, but no one showed up.

Answer: Try and arrange for workers to have access to your property while you are away. To prevent wasted time and unhappy customers, our crews have to juggle schedules. If we're painting Mrs. Smith's kitchen in the morning, and figure we'll be done by noon, we'll schedule *your* kitchen painting for 1 o'clock. But what if a snag comes up at Mrs. Smith's? We can't leave her kitchen half-painted to come to your job on time. We have to finish. Of course, we'd extend you the same courtesy. So our crews can't always arrive on a job at a preset time, though we do try. If you want to talk about your job, please call our office and make an appointment with our superintendent or manager.

Homeowner: If your workers hadn't done things wrong, our bathroom would have been finished sooner.

Answer: I'd like to say our crews *never* mess up. But we don't walk on water. Sometimes mistakes happen. Believe me, when a mistake happens, while it inconveniences *you*, it *costs* me — sometimes a large part of my profit on a job. I am even more anxious to prevent mistakes than you are. But when a mistake on our part happens, we make every effort to correct it to your complete satisfaction and still finish the job in the time allowed by the contract.

Homeowner: Better supervision would reduce mistakes, wouldn't it?

Answer: That's true. If we had a superintendent full-time on every job, there would probably be no mistakes. But if we add the cost of that superintendent to your job, it would be far more than you'd want to pay. So we employ top-notch people to do our work, and have our superintendents and production managers look after fifteen to twenty jobs each. Actually, that's considered low (by one-half) in the industry. Most remodeling companies have only one supervisor for every *thirty* or *forty* jobs. Even then, we can't watch every worker every moment. We count on our people to do their jobs responsibly and well.

Homeowner: The finish stucco coat doesn't match the rest of our house.

Answer: As with painted siding, new color can't usually be made to *exactly* match the old color, even if the make and color coding is the same. The reason is simple. The old color has stood exposed to light and heat for many years and has oxidized. This changes the color or shade. However, the new color will probably "catch up" and match the existing shading after a period of time.

Homeowner: Your work failed to pass inspection. Is this because of poor workmanship?

Answer: Almost never. Inspectors often use their discretion in interpreting codes. One inspector may pass a certain phase of work, only to have another inspector cite it later. In any event, we don't dispute any points; we simply comply as requested.

Homeowner: Your workers ruined our lawn.

Answer: We need an accessible area in which to store raw materials and debris. This may have to be the lawn if no driveway is available. Concentrated traffic by our crews can also contribute to wear and tear on the lawn. We'll do our best to minimize any damage, but you may need to budget for lawn refurbishing once the project is complete.

Homeowner: Why don't you put on more workers so you can finish quicker?

Answer: Economics dictates that we keep our crews to the size that can most efficiently do the job. Six men could probably paint your kitchen in half the time it would take two — but they'd spend lot of time tripping over each other. And the labor cost would be *triple* — a cost that we'd have to pass on to you. Instead, by careful planning, we can reduce our labor cost and pass the *savings* on to you. Our crews are the best we can assemble. We employ our workers full-time and try to schedule and balance jobs so there is no unproductive time to add to costs.

Homeowner: Will we be without water or power any time during the project? If so, how long?

Answer: There's no reason your utilities should be interrupted for more than a few minutes at a time.

Homeowner: How long will our (bathroom) (kitchen) be "out of service?"

Answer: If you'll be unable to use your kitchen or bathroom, we'll include that information in your contract. You'll have plenty of time to make arrangements.

Homeowner: Can we arrange to do the finishing (paint, install fixtures) ourselves? Can we buy our own light fixtures, cabinet hardware, etc.?

Answer: Yes. If you want to do any of those yourself, we'll specifically exclude them from the contract.

From Your Contractor's Point of View

Unlikely as it may seem, contractors have complaints, too. You've just never heard about them — until now, that is.

A contract binds the homeowner and contractor together. It's in the best interest of both parties to cooperate fully with each other, especially under trying circumstances. We want to keep all lines of communication open. Here are some of the things that make a contractor's life miserable. If we can avoid these situations, we're much nicer to work with.

Complaint: *Profane and threatening language.*

If you're upset and angry, right or wrong, directing unbecoming language to our office manager, superintendent, worker, or anyone for that matter, won't help to resolve any situation. It will, however, create resentment and disrespect by our people.

Our personnel and subcontractors are instructed, trained, and directed not to use profane language, and certainly not to threaten and act in a disrespectful manner. To do so is cause for immediate dismissal. Therefore, a customer out of control would have a verbal advantage over our employees.

Complaint: *Harassment.*

We consider it a form of harassment if you call our office four, six, eight times a day just to find out what's happening. It's our policy to call you if there are problems or delays. Beyond that, please trust us to do what's necessary at the earliest opportunity and in the least possible time.

Complaint: *Pushing.*

Sometimes there are delays beyond our control. Occasionally we'll be held up by lenders, permit agencies, suppliers, weather, strikes, or whatever. Your demands to speed up work to make up for these events aren't justified. Rarely, we'll estimate a too-tight completion date, and will need your cooperation to reschedule.

Complaint: *You want something for nothing.*

Every item on a contract has a cost attached to it. That, among other things, is the basis for arriving at the contract price. If you want something added or altered, *there's going to be an extra charge.*

Complaint: *Outside interference.*

We're obligated under the terms of the contract to do a job for our customer. We won't tolerate interference by outsiders, and aren't required to account to anyone except those with a vested interest.

Complaint: *Late payments.*

Make your progress payments promptly when they're billed. We'll be a lot more willing to "go the extra mile" when we get our money on time.

Complaint: *Dealing direct with our workers and trades.*

Occasionally we have customers make deals with our workers and trades to do extra work for them on the side. This is a back door effort to get work done at a lower price that usually doesn't save you money in the long run. Our people are prohibited from accepting these offers (they're putting their jobs on the line if they do). Problems can arise for you as well. For instance, you would be legally bound to carry workers' compensation insurance for everyone you hire, and you're financially liable for injuries of any sort. If the worker isn't a licensed contractor, you are responsible for the work, compliance with the law, building codes, etc.

For Satisfaction in a Dispute

If you feel you have a valid claim for a deficiency, how should you go about getting it corrected? You can begin by discussing the problem with our superintendent. This will initiate immediate corrective action. But if this doesn't prove satisfactory, contact our manager, who will give your matter his immediate attention.

Before your blood pressure goes up, here are a few things to ask yourself: "Is my claim really valid?" "Could *I* be wrong?" "Are they right?"

Do you believe something was included in the contract but not delivered? Check your contract documents and the plans once more and see if what you expect was really included. Perhaps you just *assumed* it was included. If whatever you expected is not on the plans or in the contract, you weren't charged for the item. It wouldn't be reasonable to believe we should provide the item without charging for it. We simply cannot supply it free.

You expect us to do a good job for you. We expect to do a good job for you. And we expect to give you a hassle-free course of construction, high-quality workmanship, the best of materials, and on-time completion.

Appendix B

Sales Employment Agreement

A contract lets you know exactly where you stand in a business relationship. You wouldn't start work on a job without a contract, yet many contractors hire their sales staff without one. Having an employment agreement is like having a contract. It tells your new recruits exactly what you expect of them. There's little opportunity for misunderstanding, because it's all down in black and white. And just as important, it tells your employees what they can expect of you.

Employment agreements are being used more and more to clarify the relationship between employer and employee. In today's litigation-happy society, you're asking for trouble if you take on a new employee without a clear contract. On the next page is the contract I use. I've improved on it over the years, as things it never occurred to me would happen, happened. Have a good look at mine, and adapt it to suit your particular needs, and the requirements of the state you do business in.

It's probably a good idea to have your attorney check it over before you print them. You may include an item that your state prohibits.

SALES EMPLOYMENT AGREEMENT

This Agreement dated _____ day of _____ month, 19___, by and between _____, (the Company), and _____, (the Salesperson).

The Company has hired the Salesperson as a sales representative, and the Salesperson accepts the position subject to the following terms and conditions.

1) The Salesperson shall represent the Company to sell its services and products within the following territory:

_____
_____
_____
_____

2) The Company's primary business is remodeling and new construction of residential and commercial buildings.

3) The Company agrees to avail the salesperson of the Company's comprehensive Sales Training Program, which includes:

   a) One week of classroom training in sales techniques, construction methods, terminology, estimating, contract law, and company policies.

   b) Field training under the supervision of an experienced Company salesperson.

   c) Classroom materials, including study guides and reference material.

4) The Salesperson shall faithfully, diligently and to the best of his/her ability, promote and sell this Company's products and services exclusively.

5) The Company shall provide the Salesperson with adequate sales leads. All sales leads, whether furnished by the Company or obtained by the Salesperson, shall be the exclusive property of the Company.

6) All information and data on sales and leads are for the exclusive benefit of the Company, and are to be kept confidential by the Salesperson during his/her term of employment and for a period of one year thereafter.

7) The Salesperson shall not solicit or conduct sales or services of any sort on behalf of any other company, person, or entity, nor recommend any other company, person or entity to any of the Company's customers or prospective customers.

8) The Salesperson shall apply and pay for any license(s) or bond(s) required by law.

9) The Salesperson shall comply with all directives issued from time to time by the Company and carry out its policies in dealing with customer trade.

10) The Salesperson shall cooperate with the Company to the best of his/her ability in getting credit and financial information about prospective customers, and in promptly reporting pertinent information to the Company.

11) The Company shall provide services and products which are competitive with those offered by other companies with respect to quality, price, and design concept, and support the sale of its services and products with brochures, order forms, price lists, etc.

12) The Company shall have the absolute right to change and establish the following: prices, schedules, quantities, qualities, terms, conditions, payments, warranties, guarantees, discounts and any other terms of sale not specified.

13) The Salesperson shall not obligate the Company, verbally or in writing, to any customer, prospective customer, or buyer, for goods or services not specified in the sales contract. All labor and materials needed by the Company or its subcontractors or suppliers to perform on the contract shall be specified in the sales contract.

14) The Company shall pay the Salesperson a commission for each sale completed. A *completed sale* is defined as a contract completed and properly signed, deposit or down payment received and ratified by the Company, the rescission period expired, financing approved, placed, and accepted, design and drawings completed and approved by the Owner(s), all necessary permits issued, any other pertinent paperwork completed, and the project ready for construction.

   Commissions shall be paid as follows:

   50% after completion of sale

   50% after start of construction

   Disbursements of commissions earned up to Saturday of the previous week shall be paid on the Friday following.

15) Commissions shall be computed as follows:

   a) Eight percent (8%) on sales based on the Book Price list.

   b) Plus, fifty percent (50%) of the difference between the Book Price and the retail price (the actual selling price in excess of the Book Price.)

   c) Commissions for contracts sold short (less than the Book Price) and accepted by the Company shall be by negotiation.

16) The Salesperson shall supply his/her own automobile, and shall assume full responsibility for all expenses regardless of how incurred. Salesperson is required to keep a copy of his/her proof of valid insurance on file with the company at all times.

17) The term of this agreement shall be for _____ years beginning _____ and ending on _____.

18) Either party may cancel this agreement, with or without cause, by submitting _____ days' written notice. Employment is "at will."

19) Immediately upon written notice of termination by either party, the Salesperson shall return all record of sales, leads, quotations, estimates, price books, photographs, printed forms, sales contracts, copies, promotional materials, equipment, etc., whether supplied by the Company or not, pertaining to the Company's business.

20) The Company reserves the right to charge the Salesperson the sum of _____ for failure to return all Company materials and property as in (19) above.

21) In case of termination of employment by the Salesperson with less than one year of continuous full-time service, the Sales Trainee shall reimburse the Company on demand, $_____ as payment in full for having been trained in the Company's Sales Training Program. This requirement shall be waived after one year of continuous full-time service.

22) This constitutes the entire agreement between the Company and the Salesperson and may be amended only in writing with agreement by both parties.

_____
Salesperson

_____
Company

Appendix C

Sample Forms

Why do we need printed forms? To make us more efficient, to make our job simpler, and to cut down on errors of omission, that's why. If you trust to memory for including prices for every item on a job — sooner or later you're going to pay the price. Nobody can remember *everything*.

Take a look through the forms in this appendix. They probably won't fit the way you do business exactly. Your business is different from mine. But use them as a basis for your own forms. Modify them to fit the needs of *your* business. You need a clear, standard format for estimating, and to keep your record keeping on track.

Book Price List

Index no.	Category	Unit Price
1.00	**GENERAL**	
1.01	Plans & specifications	400.00 ea
1.03	Models, renderings	400.00 ea
1.05	Engineering (for 2nd floor, add $500-750)	/bid
1.10	Soil testing	/bid
1.15	Building permits	2% of project
1.16	Special permits	2% of project
1.26	Rentals - pumps, scaffolding, etc.	300.00 min.
1.32	Insurance - liability	2.5%
2.00	**DEMOLITION**	
2.01	Roof tearoff - to ceiling line & cleanup	2.00 psf
2.04	Roof stripping (shingles only)	.50 psf
2.06	Removal - concrete slab - 4" thick	1.80 psf
2.08	Removal - exterior wall - masonry	45.00 plf
2.10	Removal - exterior wall - frame/stucco	35.00 plf
	(add beam removal @ $8.00 plf)	plf
2.12	Removal - interior wall - bearing	35.00 plf
2.14	Removal - interior wall - non-bearing	33.00 plf
2.16	Removal - stucco, plaster	.80 psf
2.20	Site cleanup	3% of project
2.24	Equipment rentals	55.00 /hr
2.88	Site cleanup	3%
3.00	**EXCAVATION**	
3.01	Footings only — no concrete	plf
3.05	Soil removal	/cu yd
3.24	Tree removal	100.00/tree
4.00	**CONCRETE**	
4.05	Concrete footings — includes excavating, formwork, pouring	22.00 plf
4.06	Concrete footings — expansive soil (soft soil) concern — 2nd floor	35.00 plf
4.10	Concrete slab — 4", no R.B.	5.00 psf
4.12	slab — 6", no R.B.	7.00 psf
4.14	slab —4", no R.B., aggregate	7.00 psf
4.20	Concrete porch stairs — 36" wide	50.00/tread
4.22	porch stairs — 72" wide	65.00/tread
4.30	porch — deck 36" x 36"	200.00 ea
4.40	Fireplace foundation	400.00 ea
4.50	Wire mesh, interior gr. 6 x 6 ga	1.00 psf

Index no.	Category	Unit Price
4.52	exterior gr. 10 x 10 ga	1.50 psf
4.60	Reinforcing bars	2.00 plf
4.70	Concrete underpin — per corner	220.00 ea
4.72	Drain tile	4.00 psf
4.80	Vapor barrier	75.00 ea
4.86	Concrete pumping	200.00 min.
4.92	Concrete cutting/coring	200.00/cut
5.00	**MASONRY**	
5.01	Brick veneer	16.00 psf
5.08	Stone veneer	30.00 psf
5.22	Fireplace — single story: masonry/raised hearth/6' mantle/brick facing to ceiling	4000.00 ea
5.33	Fireplace - prefab/one story/zero clearance	1500.00 ea
5.42	Fireplace hearth	100.00 plf
5.51	Ceramic tile — standard	20.00 psf
5.72	designer	30.00 psf
5.80	Chimney - raise existing	500.00 ea
6.00	**CARPENTRY**	
6.01	Sub floor, joists, 5/8 T&G ply, R9 insulation	5.50 psf
6.04	Underlayment, 1/2" plywood	1.25 psf
6.10	Insulation: R11	.80 psf
6.12	R-19	1.30 psf
6.14	R-30	1.80 psf
6.20	Decking — treated joists & decking	8.80 psf
6.30	Handrails	20.00 plf
6.40	Wall system — studs/R-11/paperwrap	27.50 plf
6.42	studs/R-11/Alum/drywall	88.00 plf
6.44	studs/R-11/brick/drywall	165.00 plf
6.46	studs/R-11/3/8" ply sheer/plyw	38.50 plf
6.46	studs/R-11/stucco/drywall	88.00 plf
6.50	studs/R-11/stone, drywall	190.00 plf
6.52	Partitions — studs/plates only	20.00 plf
6.54	Cut opening — window/door, lintel inc.	220.00 ea
6.56	Stairs — open tread: plywood	400.00/case
6.58	closed risers: plywood	550.00/case
6.60	Stairs — open tread: plywood	35.00/tread

Book Price List

Index no.	Category	Unit Price
6.62	closed risers: plywood	40.00/tread
6.66	Roof tie-in: flashing	350.00 ea
6.68	Roof system — gable, hip/shed, rafters, joists/ply shtg/R-30/composition shingles or built-up	8.80 psf
6.70	Roofing — shingles	2.00 psf
6.72	wood shakes	4.00 psf
6.73	wood shakes — fire retardant	6.60 psf
6.74	tile	7.70 psf
6.75	hot, built-up, or clod	1.65 psf
6.76	Siding — redwood	6.50 psf
6.77	T-111 (plyw sheet)	2.75 psf
7.00	**INTERIOR FINISH**	
7.01	Drywall - standard wall	2.00 psf
7.03	- ceiling	3.00 psf
7.05	- textured ceiling	3.60 psf
7.07	- fireguard	3.00 psf
7.08	- boarding only/no tape/no finish	30.00/panel
7.09	- patching - 1 side, 1 opening	200.00/opng
7.11	Plaster - standard wall	4.00 psf
7.13	- ceiling	5.00 psf
7.15	Plaster patching - 1 side,1 opening	200.00/opng
7.17	Insulation - blown	300.00 min.
7.19	Suspended ceiling - tec bar	4.00 psf
7.21	Floor coverings - vinyl abestos	5.00 psf
7.23	- Resilient sheet	12-30/yd
7.25	- Indoor/outdoor carpets	16.00/yd
7.27	Wood panels ($20.00 panel cost)	80.00 panel
7.29	Interior doors - H.C. with passage sets	220.00 ea
7.31	- S.C. with passage sets	400.00 ea
7.33	- Pocket slide	100.00 ea
7.35	- Bifold louvered	120.00 ea
7.37	Millwork - baseboard/casting/trim.	3.00 plf
7.39	- 3.5" crown moulding	4.00 plf
7.41	- Kitchen cabinet soffits	20.00 plf
7.43	- Illuminated soffits	40.00 plf
7.45	- Sunshine ceiling	22.00 psf
7.47	Open beams - structural	55.00 plf
7.49	Open beams - false	15.00 plf

Index no.	Category	Unit Price
7.51	Kitchen cabinets - standard wall cabinets	100.00 plf
7.53	- Counter cabinets	150.00 plf
7.55	- Custom	by quote
7.61	Counter tops - plastic lam. - self edge, splash	90.00 plf
7.63	- Ceramic tile	80.00 plf
8.00	**Electrical**	
8.01	Duplex outlets	60.00 ea
8.03	Switches - standard	60.00 ea
8.05	- 3 way	120.00 ea
8.07	- dimmer	80.00 ea
8.09	Light outlet	60.00 ea
8.11	Doorbell button	60.00 ea
8.13	TV jack	60.00 ea
8.15	Dishwasher hookup	200.00 ea
8.17	Garbage disposal hookup	200.00 ea
8.21	Range hookup	300.00 ea
8.23	Bathroom exhaust fan & switch	250.00 ea
8.25	Kitchen exhaust fan & switch	450.00 ea
8.41	Circuits - 110 V	200.00 ea
8.43	Circuits - 220 V	300.00 ea
8.44	100 amp panel - relocate or install	1000.00 ea
8.45	200 amp panel - relocate or install	1400.00 ea
8.46	Side panel	250.00 ea
8.47	Service head extension	380.00 ea
8.48	Underground circuit - $200.00 min ea	12.00 plf
8.55	Ground fault circuit interrupter	250.00 ea
8.57	Thermostat	250.00 ea
8.61	Floodlighting	100.00 ea
8.63	Fluorescent lighting 4'x2' tube	200.00 ea
8.65	Incandescent lighting	90.00 ea
8.67	Smoke detector	110.00 ea
8.71	Garage door electric opener	400.00 ea
8.81	Garage door remote opener	100.00 ea
9.00	**PLUMBING**	
9.01	Bathtub - standard gr.	800.00 ea
9.03	Toilet - standard gr.	800.00 ea
9.05	Washbasin - standard gr.	800.00 ea
9.11	Color fixtures	100.00 ea

Book Price List

Index no.	Category	Unit Price
9.21	Bidet - standard grade	800.00 ea
9.23	Shower - fiberglass, curtain rod	800.00 ea
9.25	- Sliding doors	200.00 ea
9.27	- Corner swing door	600.00 ea
9.29	Kitchen S/S sink - single bowl	800.00 ea
9.31	Kitchen S/S sink - double bowl	900.00 ea
9.33	Shower head over bathtub	250.00 ea
9.35	Faucets	125.00 ea
9.37	Bar sink	800.00 ea
9.43	Laundry tray	350.00 ea
9.45	Washer standpipe	250.00 ea
9.51	Garbage disposal hookup	200.00 ea
9.53	Hot water heater	800.00 ea
9.55	- Enclosure for heater	300.00 ea
9.57	Sewer line - $250 min.	35.00 plf
9.59	Water line - $500 base plus	30.00 plf
9.71	Gas line	30.00 plf
9.81	Vent stacks - 14' H for single story	30.00 plf
9.91	Medicine cabinet - standard	100.00 ea
9.92	Tissue holder/bath curtain rod	50.00/set
10.00	**EXTERIOR FINISH**	
10.01	Stucco	4.50 psf
10.05	Siding - vinyl or aluminum	480.00 psf
10.09	- Cedar	560.00 psf

Index no.	Category	Unit Price
10.21	Stone veneer	30.00 psf
10.31	Roofing - ashalt shingles - 235 #	180.00/sq
10.33	- spanish tile	600.00/sq
10.35	- Cedar shake	400.00/sq
10.41	Windows - aluminum frame - anodized	2.25/UI
10.43	- Aluminum picture > 60 united inches	3.50/UI
10.47	- Wood frame	7.30/UI
10.49	- Glass - replace fixed	3.50/UI
10.51	Doors - S.C. with locksets	600.00 ea
10.53	Patio - aluminum sliding to 6' wide	600.00 ea
10.55	Patio - wood sliding to 6'wide	1000.00 ea
10.61	Gutters with downpipes - aluminum	10.00 plf
10.65	Fascia boards - aluminum	5.00 plf
10.67	Garage doors - std. 8'	600.00 ea
10.69	Garage doors - std. 16'	900.00 ea
10.71	Weatherstripping	40.00/door
10.73	Window screens	55.00 ea
11.00	**HVAC**	
11.09	Air conditioner	inquire
11.21	Gas furnace - wall type	1500.00 ea
11.31	Thermostat	200.00 ea
11.41	Sheet metal work - ducts: $200.00/run mi	40.00 plf

UNIT COST PRICE LIST

Name _____   Contract no. _____
Address _____   Job no. _____
City _____   Date _____
Phone _____   Prepared by _____

No.	Items	Qty	Unit	Cost	Amount
1.00	**GENERAL**				
1.01	Plans & specifications		each	400.00	$
1.03	Models, renderings		each	400.00	$
1.05	Engineering		/bid		$
	(2nd flr, + $)		/bid		$
1.10	Soil testing		/bid		$
1.15	Building permits		project	2%	$
1.16	Special permits		project	2%	$
1.26	Rentals — pumps, scaffolding, etc		min	300.00	$
1.32	Insurance —liability		project	2.5%	$
2.00	**DEMOLITION**				
2.01	Roof tearoff to ceiling line & cleanup		psf	2.00	$
2.04	Stripping (shingles only)		psf	.50	$
2.06	Remove - 4" conc. slab		psf	1.80	$
2.08	Remove - masonry wall		plf	45.00	$
2.10	Remove - frame/stucco		plf	35.00	$
	(Remove beam @ $8 plf)		plf		$
2.12	Remove - bearing wall		plf	35.00	$
2.14	Remove - nonbear wall		plf	33.00	$
2.16	Remove - stucco, plaster		psf	.80	$
2.20	Site cleanup		project	3%	$
2.24	Equipment rental		hr	55.00	$
3.00	**EXCAVATION**				
3.01	Footings - no concrete		plf		$
3.05	Soil removal		cu yd		$
3.24	Tree removal		tree	100.00	$
4.00	**CONCRETE**				
4.05	Conc. ftgs. - incl. excavating, formwork, & pouring		plf	22.00	$
4.06	Conc. ftgs - expansive soil re: 2nd floor		plf	35.00	$
4.10	4" conc. slab no R.B.		psf	5.00	$
4.12	6" conc. slab no R.B.		psf	7.00	$
4.14	4" conc. aggr. slab no R.B.		psf	7.00	$
4.20	Conc. 36" porch stairs		/trd	50.00	$
4.22	Conc. 72" porch stairs		/trd	65.00	$
4.30	Conc. porch-deck 3" x 36"		ea	200.00	$
4.40	Fireplace foundation		ea	400.00	$
4.50	Wire mesh, int. 6x6 ga		psf	1.00	$
4.52	ext. 10x10 ga		psf	1.50	$
4.60	Reinforcing bars		plf	2.00	$
4.70	Conc. underpin/corner		ea	220.00	$
4.72	Drain tile		psf	4.00	$
COLUMN 1 SUBTOTAL					$

No.	Items	Qty	Unit	Cost	Amount
4.80	Vapor barrier		ea	75.00	$
4.86	Concrete pumping		min	250.00	$
4.92	Concrete cutting/coring		ea	250.00	$
5.00	**MASONRY**				
5.01	Fireplace - shingle story: masonry/raised hearth/6' mantle/8' brick veneer		ea	3500.00	$
5.10	Brick veneer		psf	21.00	$
5.20	Stone veneer		psf	24.00	$
5.30	Stone veneer - precast		psf	21.00	$
5.40	Pre-engineered fireplace - single story: raised hearth/6' mantle/8' brk vnr.		ea	2850.00	$
	2nd floor as above add			1000.00	
5.50	Fireplace hearth		plf	77.00	$
5.54	Mex-tile		psf	22.00	$
5.70	Ceramic tile - std gr.		psf	20.00	$
5.72	Ceramic tile - designer gr.		psf	24.00	$
5.80	Raise existing chimney		plf	325.00	$
6.00	**CARPENTRY**				
6.01	Subflr., - joists, ⅝ T&G ply, R-9 insul.		psf	5.50	$
6.04	Underlayment, ½" plywood		psf	1.25	$
6.10	Insulation, R-11		psf	.80	$
6.12	R-19		psf	1.30	$
6.14	R-30		psf	1.80	$
6.20	Decking-treated jst/dckg		psf	8.80	$
6.30	Handrails		plf	20.00	$
6.32	Railing - std. wrt iron		plf	22.00	$
6.40	Wall system - Studs/R-11/paperwrap		plf	27.50	$
6.42	Studs/R-11/alum/drywall		plf	88.00	$
6.44	Studs/R-11/brk/drywall		plf	165.00	$
6.46	Studs/R-11/⅜ ply sheer/plyw		plf	38.50	$
6.48	Studs/R-11/stucco, drywall		plf	88.00	$
6.50	Studs/R-11/stone, drywall		plf	190.00	$
6.52	Partitions-studs/plates only		plf	20.00	$
6.54	Cut opening - window/door, lintel incl		ea	220.00	$
6.56	Stairs-open tread: plywood		/cs	400.00	$
6.58	Closed raisers: plywood		/cs	550.00	$
6.60	Stairs-open tread: plywood		/trd	35.00	$
6.62	Closed risers: plywood		/trd	40.00	$
6.66	Roof tie-in: flashing		ea	350.00	$
COLUMN 2 SUBTOTAL					$

No.	Items	Qty	Unit	Cost	Amount
6.68	Roof system - gable, hip-shed, rafters, joists/ply shtg/R-30/composition/shingles or built-up		psf	8.80	$
6.70	Roofing - shingles		psf	2.00	$
6.72	Roofing - wood shakes		psf	4.00	$
6.73	Roofing - wood shakes - fire retardant		psf	6.60	$
6.74	Roofing - tile		psf	7.70	$
6.75	Roofing - hot, blt-up, or cold		psf	1.65	$
6.76	Siding - redwood		psf	6.50	$
6.77	Siding - T-111 (ply sht)		psf	2.75	$
7.00	INTERIOR FINISH				
7.01	Drywall - standard wall		psf	2.00	$
7.03	Drywall - ceiling		psf	3.00	$
7.05	Drywall - textured ceiling		psf	1.95	$
7.07	Drywall - fireguard		psf	3.00	$
7.08	Drywall - boarding only/no tape/no finish		/panel	30.00	$
7.09	Drywall patching - 1 side, 1 opng		/opng	200.00	$
7.11	Plaster- standard wall		psf	4.00	$
7.13	Plaster - ceiling		psf	5.00	$
7.15	Plaster patching - 1 side, 1 opng		/opng	200.00	$
7.17	Insulation - blown		min	300.00	$
7.19	Suspended ceiling - Tec bar		psf	4.00	$
7.21	Floor covering - vinyl asbestos		psf	5.00	$
7.23	Floor covering - resilient sheet		/yd	12-30	$
7.25	Floor covering - indr/outdr carpets		/yd	16.00	$
7.25	Wood panels ($20 panel cost)		panel	80.00	$
7.29	Interior doors - H.C. with passage sets		ea	220.00	$
7.31	- S.C. with passage sets		ea	400.00	$
7.33	- Pocket slide		ea	100.00	$
7.35	- Bi-fold louvered		ea	120.00	$
7.37	Millwork - baseboard/casing/trim		plf	3.00	$
7.39	3.5" crown moulding		plf	4.00	$
7.41	Kitchen cabinet soffits		plf	20.00	$
7.43	– Illuminated soffits		plf	40.00	$
7.45	– Sunshine ceiling		psf	22.00	$
7.47	Open beams - structural		plf	55.50	$
COLUMN 3 SUBTOTAL					$

No.	Items	Qty	Unit	Cost	Amount
7.49	Open beams - false		plf	15.00	$
7.51	Kitchen cabinets - standard, - wall cabinets		plf	100.00	$
7.53	- Counter cabinets		plf	150.00	$
7.55	- Kitchen cabinets - custom		by quote		$
7.61	Counter tops - plastic lam. - self edge, splash		plf	90.00	$
7.63	- Ceramic tile		plf	80.00	$
8.00	ELECTRICAL				$
8.01	Duplex outlets		ea	60.00	$
8.03	Switches - standard		ea	60.00	$
8.05	Switches - 3 way		ea	120.00	$
8.07	Switches dimmer		ea	80.00	$
8.09	Light outlet		ea	60.00	
8.11	Doorbell button		ea	60.00	$
8.13	TV jack		ea	60.00	$
8.15	Dishwasher hookup		ea	200.00	$
8.17	Garbage disposal hookup		ea	200.00	$
8.21	Range hookup		ea	300.00	$
8.23	Bathroom exhaust fan & switch		ea	250.00	$
8.25	Kitchen exhaust fan & switch		ea	450.00	$
8.41	Circuits - 110 V		ea	200.00	$
8.43	Circuits - 220 V		ea	300.00	$
8.44	100 amp panel - relocate or install		ea	1000.00	$
8.45	200 amp panel - relocate or install		ea	1400.00	$
8.46	Sidepanel		ea	250.00	$
8.47	Service head - extension		ea	380.00	$
8.48	Underground circuit - $200.00 min. ea		plf	12.00	$
8.55	Ground fault circuit interuptor		ea	250.00	$
8.57	Thermostat		ea	250.00	$
8.61	Floodlighting		ea	100.00	$
8.63	Flourescent lighting 4'x2 tube		ea	200.00	$
8.65	Incandescent lighting		ea	90.00	$
8.67	Smoke detector		ea	110.00	$
8.71	Garage door electric opener		ea	400.00	$
8.81	Garage door remote opener		ea	100.00	$
9.00	PLUMBING				
9.01	Bathtub - standard grade		ea	800.00	
COLUMN 4 SUBTOTAL					$

No.	Items	Qty	Unit	Cost	Amount
9.03	Toilet - standard grade		ea	800.00	$
9.05	Washbasin - standard grade		ea	800.00	$
9.11	Color fixtures		ea	100.00	$
9.21	Bidet - standard grade		ea	800.00	$
9.23	Shower - fiberglass, curtain rod		ea	800.00	$
9.25	Shower - sliding doors		ea	200.00	$
9.27	Shower - corner swing door		ea	600.00	$
9.29	Kitchen S/S sink - single bowl		ea	800.00	$
9.31	Kitchen S/S sink - double bowl		ea	900.00	$
9.33	Shower head over bathtub		ea	250.00	$
9.35	Faucets		ea	125.00	$
9.37	Bar sink		ea	800.00	$
9.43	Laundry tray		ea	350.00	$
9.45	Washer standpipe		ea	250.00	$
9.51	Garbage disposal hookup		ea	200.00	$
9.53	Hot water heater		ea	800.00	$
9.55	- enclosure for heater		ea	300.00	$
9.57	Sewer line - $250.00 min.		plf	35.00	$
9.59	Water line - $500 base plus		plf	30.00	$
9.71	Gas line		plf	30.00	$
9.81	Vent stack - 14' H for single story		plf	30.00	$
9.91	Medicine cabinet - standard		ea	100.00	$
9.92	Tissue holder/bath curtain rod		set	50.00	$
10.00	**EXTERIOR FINISH**				
10.01	Stucco		psf	4.50	$
10.05	Siding - vinyl or aluminum		/sq	480.00	$
10.09	- Cedar		/sq	560.00	$
COLUMN 5 SUBTOTAL					$

No.	Items	Qty	Unit	Cost	Amount
10.21	Stone veneer		psf	30.00	$
10.25	Brick veneer		psf	16.00	$
10.31	Roofing - asphalt shingles - 235#		/sq	180.00	$
10.33	Spanish tile		/sq	600.00	$
10.35	Cedar shake		/sq	400.00	$
10.41	Windows - aluminum frame - anodized		UI	2.25	$
10.43	- Aluminum picture 60 united inches		UI	3.50	$
10.47	- Wood frame		UI	7.30	$
10.49	- Glass - replace fixed		UI	3.50	$
10.51	Doors - S.C. with locksets		ea	600.00	$
10.53	- Patio - aluminum sliding to 6' wide		ea	600.00	$
10.55	- Patio - wood sliding to 6' wide		ea	1,000.00	$
10.61	Gutters with downpipes - aluminum		plf	10.00	$
10.65	Fascia boards - aluminum		plf	5.00	$
10.67	Garage doors - std. 8'		ea	600.00	$
10.69	Garage doors - std. 16'		ea	900.00	$
10.71	Weatherstripping		/door	40.00	$
10.73	Window screens		ea	55.00	$
11.00	**HVAC**				
11.09	Air conditioner			inquire	$
11.21	Gas furnace - wall type		ea	1500.00	$
11.31	Thermostat		ea	200.00	$
11.41	Sheet metal work - ducts: $20/run mi		plf	40.00	$
COLUMN 6 SUBTOTAL					$

Notes

Size

Width _____ lf
Length _____ lf
Area _____ sf

Subtotals

Column 1 $ _____
Column 2 $ _____
Column 3 $ _____
Column 4 $ _____
Column 5 $ _____
Column 6 $ _____

TOTAL $ _____
Contingencies $ _____
Sales tax $ _____

TOTAL $ _____
Escrow fee $ _____

TOTAL $ _____

_____% interest

Approximate monthly
Payment $_____ Years _____

Notes

JOB PROGRESS REPORT

Job no. _____

Name _____

Project: _____

Location: _____

Job tel. no.: _____

Report no._____

Date:_____

Weather:_____

Work performed by General Contractor:
_____
_____
_____
_____
_____

Work performed by subcontractors:
_____
_____
_____
_____
_____

Other activities:
_____
_____
_____
_____
_____

Comments:
_____
_____
_____

Superintendent

INDEX

Practical References for Builders

Estimating Remodeling Audiotapes

Listen to the "hands-on" estimating instruction in this popular remodeling seminar. Make your own unit price estimate based on the prints enclosed. Then check your completed estimate with those prepared in the actual seminar. After listening to these tapes you will know how to establish an operating budget for your business, determine indirect costs and profit, and estimate remodeling with the unit cost method. Includes seminar workbook, project survey and unit price estimating forms, and six 20-minute cassettes. **$65.00**

Project Survey Forms

Here are the actual forms used in the Estimating Remodeling Audiotape. Use them for walk-throughs with the homeowners so that every item is checked off as being included or excluded in your bid. These forms can save you hours of time and help prevent expensive mistakes and misunderstandings. **100 forms, 11 x 25, $35.00**

Unit Price List Forms

Here are the price list forms from the Estimating Remodeling Audiotape with actual unit prices for each area of remodeling. These forms can help you quickly and accurately create a unit price estimate on your jobs — just like the one you followed through with the seminar tape. **100 forms, 11 x 17, $35.00**

Manual of Professional Remodeling

This is the practical manual of professional remodeling written by an experienced and successful remodeling contractor. Shows how to evaluate a job and avoid 30-minute jobs that take all day, what to fix and what to leave alone, and what to watch for in dealing with subcontractors. Includes chapters on calculating space requirements, repairing structural defects, remodeling kitchens, baths, walls and ceilings, doors and windows, floors, roofs, installing fireplaces and chimneys (including built-ins), skylights, and exterior siding. Includes blank forms, checklists, sample contracts, and proposals you can copy and use. **400 pages, 8-1/2 x 11, $19.75**

How to Sell Remodeling

Proven, effective sales methods for repair and remodeling contractors: finding qualified leads, making the sales call, identifying what your prospects really need, pricing the job, arranging financing, and closing the sale. Explains how to organize and staff a sales team, how to bring in the work to keep your crews busy and your business growing, and much more. Includes blank forms, tables, and charts. **240 pages, 8-1/2 x 11, $17.50**

Estimating Electrical Construction

A practical approach to estimating materials and labor for residential and commercial electrical construction. Written by the A.S.P.E. National Estimator of the Year, it explains how to use labor units, the plan take-off and the bid summary to establish an accurate estimate. Provides extensive labor unit tables, and blank forms for use in estimating your next electrical job. **272 pages, 8-1/2 x 11, $19.00**

Remodeler's Handbook

The complete manual of home improvement contracting: Planning the job, estimating costs, doing the work, running your company and making profits. Pages of sample forms, contracts, documents, clear illustrations and examples. Chapters on evaluating the work, rehabilitation, kitchens, bathrooms, adding living area, reflooring, residing, reroofing, replacing windows and doors, installing new wall and ceiling cover, repainting, upgrading insulation, combating moisture damage, estimating, selling your services, and bookkeeping for remodelers. **416 pages, 8-1/2 x 11, $23.00**

Remodeling Kitchens & Baths

This book is your guide to succeeding in a very lucrative area of the remodeling market: how to repair and replace damaged floors; how to redo walls, ceilings, and plumbing; and how to modernize the home wiring system to accommodate today's heavy electrical demands. Show how to install new sinks and countertops, ceramic tile, sunken tubs, whirlpool baths, luminous ceilings, skylights, and even special lighting effects. Completely illustrated, with manhour tables for figuring your labor costs. **384 pages, 8-1/2 x 11, $26.25**

Running Your Remodeling Business

Everything you need to know about operating a remodeling business, from making your first sale to ensuring your profits: how to advertise, write up a contract, estimate, schedule your jobs, arrange financing (for both you and your customers), and when and how to expand your business. Explains what you need to know about insurance, bonds, and liens, and how to collect the money you've earned. Includes sample business forms for your use. **272 pages, 8-1/2 x 11, $21.00**

Builder's Guide to Accounting Revised

Step-by-step, easy to follow guidelines for setting up and maintaining an efficient record-keeping system for your building business. Not a book of theory, this practical, newly-revised guide to all accounting methods shows how to meet state and federal accounting requirements, including new depreciation rules, and explains what the Tax Reform Act of 1986 can mean to your business. Full of charts, diagrams, blank forms, simple directions and examples. **304 pages, 8-1/2 x 11, $17.25**

Builder's Office Manual Revised

Explains how to create routine ways of doing all the things that must be done in every construction office — in the minimum time, at the lowest cost, and with the least supervision possible: organizing the office space, establishing effective procedures and forms, setting priorities and goals, finding and keeping an effective staff, getting the most from your record-keeping system (whether manual or computerized). Loaded with practical tips, charts and sample forms for your use. **192 pages, 8-1/2 x 11, $15.50**

Bookkeeping for Builders

This book will show you simple, practical instructions for setting up and keeping accurate records — with a minimum of effort and frustration. Shows how to set up the essentials of a record-keeping system: the payment journal, income journal, general journal, records for fixed assets, accounts receivable, payables and purchases, petty cash, and job costs. You'll be able to keep the records required by the I.R.S., as well as accurate and organized business records for your own use. **208 pages, 8-1/2 x 11, $19.75**

Builder's Comprehensive Dictionary

Never let a construction term stump you. Here you'll find almost 10,000 construction term definitions, over 1,000 detailed illustrations of tools, techniques and systems, and a separate section containing most often used legal, real estate, and management terms. **532 pages, 8-1/2 x 11, $24.95**

Contractor's Survival Manual

How to survive hard times in construction and take full advantage of the profitable cycles. Shows what to do when the bills can't be paid, finding money and buying time, transferring debt, and all the alternatives to bankruptcy. Explains how to build profits, avoid problems in zoning and permits, taxes, time-keeping, and payroll. Unconventional advice includes how to invest in inflation, get high appraisals, trade and postpone income, and how to stay hip-deep in profitable work. **160 pages, 8-1/2 x 11, $16.75**

Video: Stair Framing

Shows how to use a calculator to figure the rise and run of each step, the height of each riser, the number of treads, and the tread depths. Then watch how to take these measurements to construct an actual set of stairs. You'll see how to mark and cut your carriages, treads, and risers, and install a stairway that fits your calculations for the perfect set of stairs. **60 minutes, VHS, $24.75**

Roof Framing

Frame any type of roof in common use today, even if you've never framed a roof before. Shows how to use a pocket calculator to figure any common, hip, valley, and jack rafter length in seconds. Over 400 illustrations take you through every measurement and every cut on each type of roof: gable, hip, Dutch, Tudor, gambrel, shed, gazebo and more. **480 pages, 5-1/2 x 8-1/2, $22.00**

Video: Roof Framing 1

A complete step-by-step training video on the basics of roof cutting by Marshall Gross, the author of the book Roof Framing. Shows and explains calculating rise, run, and pitch, and laying out and cutting common rafters. **90 minutes, VHS, $80.00**

Video: Roof Framing 2

A complete training video on the more advanced techniques of roof framing by Marshall Gross, the author of Roof Framing. Shows and explains layout and framing an irregular roof, and making tie-ins to an existing roof. **90 minutes, VHS, $80.00**

Contractor's Guide to the Building Code Revised

This completely revised edition explains in plain English exactly what the Uniform Building Code requires and shows how to design and construct residential and light commercial buildings that will pass inspection the first time. Suggests how to work with the inspector to minimize construction costs, what common building shortcuts are likely to be cited, and where exceptions are granted. **544 pages, 5-1/2 x 8-1/2, $24.25**

Spec Builder's Guide

Explains how to plan and build a home, control your construction costs, and then sell the house at a price that earns a decent return on the time and money you've invested. Includes professional tips to ensure success as a spec builder: how government statistics help you judge the housing market, cutting costs at every opportunity without sacrificing quality, and taking advantage of construction cycles. Every chapter includes checklists, diagrams, charts, figures, and estimating tables. **448 pages, 8-1/2 x 11, $27.00**

Blueprint Reading for the Building Trades

How to read and understand construction documents, blueprints, and schedules. Includes layouts of structural, mechanical and electrical drawings, how to interpret sectional views, how to follow diagrams (plumbing, HVAC and schematics) and common problems experienced in interpreting construction specifications. This book is your course for understanding and following construction documents. **192 pages, 5-1/2 x 8-1/2, $11.25**

Drywall Contracting

How to do professional quality drywall work, how to plan and estimate each job, and how to start and keep your drywall business thriving. Covers the eight essential steps in making any drywall estimate, how to achieve the six most commonly-used surface treatments, how to work with metal studs, and how to solve and prevent most common drywall problems. **288 pages, 5-1/2 x 8-1/2, $18.25**

Video: Drywall Contracting 1

How to measure, cut, and hang: the tools you need and how to use them to do top quality work on any job in the shortest time possible. Explains how to plan the job for top productivity, straighten studs, use nails, screws or adhesive to best advantage, and make the most of labor-saving tools. **33 minutes, VHS, $24.75**

Video: Drywall Contracting 2

How to use mechanical taping tools, mix and apply compound, use corner bead, finish and texture board and solve the most common drywall problems. Includes tips for making a good living in the drywall business. **38 minutes, VHS, $24.75**

Construction Estimating Reference Data

Collected in this single volume are the building estimator's 300 most useful estimating reference tables. Labor requirements for nearly every type of construction are included: site work, concrete work, masonry, steel, carpentry, thermal & moisture protection, doors and windows, finishes, mechanical and electrical. Each section explains in detail the work being estimated and gives the appropriate crew size and equipment needed. **368 pages, 11 x 8-1/2, $26.00**

National Construction Estimator

Current building costs in dollars and cents for residential, commercial and industrial construction. Prices for every commonly used building material, and the proper labor cost associated with installation of the material. Everything figured out to give you the "in place" cost in seconds. Many time-saving rules of thumb, waste and coverage factors and estimating tables are included. **544 pages, 8-1/2 x 11, $19.50. Revised annually**

Building Cost Manual

Square foot costs for residential, commercial, industrial, and farm buildings. In a few minutes you work up a reliable budget estimate based on the actual materials and design features, area, shape, wall height, number of floors and support requirements. Most important, you include all the important variables that can make any building unique from a cost standpoint. **240 pages, 8-1/2 x 11, $14.00. Revised annually**

Estimating Tables for Home Building

Produce accurate estimates in minutes for nearly any home or multi-family dwelling. This handy manual has the tables you need to find the quantity of materials and labor for most residential construction. Includes overhead and profit, how to develop unit costs for labor and materials, and how to be sure you've considered every cost in the job. **336 pages, 8-1/2 x 11, $21.50**

Estimating Home Building Costs

Estimate every phase of residential construction from site costs to the profit margin you should include in your bid. Shows how to keep track of manhours and make accurate labor cost estimates for footings, foundations, framing and sheathing, finishes, electrical, plumbing and more. Explains the work being estimated and provides sample cost estimate worksheets with complete instructions for each job phase. **320 pages, 5-1/2 x 8-1/2, $17.00**

Cost Records for Construction Estimating

How to organize and use cost information from jobs just completed to make more accurate estimates in the future. Explains how to keep the cost records you need to reflect the time spent on each part of the job. Shows the best way to track costs for site work, footing, foundations, framing, interior finish, siding and trim, masonry, and subcontract expense. Provides sample forms. **208 pages, 8-1/2 x 11, $15.75**

Carpentry Estimating

Simple, clear instructions show you how to take off quantities and figure costs for all rough and finish carpentry. Shows how much overhead and profit to include, how to convert piece prices to MBF prices or linear foot prices, and how to use the tables included to quickly estimate manhours. All carpentry is covered; floor joists, exterior and interior walls and finishes, ceiling joists and rafters, stairs, trim, windows, doors, and much more. Includes sample forms, checklists, and the author's factor worksheets to save you time and help prevent errors. **320 pages, 8-1/2 x 11, $25.50**

Wood-Frame House Construction

From the layout of the outer walls, excavation and formwork, to finish carpentry, and painting, every step of construction is covered in detail with clear illustrations and explanations. Everything the builder needs to know about framing, roofing, siding, insulation and vapor barrier, interior finishing, floor coverings, and stairs. . .complete step-by-step "how to" information on what goes into building a frame house. **240 pages, 8-1/2 x 11, $14.25. Revised edition**

Rough Carpentry

All rough carpentry is covered in detail: sills, girders, columns, joists, sheathing, ceiling, roof and wall framing, roof trusses, dormers, bay windows, furring and grounds, stairs and insulation. Many of the 24 chapters explain practical code-approved methods for saving lumber and time without sacrificing quality. Chapters on columns, headers, rafters, joists and girders show how to use simple engineering principles to select the right lumber dimension for whatever species and grade you are using. **288 pages, 8-1/2 x 11, $17.00**

Roofers Handbook

The journeyman roofer's complete guide to wood and asphalt shingle application on both new construction and reroofing jobs: how professional roofers make smooth tie-ins on any job, the right way to cover valleys and ridges, how to handle and prevent leaks, how to set up and run your own roofing business and sell your services as a professional roofer. Over 250 illustrations and hundreds of trade tips. **192 pages, 8-1/2 x 11, $14.00**

Carpentry Layout

Explains the easy way to figure: cuts for stair carriages, treads and risers; lengths for common, hip and jack rafters; spacing for joists, studs, rafters and pickets; layout for rake and bearing walls. Shows how to set foundation corner stakes — even for a complex home on a hillside. Practical examples show how to use a hand-held calculator as a powerful layout tool. Written in simple language any carpenter can understand. **240 pages, 5-1/2 x 8-1/2, $16.25**

Construction Surveying and Layout

A practical guide to simplified construction surveying: how land is divided, how to use a transit and tape to find a known point, how to draw an accurate survey map from your field notes, how to use topographic surveys, and the right way to level and set grade. You'll learn how to make a survey for any residential or commercial lot, driveway, road, or bridge — including how to figure cuts and fills and calculate excavation quantities. If you've been wanting to make your own surveys, or just read and verify the accuracy of surveys made by others, you should have this guide. **256 pages, 5-1/2 x 8-1/2, $19.25**

Paint Contractor's Manual

How to start and run a profitable paint contracting company: getting set up and organized to handle volume work, avoiding the mistakes most painters make, getting top production from your crews and the most value from your advertising dollar. Shows how to estimate all prep and painting. Loaded with manhour estimates, sample forms, contracts, charts, tables and examples you can use. **224 pages, 8-1/2 x 11, $19.25**

Painter's Handbook

Loaded with "how-to" information you'll use every day to get professional results on any job: the best way to prepare a surface for painting or repainting; selecting and using the right materials and tools (including airless spray); tips for repainting kitchens, bathrooms, cabinets, eaves and porches; how to match and blend colors; why coatings fail and what to do about it. Thirty profitable specialties that could be your gravy train in the painting business. Every professional painter needs this practical handbook. **320 pages, 8-1/2 x 11, $21.25**

Estimating Painting Costs

Here is an accurate step-by-step estimating system, based on a set of easy-to-use manhour tables that anyone can use for estimating painting costs: from simple residential repaints to complicated commercial jobs — even heavy industrial and government work. Explains taking field measurements, doing take-offs from plans and specs, predicting productivity, figuring labor, material costs, overhead and profit. Includes manhour and material tables, plus samples, forms, and checklists for your use. **448 pages, 8-1/2 x 11, $28.00**

Residential Wiring

Shows how to install rough and finish wiring in both new construction and alterations and additions. Complete instructions are included on troubleshooting and repairs. Every subject is referenced to the 1987 National Electrical Code, and over 24 pages of the most needed NEC tables are included to help you avoid errors so your wiring passes inspection — the first time. **352 pages, 5-1/2 x 8-1/2, $18.25**

Residential Electrician's Handbook

Simple, clear instructions for wiring homes and apartments: understanding plans and specs, following the NEC, making simple load calculations, sizing wire and service equipment, installing branch and feeder circuits, and running wire. Explains how to estimate the cost of residential electrical systems, speed and simplify your estimates using composite unit prices, and provides the forms and labor and material tables you need. **240 pages, 5-1/2 x 8-1/2, $16.75**

Home Wiring: Improvement, Extension, Repairs

How to repair electrical wiring in older homes, extend or expand an existing electrical system in homes being remodeled, and bring the electrical system up to modern standards in any residence. Shows how to use the anticipated loads and demand factors to figure the amperage and number of new circuits needed, and how to size and install wiring, conduit, switches, and auxiliary panels and fixtures. Explains how to test and troubleshoot fixtures, circuit wiring, and switches, as well as how to service or replace low voltage systems. **224 pages, 5-1/2 x 8-1/2, $15.00**

Electrical Blueprint Reading

Shows how to read and interpret electrical drawings, wiring diagrams and specifications for construction of electrical systems in buildings. Shows how a typical lighting plan and power layout would appear on the plans and explains what the contractor would do to execute this plan. Describes how to use a panelboard or heating schedule and includes typical electrical specifications. **128 pages, 8-1/2 x 11, $13.75**

Plumber's Handbook Revised

This new edition shows what will and what will not pass inspection in drainage, vent, and waste piping, septic tanks, water supply, fire protection, and gas piping systems. All tables, standards, and specifications are completely up-to-date with recent changes in the plumbing code. Covers common layouts for residential work, how to size piping, selecting and hanging fixtures, practical recommendations and trade tips. This book is the approved reference for the plumbing contractor's exam in many states. **240 pages, 8-1/2 x 11, $18.00**

Basic Plumbing with Illustrations

The journeyman's and apprentice's guide to installing plumbing, piping and fixtures in residential and light commercial buildings: how to select the right materials, lay out the job and do professional quality plumbing work. Explains the use of essential tools and materials, how to make repairs, maintain plumbing systems, install fixtures and add to existing systems. **320 pages, 8- 1/2 x 11, $22.00**

Planning Drain, Waste, and Vent Systems

How to design plumbing systems in residential, commercial, and industrial buildings that will be approved without expensive delays. Covers designing systems that meet code requirements for homes, commercial buildings, private sewage disposal systems, and even mobile home parks. Includes relevant code sections and many illustrations to guide you through what the code requires in designing drainage, waste, and vent systems. **192 pages, 8-1/2 x 11, $19.25**

HVAC Contracting

Your guide to setting up and running a successful HVAC contracting company. Shows how to plan and design all types of systems for maximum efficiency and lowest cost — and explains how to sell your customers on the designs you propose. Describes the right way to use all the instruments, equipment and reference materials essential to HVAC contracting. Includes a full chapter on estimating, bidding, and contract procedure. **256 pages, 8-1/2 x 11, $24.50**

Estimating Plumbing Costs

Offers a basic procedure for estimating materials, labor, and direct and indirect costs for residential and commercial plumbing jobs. Explains how to interpret and understand plot plans, design drainage, waste, and vent systems, meet code requirements, and make an accurate take-off for materials and labor. Includes sample cost sheets, manhour production tables, complete illustrations, and all the practical information you need to accurately estimate plumbing costs. **224 pages, 8-1/2 x 11, $17.25**

Craftsman Book Company
6058 Corte del Cedro
P. O. Box 6500
Carlsbad, CA 92008

Phone Orders
For charge card orders call *1-800-829-8123*.
Your order will be shipped within 48 hours of your call.

Mail Orders
We pay shipping when you use your charge card or when your check covers your order in full.

These books are tax deductible when used to improve or maintain your professional skill.

Name (Please print clearly)
_____

Company
_____

Address
_____

City / State / Zip
_____

Send check or money order _____ total enclosed
(In California add 6% tax)

If you prefer use your:
☐ Visa ☐ MasterCard or ☐ American Express

Card number _____

Expiration date_____Initials_____

10 Day Money Back GUARANTEE

☐ 22.00 Basic Plumbing with Illustrations
☐ 11.25 Blueprint Reading for Building Trades
☐ 19.75 Bookkeeping for Builders
☐ 24.95 Builder's Comprehensive Dictionary
☐ 17.25 Builder's Guide to Accounting Revised
☐ 15.50 Builder's Office Manual Revised
☐ 14.00 Building Cost Manual
☐ 25.50 Carpentry Estimating
☐ 16.25 Carpentry Layout
☐ 26.00 Construction Estimating Reference Data
☐ 19.25 Construction Surveying and Layout
☐ 24.25 Contractor's Guide to the Building Code Revised
☐ 16.75 Contractor's Survival Manual
☐ 15.75 Cost Records for Construction Estimating
☐ 18.25 Drywall Contracting
☐ 13.75 Electrical Blueprint Reading
☐ 19.00 Estimating Electrical Construction
☐ 17.00 Estimating Home Building Costs
☐ 28.00 Estimating Painting Costs
☐ 17.25 Estimating Plumbing Costs
☐ 65.00 Estimating Remodeling Audiotapes
☐ 21.50 Estimating Tables for Home Building
☐ 15.00 Home Wiring: Improvement, Extension, Repairs
☐ 17.50 How to Sell Remodeling
☐ 24.50 HVAC Contracting
☐ 19.75 Manual of Professional Remodeling
☐ 19.50 National Construction Estimator
☐ 19.25 Paint Contractor's Manual
☐ 21.25 Painter's Handbook
☐ 19.25 Planning Drain, Waste & Vent Systems
☐ 18.00 Plumbers Handbook Revised
☐ 35.00 Project Survey Forms
☐ 23.00 Remodeler's Handbook
☐ 26.25 Remodeling Kitchens & Baths
☐ 16.75 Residential Electrician's Handbook
☐ 18.25 Residential Wiring
☐ 22.00 Roof Framing
☐ 14.00 Roofers Handbook
☐ 17.00 Rough Carpentry
☐ 21.00 Running Your Remodeling Business
☐ 27.00 Spec Builder's Guide
☐ 35.00 Unit Price List Forms
☐ 24.75 Video: Drywall Contracting 1
☐ 24.75 Video: Drywall Contracting 2
☐ 80.00 Video: Roof Framing 1
☐ 80.00 Video: Roof Framing 2
☐ 24.75 Video: Stair Framing
☐ 14.25 Wood-Framing House Construction
☐ 18.25 Remodeling Contractor's Handbook

Craftsman Book Co
6058 Corte del Cedro
P. O. Box 6500
Carlsbad, CA 92008

In a hurry?
We accept phone orders charged to your MasterCard, Visa or American Express
Call 1-800-829-8123

Name (Please print clearly) ____________________

Company ____________________

Address ____________________

City/State/Zip ____________________

Total Enclosed ____________________
(In California add 6% tax)

Use your ☐Visa ☐MasterCard ☐American Express

Card # ____________________

Exp. date __________ Initials ____

10-Day Money Back GUARANTEE

- ☐ 95.00 Audio: Construction Field Sup.
- ☐ 65.00 Audio: Estimating Remodeling
- ☐ 19.95 Audio: Plumbers Examination
- ☐ 22.00 Basic Plumbing with Illustration
- ☐ 30.00 Berger Building Cost File
- ☐ 11.25 Blprt Reading for Bldg Trades
- ☐ 19.75 Bookkeeping for Builders
- ☐ 24.95 Builder's Comp. Dictionary
- ☐ 17.25 Blder's Guide to Acct. Rev.
- ☐ 15.25 Blder's Guide to Const. Fin.
- ☐ 15.50 Blder's Office Manual Rev.
- ☐ 14.00 Building Cost Manual
- ☐ 11.75 Building Layout
- ☐ 25.50 Carpentry Estimating
- ☐ 19.75 Carpentry for Resi. Const.
- ☐ 19.00 Carpentry in Com. Const.
- ☐ 16.25 Carpentry Layout
- ☐ 17.75 Compt: Builder's New Tool
- ☐ 14.50 Concrete and Formwork
- ☐ 20.50 Concrete Const. & Estimating
- ☐ 26.00 Const. Estimating Ref. Data
- ☐ 22.00 Construction Superintendent
- ☐ 19.25 Const. Surveying & Layout
- ☐ 19.00 Cont. Growth & Profit Guide
- ☐ 24.25 Cont. Guide Build.Code Rev.
- ☐ 16.75 Contractor's Survival Manual.
- ☐ 16.50 Cont. Year-Rd Tax Guide
- ☐ 15.75 Cost Record for Const. Est.
- ☐ 9.50 Dial-A-Length Rafterule
- ☐ 18.25 Drywall Contracting
- ☐ 13.75 Electrical Blueprint Reading
- ☐ 25.00 Electrical Const. Estimator
- ☐ 19.00 Estimating Electrical Const.
- ☐ 17.00 Estimating Home Blding Costs
- ☐ 28.00 Estimating Painting Costs
- ☐ 17.25 Estimating Plumbing Costs
- ☐ 21.50 Est. Tables for Home Building
- ☐ 22.75 Exca. & Grading Hndbk Rev.
- ☐ 9.25 E-Z Square
- ☐ 15.25 Finish Carpentry
- ☐ 23.00 Kitchen Designer
- ☐ 24.75 Hdbk of Const. Cont. Vol. 1
- ☐ 24.75 Hdbk of Const. Cont. Vol. 2
- ☐ 14.75 Hdbk of Modern Elec. Wiring
- ☐ 15.00 Home Wiring: Imp., Ext., Repr
- ☐ 17.50 How to Sell Remodeling
- ☐ 24.50 HVAC Contracting
- ☐ 20.25 Manual of Electrical Cont.
- ☐ 19.75 Manual of Prof. Remodeling
- ☐ 17.25 Masonry & Concrete Const.
- ☐ 26.50 Masonry Estimating
- ☐ 19.50 National Const. Estimator
- ☐ 19.25 Paint Contractor's Manual
- ☐ 21.25 Painter's Handbook
- ☐ 23.50 Pipe & Excavation Contracting
- ☐ 13.00 Plan. and Design. Plumb. Sys.
- ☐ 19.25 Plan. Drain, Waste & Vent
- ☐ 21.00 Plumber's Exam Prep. Guide
- ☐ 18.00 Plumber's Hndbok Rev.
- ☐ 15.75 Rafter Length Manual
- ☐ 23.00 Remodeler's Handbook
- ☐ 18.25 Remodeling Contractor's Hdbk
- ☐ 26.25 Remodeling Kitchens & Baths
- ☐ 11.50 Residential Electrical Design
- ☐ 16.75 Residential Electrician's Hdbk.
- ☐ 18.25 Residential Wiring
- ☐ 22.00 Roof Framing
- ☐ 14.00 Roofers Handbook
- ☐ 17.00 Rough Carpentry
- ☐ 21.00 Run. Your Remodeling Bus.
- ☐ 27.00 Spec Builder's Guide
- ☐ 15.50 Stair Builder's Handbook
- ☐ 15.50 Video: Asphalt Shingle Roof.
- ☐ 15.50 Video: Bathroom Tile
- ☐ 15.50 Video: Contracting a Home 1
- ☐ 15.50 Video: Contracting a Home 2
- ☐ 32.00 Video: Design Your Kitchen
- ☐ 24.75 Video: Drywall Contruction 1
- ☐ 24.75 Video: Drywall Contruction 2
- ☐ 15.50 Video: Electrical Wiring
- ☐ 15.50 Video: Exterior Painting
- ☐ 15.50 Video: Finish Carpentry
- ☐ 15.50 Video: Hang an Exterior Door
- ☐ 15.50 Video: Int. Paint & Wallpaper
- ☐ 15.50 Video: Kitchen Renovation
- ☐ 24.75 Video: Paint Contractor's 1
- ☐ 24.75 Video: Paint Contractor's 2
- ☐ 15.50 Video: Plumbing
- ☐ 80.00 Video: Roof Framing 1
- ☐ 80.00 Video: Roof Framing 2
- ☐ 15.50 Video: Rough Carpentry
- ☐ 24.75 Video: Stair Framing
- ☐ 15.50 Video: Windows & Doors
- ☐ 15.50 Video: Wood Siding
- ☐ 9.50 Visual Stairule
- ☐ 14.25 Wood-Frame House Const

Charge Card Phone Orders - Call *1-800-829-8123*

Craftsman Book Co
6058 Corte del Cedro
P. O. Box 6500
Carlsbad, CA 92008

In a hurry?
We accept phone orders charged to your MasterCard, Visa or American Express
Call 1-800-829-8123

Name (Please print clearly ____________________

Company ____________________

Address ____________________

City/State/Zip ____________________

Total Enclosed ____________________
(In California add 6% tax)

Use your ☐Visa ☐MasterCard or ☐American Express

Card # ____________________

Exp. date __________ Initials ____

10-Day Money Back GUARANTEE

- ☐ 95.00 Audio: Construction Field Sup.
- ☐ 65.00 Audio: Estimating Remodeling
- ☐ 19.95 Audio: Plumbers Examination
- ☐ 22.00 Basic Plumbing with Illustration
- ☐ 30.00 Berger Building Cost File
- ☐ 11.25 Blprt Reading for Bldg Trades
- ☐ 19.75 Bookkeeping for Builders
- ☐ 24.95 Builder's Comp. Dictionary
- ☐ 17.25 Blder's Guide to Acct. Rev.
- ☐ 15.25 Blder's Guide to Const. Fin.
- ☐ 15.50 Blder's Office Manual Rev.
- ☐ 14.00 Building Cost Manual
- ☐ 11.75 Building Layout
- ☐ 25.50 Carpentry Estimating
- ☐ 19.75 Carpentry for Resi. Const.
- ☐ 19.00 Carpentry in Com. Const.
- ☐ 16.25 Carpentry Layout
- ☐ 17.75 Compt: Builder's New Tool
- ☐ 14.50 Concrete and Formwork
- ☐ 20.50 Concrete Const. & Estimating
- ☐ 26.00 Const. Estimating Ref. Data
- ☐ 22.00 Construction Superintendent
- ☐ 19.25 Const. Surveying & Layout
- ☐ 19.00 Cont. Growth & Profit Guide
- ☐ 24.25 Cont. Guide Build.Code Rev.
- ☐ 16.75 Contractor's Survival Manual.
- ☐ 16.50 Cont. Year-Rd Tax Guide
- ☐ 15.75 Cost Record for Const. Est.
- ☐ 9.50 Dial-A-Length Rafterule
- ☐ 18.25 Drywall Contracting
- ☐ 13.75 Electrical Blueprint Reading
- ☐ 25.00 Electrical Const. Estimator
- ☐ 19.00 Estimating Electrical Const.
- ☐ 17.00 Estimating Home Blding Costs
- ☐ 28.00 Estimating Painting Costs
- ☐ 17.25 Estimating Plumbing Costs
- ☐ 21.50 Est. Tables for Home Building
- ☐ 22.75 Exca. & Grading Hndbk Rev.
- ☐ 9.25 E-Z Square
- ☐ 15.25 Finish Carpentry
- ☐ 23.00 Kitchen Designer
- ☐ 24.75 Hdbk of Const. Cont. Vol. 1
- ☐ 24.75 Hdbk of Const. Cont. Vol. 2
- ☐ 14.75 Hdbk of Modern Elec. Wiring
- ☐ 15.00 Home Wiring: Imp., Ext., Repr
- ☐ 17.50 How to Sell Remodeling
- ☐ 24.50 HVAC Contracting
- ☐ 20.25 Manual of Electrical Cont.
- ☐ 19.75 Manual of Prof. Remodeling
- ☐ 17.25 Masonry & Concrete Const.
- ☐ 26.50 Masonry Estimating
- ☐ 19.50 National Const. Estimator
- ☐ 19.25 Paint Contractor's Manual
- ☐ 21.25 Painter's Handbook
- ☐ 23.50 Pipe & Excavation Contracting
- ☐ 13.00 Plan. and Design. Plumb. Sys.
- ☐ 19.25 Plan. Drain, Waste & Vent
- ☐ 21.00 Plumber's Exam Prep. Guide
- ☐ 18.00 Plumber's Hndbok Rev.
- ☐ 15.75 Rafter Length Manual
- ☐ 23.00 Remodeler's Handbook
- ☐ 18.25 Remodeling Contractor's Hdbk
- ☐ 26.25 Remodeling Kitchens & Baths
- ☐ 11.50 Residential Electrical Design
- ☐ 16.75 Residential Electrician's Hdbk.
- ☐ 18.25 Residential Wiring
- ☐ 22.00 Roof Framing
- ☐ 14.00 Roofers Handbook
- ☐ 17.00 Rough Carpentry
- ☐ 21.00 Run. Your Remodeling Bus.
- ☐ 27.00 Spec Builder's Guide
- ☐ 15.50 Stair Builder's Handbook
- ☐ 15.50 Video: Asphalt Shingle Roof.
- ☐ 15.50 Video: Bathroom Tile
- ☐ 15.50 Video: Contracting a Home 1
- ☐ 15.50 Video: Contracting a Home 2
- ☐ 32.00 Video: Design Your Kitchen
- ☐ 24.75 Video: Drywall Contruction 1
- ☐ 24.75 Video: Drywall Contruction 2
- ☐ 15.50 Video: Electrical Wiring
- ☐ 15.50 Video: Exterior Painting
- ☐ 15.50 Video: Finish Carpentry
- ☐ 15.50 Video: Hang an Exterior Door
- ☐ 15.50 Video: Int. Paint & Wallpaper
- ☐ 15.50 Video: Kitchen Renovation
- ☐ 24.75 Video: Paint Contractor's 1
- ☐ 24.75 Video: Paint Contractor's 2
- ☐ 15.50 Video: Plumbing
- ☐ 80.00 Video: Roof Framing 1
- ☐ 80.00 Video: Roof Framing 2
- ☐ 15.50 Video: Rough Carpentry
- ☐ 24.75 Video: Stair Framing
- ☐ 15.50 Video: Windows & Doors
- ☐ 15.50 Video: Wood Siding
- ☐ 9.50 Visual Stairule
- ☐ 14.25 Wood-Frame House Const

Charge Card Phone Orders - Call *1-800-829-8123*

Craftsman Book Co.
6058 Corte del Cedro
P. O. Box 6500
Carlsbad, CA 92008

In a hurry?
We accept phone orders charged to your MasterCard, Visa or American Express
Call 1-800-829-8123

Name (Please print clearly) ____________________

Company ____________________

Address ____________________

City/State/Zip ____________________

Total Enclosed ____________________
(In California add 6% tax)

Use your ☐Visa ☐MasterCard or ☐American Express

Card # ____________________

Exp. date __________ Initial ____

These books are tax deductible when used to improve or maintain your professional skill.

10-Day Money Back GUARANTEE

- ☐ 95.00 Audio: Construction Field Sup.
- ☐ 65.00 Audio: Estimating Remodeling
- ☐ 19.95 Audio: Plumbers Examination
- ☐ 22.00 Basic Plumbing with Illustration
- ☐ 30.00 Berger Building Cost File
- ☐ 11.25 Blprt Reading for Bldg Trades
- ☐ 19.75 Bookkeeping for Builders
- ☐ 24.95 Builder's Comp. Dictionary
- ☐ 17.25 Blder's Guide to Acct. Rev.
- ☐ 15.25 Blder's Guide to Const. Fin.
- ☐ 15.50 Blder's Office Manual Rev.
- ☐ 14.00 Building Cost Manual
- ☐ 11.75 Building Layout
- ☐ 25.50 Carpentry Estimating
- ☐ 19.75 Carpentry for Resi. Const.
- ☐ 19.00 Carpentry in Com. Const.
- ☐ 16.25 Carpentry Layout
- ☐ 17.75 Compt: Builder's New Tool
- ☐ 14.50 Concrete and Formwork
- ☐ 20.50 Concrete Const. & Estimating
- ☐ 26.00 Const. Estimating Ref. Data
- ☐ 22.00 Construction Superintendent
- ☐ 19.25 Const. Surveying & Layout
- ☐ 19.00 Cont. Growth & Profit Guide
- ☐ 24.25 Cont. Guide Build.Code Rev.
- ☐ 16.75 Contractor's Survival Manual.
- ☐ 16.50 Cont. Year-Rd Tax Guide
- ☐ 15.75 Cost Record for Const. Est.
- ☐ 9.50 Dial-A-Length Rafterule
- ☐ 18.25 Drywall Contracting
- ☐ 13.75 Electrical Blueprint Reading
- ☐ 25.00 Electrical Const. Estimator
- ☐ 19.00 Estimating Electrical Const.
- ☐ 17.00 Estimating Home Blding Costs
- ☐ 28.00 Estimating Painting Costs
- ☐ 17.25 Estimating Plumbing Costs
- ☐ 21.50 Est. Tables for Home Building
- ☐ 22.75 Exca. & Grading Hndbk Rev.
- ☐ 9.25 E-Z Square
- ☐ 15.25 Finish Carpentry
- ☐ 23.00 Kitchen Designer
- ☐ 24.75 Hdbk of Const. Cont. Vol. 1
- ☐ 24.75 Hdbk of Const. Cont. Vol. 2
- ☐ 14.75 Hdbk of Modern Elec. Wiring
- ☐ 15.00 Home Wiring: Imp., Ext., Repr
- ☐ 17.50 How to Sell Remodeling
- ☐ 24.50 HVAC Contracting
- ☐ 20.25 Manual of Electrical Cont.
- ☐ 19.75 Manual of Prof. Remodeling
- ☐ 17.25 Masonry & Concrete Const.
- ☐ 26.50 Masonry Estimating
- ☐ 19.50 National Const. Estimator
- ☐ 19.25 Paint Contractor's Manual
- ☐ 21.25 Painter's Handbook
- ☐ 23.50 Pipe & Excavation Contracting
- ☐ 13.00 Plan. and Design. Plumb. Sys.
- ☐ 19.25 Plan. Drain, Waste & Vent
- ☐ 21.00 Plumber's Exam Prep. Guide
- ☐ 18.00 Plumber's Hndbok Rev.
- ☐ 15.75 Rafter Length Manual
- ☐ 23.00 Remodeler's Handbook
- ☐ 18.25 Remodeling Contractor's Hdbk
- ☐ 26.25 Remodeling Kitchens & Baths
- ☐ 11.50 Residential Electrical Design
- ☐ 16.75 Residential Electrician's Hdbk.
- ☐ 18.25 Residential Wiring
- ☐ 22.00 Roof Framing
- ☐ 14.00 Roofers Handbook
- ☐ 17.00 Rough Carpentry
- ☐ 21.00 Run. Your Remodeling Bus.
- ☐ 27.00 Spec Builder's Guide
- ☐ 15.50 Stair Builder's Handbook
- ☐ 15.50 Video: Asphalt Shingle Roof.
- ☐ 15.50 Video: Bathroom Tile
- ☐ 15.50 Video: Contracting a Home 1
- ☐ 15.50 Video: Contracting a Home 2
- ☐ 32.00 Video: Design Your Kitchen
- ☐ 24.75 Video: Drywall Contruction 1
- ☐ 24.75 Video: Drywall Contruction 2
- ☐ 15.50 Video: Electrical Wiring
- ☐ 15.50 Video: Exterior Painting
- ☐ 15.50 Video: Finish Carpentry
- ☐ 15.50 Video: Hang an Exterior Door
- ☐ 15.50 Video: Int. Paint & Wallpaper
- ☐ 15.50 Video: Kitchen Renovation
- ☐ 24.75 Video: Paint Contractor's 1
- ☐ 24.75 Video: Paint Contractor's 2
- ☐ 15.50 Video: Plumbing
- ☐ 80.00 Video: Roof Framing 1
- ☐ 80.00 Video: Roof Framing 2
- ☐ 15.50 Video: Rough Carpentry
- ☐ 24.75 Video: Stair Framing
- ☐ 15.50 Video: Windows & Doors
- ☐ 15.50 Video: Wood Siding
- ☐ 9.50 Visual Stairule
- ☐ 14.25 Wood-Frame House Const

Craftsman Book Company, 6058 Corte del Cedro, Carlsbad, CA 92009

BUSINESS REPLY MAIL
FIRST CLASS MAIL   PERMIT NO.271   CARLSBAD, CA

POSTAGE WILL BE PAID BY ADDRESSEE

Craftsman Book Company
6058 Corte Del Cedro
P. O. Box 6500
Carlsbad, CA 92008-0992

BUSINESS REPLY MAIL
FIRST CLASS MAIL   PERMIT NO.271   CARLSBAD, CA

POSTAGE WILL BE PAID BY ADDRESSEE

Craftsman Book Company
6058 Corte Del Cedro
P. O. Box 6500
Carlsbad, CA 92008-0992

BUSINESS REPLY MAIL
FIRST CLASS MAIL   PERMIT NO.271   CARLSBAD, CA

POSTAGE WILL BE PAID BY ADDRESSEE

Craftsman Book Company
6058 Corte Del Cedro
P. O. Box 6500
Carlsbad, CA 92008-0992